P9-BZS-837

S. S. Hayten

TRANSIENT ELECTRIC CURRENTS

McGraw-Hill Electrical and Electronic Engineering Series

FREDERICK EMMONS TERMAN, *Consulting Editor*
W. W. HARMAN and J. G. TRUXAL, *Associate Consulting Editors*

TRANSIENT ELECTRIC CURRENTS

HUGH HILDRETH SKILLING, Ph.D.

PROFESSOR OF ELECTRICAL ENGINEERING
STANFORD UNIVERSITY

SECOND EDITION

NEW YORK   TORONTO   LONDON

McGRAW-HILL BOOK COMPANY, INC.

1952

TRANSIENT ELECTRIC CURRENTS

Copyright, 1937, 1952, by the McGraw-Hill Book Company, Inc. Printed in the United States of America. All rights reserved. This book, or parts thereof, may not be reproduced in any form without permission of the publishers.

Library of Congress Catalog Card Number: 51-12577

v

PREFACE

Since the first edition of "Transient Electric Currents" was published, circuit analysis by Laplace transformation has been developed into an effective tool. One of the major purposes of this second edition is to present the Laplace transformation method of solution of transient problems in addition to the more familiar treatment that has come to be called the "classic" method.

Laplace transformation is an outgrowth of operational circuit analysis and has largely replaced it. Those who know and like the Heaviside operational calculus will find that the Laplace method is not unfamiliar. In application, the operational and transformation methods are very similar indeed. The mathematical underpinning of the Laplace transformation, on the other hand, is completely different and, as a matter of fact, is much less difficult.

The Laplace transformation method is presented in Chap. X of this new edition. The presentation is arranged for engineering students. Physical concepts are stressed. The work is, of course, mathematical, but needless elaboration is avoided. The Laplace transformation is first related to familiar ideas such as the Fourier series. The method is then developed to make it readily useful in solving problems. Frequent examples are fully worked out, and most of the examples are compared with "classic" solutions to give the student confidence that the Laplace method is not only quick and easy but dependable.

The other chapters of the book are not greatly changed. It has been most encouraging to receive favorable comments from users of the first edition, speaking well of the arrangement of material and careful explanations. In this edition, as in the first, an understanding of the physical nature of transient phenomena is considered of primary importance. Basic principles are emphasized, for it is neither feasible nor desirable to study every possible situation. Rather, the purpose of the book is to prepare the student to attack with reasonable confidence any sort of transient problem that may arise.

Prerequisities for study of this book are elementary calculus and as much electricity as is commonly taught in a general physics course. The first edition has most commonly been used in fourth-year college courses, but students in the third year would have no trouble with the material.

The author has used the book as text in a 12-weeks course, covering the first seven of the ten chapters. Others use it for a semester of about 16 weeks. It seems that the new edition will work out particularly well for a semester course to include both the "classic" development and the Laplace transformation method.

Although the Laplace transformation method is presented in the final chapter of the book, it need not be taught last. Experience shows that it combines well with the presentation of the "classic" material. A suggestion might be made to introduce Laplace transformation after Chap. IV, using the first eleven sections of Chap. X at that time. Then the rest of Chap. X can be given at a later time, following Chaps. V or VI, as the teacher finds suitable.

The Laplace transformation chapter can, indeed, be studied by itself. It will be entirely practical for a reader with some slight knowledge of transients to turn at once to the Laplace transform method and to read Chap. X without necessarily referring to the rest of the book. This suggestion is more for the individual reader, no doubt, than for class work.

Indebtedness to Dr. Vannevar Bush, Dean H. E. Clifford, and Dean B. L. Robertson is acknowledged for the second edition as for the first. Special gratitude is owing to Dr. F. E. Terman, Dean of Engineering at Stanford University, who has provided both encouragement and opportunity for writing. The liberal policy of Stanford University, remarked in the first edition, continues under the presidency of Dr. J. E. Wallace Sterling.

The aid of my wife, Hazel Skilling, is as indispensable as it was fifteen years ago. She is even now working on the new manuscript as I write this preface.

HUGH HILDRETH SKILLING

STANFORD, CALIF.
November, 1951

CONTENTS

TRANSIENT ELECTRIC CURRENTS

INTRODUCTION

> I often say that when you can measure what you are speaking about, and express it in numbers, you know something about it, but when you cannot measure it, when you cannot express it in numbers, your knowledge is of a meagre and unsatisfactory kind; it may be the beginning of knowledge, but you have scarcely in your thoughts advanced to the stage of science, whatever the matter may be.— WILLIAM THOMSON, LORD KELVIN.

What is electricity?

An impression has been created, probably by expositors of popular science, that there is something mystic about electricity. Even today, when electricity is used in nearly every room of nearly every house, it is not uncommon to hear that we really know nothing of it, and that it is in some way less real than earth, air, fire, and water.

One does not, indeed, see electricity. Nor can one touch it, hear it, taste it, or smell it. But it is commonly used, easily measured, and its behavior can be predicted with great accuracy. What can be meant, then, by saying that we do not know what it is?

To Lord Kelvin it appeared that when you can measure what you are speaking about, and express it in numbers, you know something about it. And there is hardly anything that can be measured more satisfactorily, or expressed in numbers so precisely, as electricity. There is hardly anything, in other words, so well known, despite its lack of appeal to the senses. Let us consider what is known about electricity.

The predominant characteristic of electricity is its ability to convey energy. For two thousand years it was known that certain substances, after they had acquired energy by being touched with other substances, would exert a force on light

1

objects near them. Specifically, it is mentioned in the Greek records that Thales, about 600 B.C., discovered that amber rubbed with wool would attract splinters and bits of straw. This was the meaning of electricity and the total knowledge of it for many, many centuries, and it was from ἤλεκτρον, amber, that electricity took its name.

It was not until about A.D. 1600, as far as one can tell from the very scant information that is available, that electricity was studied further; Gilbert, best known for his work on magnetism, gave some attention to electricity also. That was in the time of Shakespeare. Two generations later, sparks were observed by Guericke and were associated with electricity, and Guericke was also the first to discover that under certain circumstances electricity would exert a repulsive force. Sparks represent one of the energy characteristics of electricity, for they occur when the electrical energy of amber is changed to heat and light.

Just recently—almost within a century—Volta found that chemical energy could be carried about in wires, and the fact that it, too, would produce sparks, led to the belief that it was a different aspect of electricity. This belief was greatly strengthened when it was discovered that the well-known attractive and repulsive forces of frictional electricity were displayed by this new voltaic electricity also. And further evidence of the energy nature of electricity was discovered by observing that a fine wire would become red hot when connected to a chemical battery.

Then a relationship between electricity and magnetism was found. When electricity flowed through a wire it would move a magnet. This is yet another indication of energy. It has, in fact, been the most useful one, for the interaction of wires and magnets is the source of all commercial electricity today, and the means of utilizing most of it.

But with all the present uses of electricity—whether it warms a room or turns a motor or lights a lamp, whether it is in a meter, a telephone, or a spark plug—electricity is known only because it does work. Electricity, in short, is energy.

2. Energy. It is now known that electrical energy may be derived from mechanical or chemical energy, as in the generator and battery; it may be obtained from heat, as in the thermocouple, or from light, as in the photovoltaic cell. It may be changed back into any of these other forms. But while it exists as electrical energy it is either electrostatic (as in amber) or electromagnetic (which attracts iron).

Electromagnetic energy is associated with inductance. Electromagnetic energy increases as current increases. Work is done in forcing current to increase through an inductance, and as long as current continues to flow the energy remains stored. It is given up as current diminishes.

The amount of electromagnetic energy is proportional to the square of the current, being, in joules, $\frac{1}{2}Li^2$ (L is inductance in henrys, and i is amperes of current). Electromagnetic energy is analogous to the kinetic mechanical energy of a moving body, which increases as velocity increases, and is $\frac{1}{2}Mv^2$.

Electrostatic energy is developed when positive electric charge and negative electric charge are separated, as in a condenser. Work must be done in separating the charges of opposite polarity, and while they are held apart the energy is in electrostatic form. As the charges approach each other again the stored energy is released.

The amount of electrostatic energy, in joules, is $\frac{1}{2}Ce^2$ (C is capacitance in farads, and e is volts). Electrostatic energy is analogous to potential mechanical energy in a strained elastic body, such as a stretched spring; the energy of the spring is proportional to the square of the force exerted, being $\frac{1}{2}\frac{1}{k}f^2$.

Electric energy is changed into heat by the passage of electric current through resistance. This transformation to heat is of outstanding importance because it is always present; no circuit can be without resistance, and no dielectric is perfectly non-conducting. Electric energy cannot be stored indefinitely in either the electromagnetic or electrostatic form, for it is gradually wasted away as heat.

The amount of energy lost as heat when a charge q is driven through a resistance by a voltage e is eq. This is only one of many ways of expressing the loss, but it is interesting because of analogy to the energy lost in mechanical friction. When a force f is exerted in overcoming friction, and it results in motion through a distance s, the amount of energy changed to heat is fs, which is analogous to the electrical loss eq.

The change to heat is only one of the ways in which electric energy can be transformed to energy of some other kind.

Other important examples are the change to mechanical energy whenever electric or magnetic forces are allowed to produce motion, as in the electric motor, and the change to chemical energy by electrolytic processes, as in the storage battery.

3. Electrical Units.   To account in quantitative manner for the various manifestations and properties of electric energy, an extensive and beautiful mathematical system has been developed. Certain relations appear quite frequently in the mathematics, and they have been given such names as *voltage, current, inductance, capacitance, resistance,* and *charge.*   It is usually easier to compute and to think in terms of these relations than in terms of energy, and some of them are particularly easy to measure. They fill the same place in the electrical system that force, velocity, mass, elastance, friction, and distance occupy in the mechanical system.   Most equations of electricity are written in terms of the electrical units, and although energy is the essence of all electrical behavior, it does not often appear explicitly in the mathematics.

Most of the equations of this book are based on one of the simplest and most valuable relations among the electrical quantities.   It was first stated by Kirchhoff for the steady state of direct current, but when written as follows it applies equally well to the instantaneous conditions in any network: *The sum of the voltages around any closed circuit is zero.*

It is often possible to gain an excellent qualitative understanding of the transient operation of a circuit or network from energy considerations.   Applications of this method are introduced from time to time throughout the text.   The essential nature of energy must never be forgotten; but in most cases the quantitative relations are most readily determined from an equation in which the sum of the voltages in a circuit is equated to zero, or—what amounts to the same thing—when the applied voltage is equated to the sum of the voltages across the elements of the circuit.

4. Electrical and Mechanical Analogues.   It has been mentioned that there are analogous relations in electricity and mechanics.   Two systems are analogous when the same equation will describe the action of either, the mathematical symbols being assigned different meanings.   For instance, there are the analogous expressions for magnetic energy and kinetic energy,

$\frac{1}{2}Li^2$ and $\frac{1}{2}Mv^2$; in these equations inductance is analogous to mass and current to velocity. Further, in the electrical equation $e = L\dfrac{di}{dt}$, and the equation that expresses Newton's second law, $f = M\dfrac{dv}{dt}$, it will be seen that there is also analogy between voltage and force. These equations, with others that extend the analogy, are shown in the following table:

ANALOGOUS RELATIONS

Electrical	Mechanical	Analogues	
$E = \frac{1}{2}Li^2$	$E = \frac{1}{2}Mv^2$	Inductance, L Current, i	Mass, M Velocity, v
$e = L\dfrac{di}{dt}$	$f = M\dfrac{dv}{dt}$	Voltage, e	Force, f
$i = \dfrac{dq}{dt}$	$v = \dfrac{ds}{dt}$	Charge, q	Displacement, s
$q = Ce$	$s = \dfrac{1}{k}f$	Capacitance, C	Reciprocal of stiffness, $\dfrac{1}{k}$

Analogy is useful when it is desired to compare an unfamiliar system with one that is better known. Sometimes it is helpful to consider electric circuits in terms of their mechanical analogues; on other occasions there is much to be gained by considering the electric analogue of a mechanical problem. Relations are more easily visualized in the more familiar system, and mathematical solutions are more readily handled. But it is probable that the chief value of analogy is that through its use the extension of a line of reasoning into unexplored territory is frequently made possible. If two systems are analogous in one case, may they not also be analogous in another? Sometimes they prove to be, sometimes they do not. Since there are so many analogies between electrical and mechanical systems, may there not be an electric analogue of momentum? There is, indeed: it is Li, called by Maxwell the electrokinetic momentum. Since frictional loss in heat is analogous to resistance loss in heat, is there not analogy between mechanical friction and electrical resistance? By no means.

It must be clearly understood that analogy between two systems is helpful in suggesting new relations, but it does not prove their validity. Unless equations describing the action of friction and resistance are of the same form, these quantities are not analogous. But it is known that the electromotive force of resistance is proportional to current ($e = Ri$), whereas the mechanical force of friction is not proportional to velocity except in certain special cases of fluid friction. Resistance, therefore, is not analogous to friction.

While no system is completely analogous to any other, there are limited analogies between most physical systems. The mechanical system considered in the table relates specifically to translatory motion of a rigid body. If rotational motion is to be considered, the analogues of voltage, current, charge, and inductance are (respectively) torque, angular velocity, angle, and moment of inertia. Analogues of the same electrical quantities in the flow of liquid along a pipe are pressure, rate of flow expressed as volume per unit area of cross section per unit time, volume of flow per unit area, and density of liquid times length of pipe. Comparing equations of heat flow to equations of the electric circuit, analogues are temperature and voltage, flow of heat and current, thermal and electrical conductivity, specific heat and capacitance. It is interesting that there is no detectable thermal analogue of inductance.

5. The Transient Period. It seems to be generally true that energy cannot be changed from one form to another instantaneously. Time is required, for instance, for a locomotive to bring a train to its full speed; it must add gradually to the kinetic energy of the train as the speed increases. An automobile comes slowly to a stop after its brakes are applied, while kinetic energy is being changed to heat through the agency of friction. There is an exceedingly rapid change from kinetic energy to heat when a bullet is stopped by striking a sheet of steel, and the release of energy in the form of heat is almost explosive, but in even this extreme case some short time is required. A stone that is shot from a catapult is accelerated during a short but finite length of time while the potential energy of the catapult is being changed to kinetic energy in the stone. Such intervals of energy transfer are spoken of as *transient* intervals, as distinct from the final *steady state*.

It is equally true that changes of the form of electrical energy must be made gradually. Time is required for a battery to bring the current in an inductive circuit to its final steady value; it must add gradually to the magnetic energy of the circuit as the current increases. The final value of steady current, E/R, will be the ratio of the applied voltage to the circuit resistance. When this value of current is reached there must be a definite amount of energy stored in the magnetic field of the circuit; the amount is $\frac{1}{2}LI^2$, I being the steady current. But this energy must be obtained by the magnetic field from the current, while at the same time the current must remain in proportion to the square root of the energy, so both stored energy and current must grow, together, gradually, until the steady state is attained. The increase of current is analogous to the increase of velocity as a railroad train is accelerated by its locomotive.

If the driving force of the battery is removed from an inductive circuit, without breaking the circuit, the flow of current must eventually cease, but (as brakes retard an automobile) the current diminishes gradually as magnetic energy is changed to heat by resistance. If the circuit is opened suddenly while current is flowing, the action is analogous to stopping a bullet: the current stops suddenly, but not instantly, and magnetic energy of the circuit is changed to heat in a very short time by the explosive formation of a spark as the circuit is broken.

Electric energy can be changed from the electrostatic form to the electromagnetic form, as the catapult exchanges potential energy for kinetic, if a charged condenser is allowed to discharge through an inductive circuit. A less limited analogy, however, is found between such a circuit and a pendulum which is moved to one side and then, released, is allowed to swing. At the moment of release, the bob of the pendulum has potential energy. As the bob swings downward, its potential energy is lost, but kinetic energy is gained; at the mid-point of the swing there is no potential energy, but the kinetic energy is maximum and the pendulum must swing on. The energy becomes again potential. Until the initial store of energy has been lost, owing to friction, the pendulum cannot cease to swing.

When a charged condenser is suddenly connected to an inductive coil there is energy in the condenser but none in the coil. Charge flows out of the condenser, however, and the electrostatic field loses its stored energy, until the condenser is fully discharged. But the current flowing out of the condenser must pass through the coil, giving energy to the magnetic field; as energy is drained from the electrostatic field of the condenser it is added to the magnetic field of the coil (except for that part of the energy which is changed to heat by the resistance of the circuit). Although the condenser becomes fully discharged, current cannot cease to flow in the circuit, because there is electromagnetic energy in the magnetic field of the coil: current will continue, and the condenser will be charged with the opposite polarity, regaining energy at the expense of the energy of the coil. When all of the magnetic energy has again become electrostatic, current ceases momentarily, but equilibrium does not exist and the condenser will at once begin to discharge, and there will be current in the opposite direction. So the condenser continues to charge and discharge, and current continues to flow back and forth. The energy is transferred from condenser to coil, and from coil to condenser, and the transient flow cannot cease until all of the initial energy has been lost as heat in the resistance.

6. Duration of the Transient State. The duration of the transient state is indefinite. There is rarely any sharp distinction between transient and steady states; one merges into the other so gradually that a theoretical end to the transient interval is not only imperceptible but actually nonexistent. It becomes necessary, then, to accept this purely pragmatic definition: the transient change has ceased when it is no longer measurable.

Illustrations in the field of mechanics are obvious. A railroad train, for example, has ceased to be accelerated when its speed is not perceptibly different from its final speed. It must be observed that the weakness of this definition lies in the fact that the end of the transient interval will appear at different times to different observers, depending on the delicacy of the method of observation. The engineer with a speedometer can recognize that acceleration is taking place after it is no longer apparent to a passenger.

The transient phenomena of electricity are of a similar nature, and the steady state of energy distribution is usually approached at a constantly decreasing rate. A termination of the transient interval can only mean a time at which the most sensitive available meters or oscillographs will fail to distinguish any difference from the steady state.

This definition is theoretically unsatisfactory, for the transient interval is mathematically of infinite duration, but practically it sets a limit beyond which the transient current can be of no importance.

7. Transient Phenomena in Engineering. Transient interchanges of energy are associated with electrical circuits containing inductance or capacitance and with mechanical systems having inertia or elasticity. Every time a switch is closed or opened, when the load on a motor is changed, in case of any alteration of resistance, inductance, or other parameters of a circuit while it is carrying current, there is a transient electric disturbance. This may or may not be coupled with a transient mechanical disturbance. Some transient currents are harmful and must be avoided, others are of the greatest value.

Automobile ignition is perhaps the most common practical utilization of a transient surge: each spark in a cylinder is a carefully engineered transient current. Lightning, on the other hand, is the most dreaded and also the most spectacular of transient disturbances. The traveling waves on transmission lines that result from lightning have potentials of many million volts and are highly dangerous although their duration is measured in millionths of a second. To simulate their action, transient surges of short duration are developed by "lightning generators" in electrical testing laboratories.

Other transient phenomena appear on transmission lines when switches are operated, and, since these may result in application of twice normal voltage to the power system, they must be considered in design of insulation.

A sudden change of load, such as short-circuit of part of the system, or the starting of a large machine, will produce a complex series of electrical transients in the field and armature circuits of the machines of a power system, combined with mechanical oscillations of the rotating machines. The various electrical and mechanical disturbances are by no means independent; each affects the others, and there is in reality one inclusive transient state throughout the entire electromechanical system. Such disturbances endanger power-system stability and involve tremendous surges of energy that may continue for several seconds.

Transient currents of great importance appear in telephone and radio circuits. Some, such as the atmospheric disturbances called "static," and noise-producing currents induced by surges on near-by power lines, are highly undesirable. But another, that is in some sense a transient phenomenon, is the very life of modern communication: it is the oscillator. In all ordinary circuits, transient oscillations die away as energy is dissipated by resistance, but it is possible so to connect an amplifying vacuum tube that the energy of the oscillating current is increased instead of being dissipated. The effective resistance of the circuit is negative. The circuit is dynamically unstable. In such a circuit any small fluctuation will be the beginning of a transient current that will grow in amplitude (instead of diminishing) until the vacuum tube can supply no more power; the oscillations then continue without further increase. The vacuum tube acts in a manner analogous to the escapement of a clock: when the pendulum of the clock is given a small swing, to allow the escapement to act, a transient oscillation of the pendulum will begin—transient in the sense that there is never a stable equilibrium of energy. The pendulum will swing through an increasingly wider arc until the power supplied by the clock's spring, through the escapement, is equal to the power consumed by friction. Thereafter, the oscillations, as in an electric oscillator, will continue in a quasi-steady state.

In the coming pages it will not be possible to discuss all the transient phenomena that arise in the practice of electrical engineering, but a few fundamental principles and general examples point the way to the solution of many problems. The underlying thought, and even the methods of solution, are much the same for all transient circuit problems, regardless of widely different superficial appearances. It is usually necessary to idealize and simplify the networks that occur in practice and then, with the network reduced to a familiar form, its transient behavior can be found by one of three or four general methods of attack.

CHAPTER I

THE BEHAVIOR OF INDUCTANCE

1. An Inductive Circuit. When direct current is flowing continuously through a circuit, the amount of current can be read on an ammeter, which will indicate a certain number of amperes. The flow of current is unchanging, and when it is specified as 1 ampere it is not necessary to say that it was 1 ampere at a certain instant of time, for it does not change from one time to another. This is called the steady-state condition of the current, and the relation between the amount of current, voltage, and resistance is given by the familiar Ohm's law.

But when current is being started, and a battery is first connected to a circuit, or when the current is being stopped, or its amount changed, the steady-state condition will not exist and the current will be a transient current. For instance, in the circuit of Fig. 1, where a switch is suddenly closed to permit current to flow through an inductance coil, current will begin to flow gradually. Starting at zero, the current will increase rapidly at first, and then the increase will become more and more gradual. Finally the current will cease to change perceptibly, and it will then have the steady-state value of E/R. The transient condition is over when the steady-state value of current is reached and maintained.

In general, in any circuit containing inductance or capacitance there will be a transient current. The amount of transient current will vary as a function of time until, after a short period that generally is not more than a few seconds, it will have become so very nearly equal to the steady-state current that one may say the transient state is passed.

2. Examples of Transient Currents in Inductive Circuits. In spite of the short time that the transient current usually lasts, it is of very great importance. The current in an automobile ignition system is just a succession of transient currents that result from operation of the timing mechanism; steady-state is

11

never reached, and good ignition is dependent on a proper sort of transient current. The coil of Fig. 1 might well be the coil of an automobile engine, and the switch of the diagram the timer points of the engine, opened and closed by a cam. A lightning stroke is a transient electric current. So are the dots and dashes of a telegraph, and again in Fig. 1 the coil might be a sounder or

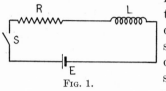

Fig. 1.

relay and the switch would then be the sending key. If steady-state current in a telegraph is reached slowly, as in the case of a very long cable from England to America, the speed of transmitting messages is reduced. The field current of an electric generator cannot be changed without a transient state; and a vibrating voltage regulator of the type commonly used never allows a steady state of field current to be established.

3. Inductance. The most generally useful concept of inductance is based on the ability of a changing current to induce a voltage. A current whose amount is changing has the property of inducing a voltage in the circuit carrying that current, and also in any other nearby circuit; inductance is a measure of that voltage-inducing ability. If the voltage is induced in the same wire that carries the current it is spoken of as "self-inductance" and in such a case it is analogous to inertia, whereas a voltage in some other circuit is due to "mutual inductance" between the two circuits. Inductance is defined by the following equation, which has already been mentioned:

$$e_L = L \frac{di}{dt} \tag{1}$$

Experiment shows that in a great many cases the inductance of a circuit is simply constant and does not change with the amount of current or with any other electrical quantities. The chief exception to this general rule appears when iron is used as the core of the coil; inductance of the coil then changes as a function of the amount of current, and in particular the inductance decreases with large values of current. But when there is neither iron nor other ferromagnetic substance in the immediate neighborhood of a circuit it is quite safe to give L, in Eq. (1), a constant value.

4. A Growing Current. When a circuit contains resistance as well as inductance, as in Fig. 1, the current that will flow at any instant will be affected by both parameters. One part of the applied voltage will have to drive current through the resistance, and according to Ohm's law this will require a voltage

$$e_R = Ri \tag{2}$$

while, during the transient period, the rest of the applied voltage is used in increasing current through the inductance. Since the voltage used in the resistance plus the voltage used in the induc-

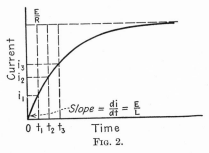

Fig. 2.

tance must equal the applied voltage, the whole operation of the circuit may be defined by a combination of Eqs. (1) and (2):

$$E = e_R + e_L = Ri + L\frac{di}{dt} \tag{3}$$

where E is the applied voltage.

When the switch is first closed in such a circuit, the current will start to increase. The current will begin at zero, and at that instant we can see from Eq. (3) that the whole applied voltage will be used in the inductance. If time is measured from the instant of closing the switch, we can write that when

$$t = 0, \quad i = 0 \tag{4}$$

and therefore $Ri = 0$ and $E = L\frac{di}{dt}$. If we plot, in Fig. 2, current as a function of time, we can start the curve from the origin [in accordance with Eq. (4)] and give it a slope equal to E/L. At a slightly later time, t_1, however, the equation's values must be revised because when $t = t_1$, $i = i_1$, the drop in the resistance equals Ri_1, and there is less voltage available to over-

come the inductance.   When the current is i_1, the rate of change
of current is

$$\frac{di}{dt} = \frac{E - Ri_1}{L} \tag{5}$$

A further section of the curve of Fig. 2 may now be drawn from
t_1 toward t_2 with a lesser slope, as determined by Eq. (5).   Current will continue to increase during this time interval, but not
so rapidly as before.   Between t_2 and t_3 there will be a further
increase of current and decrease of slope, and throughout the
entire curve the current will gradually approach its steady-state
value of E/R with the slope constantly diminishing as the
resistance of the circuit uses a larger and larger part of the
applied voltage.

The current curve in Fig. 2 is described as if its slope were
constant over the time intervals 0 to t_1, t_1 to t_2, and so on.   This
is of course not the case, for the slope diminishes gradually; the
slope is $\frac{di}{dt}$ and is always proportional to $E - Ri$ [see Eq. (5)].

The total time required for transient current in a circuit is
usually rather small.   Current in the magnet of a doorbell will
rise to its steady value in less than a tenth of a second.   In a small
radio coil, with air core, the transient state may last less than a
thousandth, or even less than a hundred thousandth of a second.
If a battery were connected to a large power transformer with heavy
copper windings on an iron core, steady-state current would not
be established for five or ten seconds.   When a direct-current shunt
motor is connected to the line, there are two transient currents,
one in the field and one in the armature, and the field current will
be established much more slowly than the armature current.

5. A Diminishing Current.   It is not only when the switch in
an inductive circuit is closed that a transient current results;
there is a somewhat similar transient condition when the switch
is opened.   Current in such a circuit as that of Fig. 1 will not
stop flowing instantly upon separation of the switch contacts,
for that would require an infinite rate of change of current and a
correspondingly high voltage across the inductance, as indicated
by Eq. (1).   Instead, there will be arcing at the switch, and current will continue to flow in the circuit even after the switch is
open, by the expedient of flowing in an arc through the air.

Such an arc will not last long, but it can easily be seen whenever a switch is opened in a highly inductive direct-current circuit such as the field circuit of a generator. The action of the current in such a case is complicated by the presence of the arc, so it is better to consider first the transient current in an inductive circuit when by some expedient the battery voltage is removed without opening the circuit.

An effective means of removing the driving voltage without opening the circuit is shown in Fig. 3.   When the short-circuiting switch is closed there will be an inductive circuit consisting of

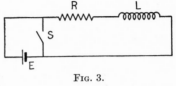

FIG. 3.

resistance, inductance, and the switch. It is this circuit that interests us; there will be another circuit consisting of the battery and the switch, but what happens in that circuit we may in theory at least disregard.

When the short-circuiting switch is closed, the current in the inductive circuit will not immediately cease, but will die out

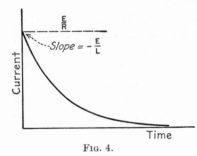

FIG. 4.

gradually as in Fig. 4.   Equation (3) still applies, but since the applied voltage is zero, (3) may be written

$$Ri + L\frac{di}{dt} = 0 \qquad (6)$$

When time equals zero, which we now specify to be at the instant of closing the short-circuiting switch, $i = E/R$, for that is the steady-state current that was established by the battery before the switch was closed. Substituting this value of i in Eq. (6) gives $\frac{di}{dt} = -\frac{E}{L}$. If we plot current as a function of time in Fig. 4, the curve will start with a current value of E/R, and at the first instant will have a slope equal to $-\frac{E}{L}$. This is the same as the initial slope in Fig. 2 but of negative sign. Since, from Eq. (6), the slope is proportional to the current, the curve will gradually approach the axis as the current dies away, as in Fig. 4.

Let us consider the flow of energy when a battery is connected, suddenly, to a circuit of inductance and resistance. Flow of energy from the battery is proportional to the current, being small at first, and increasing gradually toward a steady value. At the first instant all energy from the battery goes to the inductance for storage; but, as current begins to flow, part of the supplied energy is lost in the resistance by being changed to heat. As the current reaches its steady value, however, energy is no longer taken by the inductance, and all energy that flows from the battery during the steady state is turned to heat in the resistance.

As long as the steady-state current continues, energy remains stored in the inductance; it is $\frac{1}{2}LI^2$, where I is the steady-state current. When the battery is removed from the circuit, or when the flow of current is stopped by opening a switch, the rate of flow of current can diminish only as rapidly as is allowed by transformation of electromagnetic energy into heat. Even after the circuit is no longer receiving energy from the battery, current will flow, and energy to maintain the current will come from the inductance.

6. The Mathematical Solution. For purposes of computation, and in order to know the value of current at any particular time, it is desirable to express current as an analytic function of time. In other words, we must solve the differential equation. The solution of Eq. (6) is very simple, because it is one of that easily handled class of differential equations in which the variables may be separated. A mere algebraic transformation will change Eq. (6) to

$$\frac{1}{i}di = -\frac{R}{L}dt \qquad (7)$$

Integration of both sides is now possible, for there is only one variable on each side:

$$\int \frac{di}{i} = \int -\frac{R}{L}dt \qquad (8)$$

$$\ln i = -\frac{R}{L}t + A \qquad (9)$$

where A is a constant of integration. Since the logarithm of i is that power of ϵ that equals i,

$$i = K\epsilon^{-\frac{R}{L}t} \tag{10}$$

(The constant of integration now appears as K.)

As proof that this is a true solution of Eq. (6), we can show that its substitution will reduce (6) to an identity. If Eq. (10) gives the current, then, by differentiating,

$$\frac{di}{dt} = -\frac{R}{L}K\epsilon^{-\frac{R}{L}t} \tag{11}$$

and substitution of (10) and (11) in (6) gives

$$RK\epsilon^{-\frac{R}{L}t} - L\frac{R}{L}K\epsilon^{-\frac{R}{L}t} \equiv 0$$

This, being an identity, tells us that Eq. (10) is indeed a solution of Eq. (6).

There remains the coefficient K to be evaluated. The value of K has nothing to do with the shape of the transient current, for the shape is exponential with a rate of decay determined by the exponent, $-\frac{R}{L}$. But K can make the whole transient current larger or smaller, and we see from Fig. 4 that it must be just big enough to make the initial value of the transient current (when time is zero) equal the previously established steady current, E/R. Expressed symbolically, we know that when

$$t = 0, \qquad i = \frac{E}{R} \tag{12}$$

Let us call this value of current i_0, so

$$i_0 = \frac{E}{R} \tag{13}$$

When the values of (12) are substituted in Eq. (10), it reduces to

$$\frac{E}{R} = K$$

(because ϵ with the exponent 0 is equal to 1). This value of K, then, in Eq. (10), gives us the desired expression for current as a function of time:

$$i = \frac{E}{R}\epsilon^{-\frac{R}{L}t} = i_0\epsilon^{-\frac{R}{L}t} \tag{14}$$

The current at any time is now expressed entirely in terms of known circuit constants and the initial value of current; this is the useful form of solution.

7. Circuit Equation and Boundary Conditions. In finding Eq. (14) and in proving that it satisfies Eq. (6) we have determined once for all the current that will flow in any circuit made up of inductance and resistance after the driving voltage is removed, with the following conditions:

1. The circuit consists of self-inductance and resistance, and nothing else, and the values of inductance and resistance do not vary during the period of time in which Eq. (14) applies. This is a statement of *circuit* conditions, and this statement is written symbolically in Eq. (6).

2. At a known instant there is a known value of current flowing in the circuit. This is a statement of *boundary* condition, and is given in Eq. (12).

In all study of transient currents (and in many other fields of science and engineering) a solution is found by properly combining circuit and boundary conditions.

A fundamental idea, which is obvious when once formulated, is that a mathematical solution cannot be found until all physical conditions that bear on the problem—both circuit conditions and boundary conditions—have been written into the solution in mathematical form. For mathematics is only a system of reasoning and it can never *supply* any facts or information.

8. The Solution for Growing Current. Returning to the problem of the transient current in an inductive circuit to which voltage is suddenly applied, we need an exact solution that will express current as a function of time. Figure 2 gives an indication of the way in which current will increase, but what is much more useful is the statement of *circuit* conditions in Eq. (3):

$$E = Ri + L\frac{di}{dt} \tag{3}$$

and the statement of a *boundary* condition in Eq. (4):
when

$$t = 0, \quad i = 0 \tag{4}$$

These equations contain all the information needed to give the desired answer.

As in Sec. 6, the solution is accomplished by separation of the variables, for Eq. (3) may be written

$$dt = \frac{L\,di}{E - Ri} \qquad (15)$$

and when each side is integrated, this gives

$$t = -\frac{L}{R} \ln (E - Ri) + K' \qquad (16)$$

Then, changing the logarithmic form to the exponential,

$$E - Ri = \epsilon^{\frac{R}{L}(K' - t)} = \epsilon^{\frac{R}{L}K'} \epsilon^{-\frac{R}{L}t}$$

Finally, with K a constant different from K', but none the less arbitrary, we determine from the circuit equation alone that

$$i = K\epsilon^{-\frac{R}{L}t} + \frac{E}{R} \qquad (17)$$

But in order to evaluate K it is necessary to use the boundary condition of Eq. (4). Writing (17) when time is zero gives

$$0 = K + \frac{E}{R} \qquad \text{or} \qquad K = -\frac{E}{R} \qquad (18)$$

The expression for current is therefore written, from Eqs. (17) and (18),

$$i = \frac{E}{R}\left(1 - \epsilon^{-\frac{R}{L}t}\right) \qquad (19)$$

and the solution is complete.

9. Steady-state and Transient Components. It is interesting to note that the term K' is the steady-state current, to which a transient term is added to get total current. The exponential term is "transient" because as time passes, and t becomes larger and larger, the value of the exponential approaches zero and practically disappears. In further solutions of circuits we will find that the total current in a circuit may be analyzed into a transient component and a steady-state component. The steady-state component may often be evaluated by inspection, as might have been done in determining K' in Eq. (15). Of course, there will be cases when the steady-state current is zero; the example in which we found the diminishing current in a circuit after the applied voltage is removed is an illustration of this possibility, for there can be no steady-state current when there is no applied voltage.

But it is always true that we may find, if we wish, the steady-state term by ordinary steady-state analysis, using Ohm's law in direct-current circuits and making use of vectors and impedance when the applied voltage is alternating, and the current found in this way will always satisfy the differential equation that expresses *circuit* conditions. Then to satisfy also the *boundary* conditions, we add to the steady-state term a transient component.

In Eq. (17) the *magnitude K* of the transient component was determined by the boundary conditions, although the *form* of the transient component was determined by the circuit. The form, moreover, was identical with the form of the decaying transient current of Eq. (14); and as a general principle it may be stated that the form of the transient component can always be found by solving the circuit equation with zero substituted for the applied voltage.

10. Four Rules for Solution. In the two preceding paragraphs there are introduced a number of rules for procedure in solving for the current that flows in a circuit during the transient period. They may be summarized as follows:

1. Solve for the *form* of the transient component. To do this, write the differential equation of the circuit, with zero substituted for the applied voltage, and solve for current.

2. By any convenient method, find the steady-state current.

3. Add the transient component, whose magnitude is unknown, to the steady-state component.

4. By means of the boundary conditions, evaluate the coefficients of the transient component.

11. An Example. As an illustration of these rules, let us use them to solve again for the current in the circuit of Fig. 1, starting with Eqs. (3) and (4),

$$Ri + L\frac{di}{dt} = E \qquad\qquad (3)$$

and when

$$t = 0, \qquad i = 0 \qquad\qquad (4)$$

We know that

$$i = \text{transient component} + \text{steady component} \qquad (20)$$

To find the transient component we write, according to the **first rule,**

$$Ri + L\frac{di}{dt} = 0 \qquad (21)$$

and the solution of this is already known, from Eq. (10), to be of the form

$$\text{Transient component} = K\epsilon^{-\frac{R}{L}t} \qquad (22)$$

(Proof of the correctness of this form appears on substituting it back into Eq. (21), whereupon an identity results.) Then using the **second rule,**

$$\text{Steady-state component} = \frac{E}{R} \qquad (23)$$

Adding, in accordance with the **third rule,**

$$i = K\epsilon^{-\frac{R}{L}t} + \frac{E}{R} \qquad (24)$$

When time and current are both zero, (24) becomes

$$0 = K + \frac{E}{R}$$

so that

$$K = -\frac{E}{R} \qquad (25)$$

and having used the **fourth rule** we are able to write the complete form of the current:

$$i = \frac{E}{R}(1 - \epsilon^{-\frac{R}{L}t}) \qquad (26)$$

Rate of flow of energy is power, and either energy or power in any part of any circuit can easily be computed when the equation for current is known. Each circuit element receives power at any instant equal to the product of the current through it by the voltage across it. The power to resistance is ie_R, or $i(iR)$, or i^2R. The power to inductance is ie_L, or $iL\dfrac{di}{dt}$, and a negative value corresponds to an output of power by the inductance. These expressions for power can easily be evaluated from the equation which gives the instantaneous current.

The energy gained or lost by a circuit element through any interval of time is found by integrating the expression for power. The integration must be performed on the expression for power into which the general equation for current has been substituted; specific values of time are introduced as the limits of integration.

We find, however, that for most purposes it is the concept of the transient flow of energy, rather than its computation, that is most useful.

12. The Voltage Regulator. The vibrating voltage regulator is an interesting circuit that involves transient current in an inductance. The basic circuit of the regulator is shown in Fig. 5; the alternator whose voltage is being regulated is not shown, but the exciter

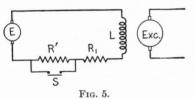

Fig. 5.

which supplies field current to the alternator is marked *Exc.* The field winding of the exciter is L, and current is supplied to it from a pilot-exciter E.

Voltage of the alternator is maintained at the correct average value by the automatic operation of the contactor S, which is continually vibrating, opening and closing at a rate of several times a second as the alternator voltage becomes a little too high and then a little too low. When the alternator voltage becomes too high, S opens; that reduces the exciter field current and so, by reducing the alternator field current, makes the alternating voltage lower. The voltage then becomes too low, and S closes; this allows more current to flow in the exciter circuit and in the main field circuit, and voltage becomes higher.

The actual operation of the vibrating regulator is complicated by having the contactor jointly controlled by the exciter voltage and the alternator voltage. This keeps the contactor in constant rapid vibration at a fixed rate; and the effect of a change of alternator voltage is to change the ratio of time open to time closed, without greatly altering the period of contactor operation.

When the contactor S operates, it alters the resistance in the exciter field circuit (see Fig. 5) and so controls the current in that circuit. Following each opening or closing there is a transient period before the steady current is established; in fact, the openings and closings come in such rapid succession that there is never time for a steady state to be reached.

For simplicity, in the first analysis, we will consider the exciter field circuit with two approximations:

1. The pilot-exciter supplies a constant voltage, E, and has negligible resistance and inductance.

2. The exciter field circuit has constant inductance, L, and any effect of saturation of iron in the exciter field system is neglected.

After the regulator has been in operation for some time, and its action has become stable, it will settle down to vibrating at a constant rate, with a constant ratio of time open to time closed for the contactor. At a time that we may designate $t = 0$ (see Fig. 6), there will be a current i_0 in the circuit; and at this instant the contactor closes. With the contactor closed, the circuit equation is similar to Eq. (3);

$$R_1 i + L \frac{di}{dt} = E \tag{27}$$

and for a boundary condition we have, when

$$t = 0, \qquad i = i_0 \tag{28}$$

In making use of the four rules for the determination of the current we **first** rewrite Eq. (27) without applied voltage as

$$R_1 i + L \frac{di}{dt} = 0 \tag{29}$$

and we know the solution of this has the form

$$\text{Transient component} = K_c \epsilon^{-\frac{R_1}{L}t} \tag{30}$$

The **second** step is to find the steady-state current:

$$\text{Steady-state component} = \frac{E}{R_1} \tag{31}$$

Third, the components are added to give

$$i = K_c \epsilon^{-\frac{R_1}{L}t} + \frac{E}{R_1} \tag{32}$$

Fourth, to evaluate the coefficient we refer back to Eq. (28) and substituting it in (32) get

$$i_0 = K_c + \frac{E}{R_1}$$

so that

$$K_c = i_0 - \frac{E}{R_1} \tag{33}$$

and

$$i = \left(i_0 - \frac{E}{R_1}\right)\epsilon^{-\frac{R_1}{L}t} + \frac{E}{R_1} \tag{34}$$

This gives current in terms of the initial current i_0, and unless we have further information about the value of i_0, this is as far as

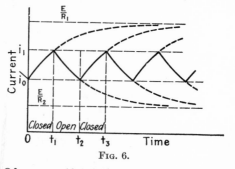

FIG. 6.

we can go. Of course, if i_0 is known to be a certain number of amperes, (34) is the complete solution, for all other coefficients on the right-hand side of the equation are known, and current is given as a function of time.

Figure 6 shows the manner in which current increases, approaching the steady-state value as time passes. But in the voltage-regulator circuit the steady state is not reached, and when time becomes t_1 the contactor S opens again. With S open, the circuit resistance is greater, and if $R_1 + R' = R_2$ the circuit equation may be written

$$R_2 i + L \frac{di}{dt} = E \tag{35}$$

First, the form of the transient will now be

$$K_o \epsilon^{-\frac{R_2}{L}t}$$

and, **second,** the steady-state component is

$$\frac{E}{R_2}$$

Third, the complete current may be written

$$i = K_o \epsilon^{-\frac{R_2}{L}t} + \frac{E}{R_2} \tag{36}$$

During the interval that the contactor was closed, from t_0 to t_1, the current increased from i_0 to a value that may be called i_1. This gives us as the boundary condition that when

$$t = t_1, \qquad i = i_1 \tag{37}$$

This combines with (36) to give

$$i_1 = K_o \epsilon^{-\frac{R_2}{L}t_1} + \frac{E}{R_2} \tag{38}$$

and, **fourth,**

$$K_o = \left(i_1 - \frac{E}{R_2}\right) \epsilon^{\frac{R_2}{L}t_1} \tag{39}$$

Equation (39) lacks the simplicity of the analogous Eq. (33) because the transient current under consideration begins at time t_1 instead of time zero. When it is substituted in (36) the complete current is seen to be

$$i = \left(i_1 - \frac{E}{R_2}\right) \epsilon^{-\frac{R_2}{L}(t - t_1)} + \frac{E}{R_2} \tag{40}$$

and this is the expression for current after time t_1. It is indicated in Fig. 6, in the time interval between t_1 and t_2. If the contactor remained open the current would approach the steady-state value of E/R_2, but when the current has been reduced to its initial value of i_0, the contactor will close again and the current will increase. Current in the period from t_2 to t_3 will duplicate the current from 0 to t_1, and may be written

$$i = \left(i_0 - \frac{E}{R_1}\right)\epsilon^{-\frac{R_1}{L}(t-t_2)} + \frac{E}{R_1} \qquad (41)$$

As long as the voltage regulator continues to operate without any change in its rate of vibration, this periodic saw-tooth current will flow in the exciter-field circuit, with the current in each period a repetition of the current in the preceding periods. This also is indicated in Fig. 6.

For the complete solution of the exciter problem it would be necessary to determine i_0 and i_1 in the current equations, for their values are probably not known. To do so it is necessary to know the length of time that the contactor is closed, and the length of time that it is open. Then, since the current must increase as much during the time the contactor is closed as it decreases while the contactor is open, it is possible to write two equations containing i_0 and i_1 as the only unknowns; these are obtained by finding from Eq. (34) the current i_1 at time t_1 in terms of i_0, and from Eq. (40) the current i_0 at time t_2 in terms of i_1. The resulting equations are then solved simultaneously for i_0 and i_1. But the complete solution need not be carried out here.

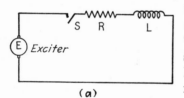

(a)

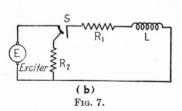

(b)

FIG. 7.

13. The Field Discharge Current. Current in an inductive circuit decreases gradually after the driving voltage has been removed, just as a moving automobile will coast to a stop after the clutch is disengaged. But an automobile cannot be stopped instantly, and if it runs into a wall the force of collision will usually be so great that something will break. An electrical "collision" occurs when the switch in an inductive circuit is suddenly opened.

If the switch in the circuit of Fig. 1 (or Fig. 7a) is closed long enough to permit the steady-state current to be established, and is then opened quickly, it will be found impossible to stop the current instantly. When the switch first begins to open, the current will start to diminish, but a change of current always induces a voltage in the inductance, proportional to the rate of change. This was stated in Eq. (1):

$$e_L = L \frac{di}{dt} \tag{1}$$

An increase of current (a positive rate of change) was found to induce a voltage that opposed the flow of current, and, similarly, a decrease of current (a negative rate of change) will induce a voltage that aids the flow of current. It is easy to remember that the induced voltage will always oppose a change of current. The induced voltage can never entirely prevent a change of current, for its very existence depends on there being a rate of change of current, but the induced voltage will in every case make a change of current more gradual.

So the inductance L, in which the opening switch has caused a negative rate of change of current, will act for the moment as a source of high voltage as it supplies energy to maintain the flow of current, and this excess voltage will appear between the blades of the opening switch—just as it would if any other source of voltage were in a circuit with an open switch. The induced voltage will be high enough to cause an arc to form at the switch blades, and the circuit current will continue to flow through the arc, although at a diminishing rate. The current will diminish just rapidly enough to supply [in agreement with Eq. (1)] the induced voltage needed to maintain the current, until the current has diminished to zero and the transient period of decaying current is ended.

There will always be a perfect balance between the voltage needed to maintain current in the circuit and the voltage induced in the inductance. If the induced voltage were too small to maintain current through the arc after the switch is open, the current would either have to cease at once or at least would diminish more rapidly. But a more rapidly diminishing current would induce a greater voltage, until the induced voltage did become sufficient to maintain the current. In the extreme case, a current stopped instantly would induce infinite voltage; but this is impossible, for an infinite voltage would maintain a current no matter how rapidly the switch was opened. The relation of the circuit voltages is expressed in a modification of Eq. (3):

$$E = Ri + L\frac{di}{dt} + e_a \tag{42}$$

in which e_a is included to represent the voltage required to maintain an arc at the opening switch. Equation (42) is like our other circuit equations in that one side of it is the applied voltage of the battery, while the other side is the sum of all the drops in the rest of the circuit. In this special case, $\frac{di}{dt}$ is negative, and e_a may be many times greater than E if the current is diminishing rapidly enough and L is sufficiently great.

Equation (42) is not an easy equation to use, for e_a is a function of current of a more or less indeterminate sort, and its value also depends on the speed with which the switch is opened. We are quite safe, however, in saying that the more rapidly the switch is opened the higher the induced voltage will be, and that the only limit to the induced voltage is the amount of voltage needed to maintain the current.

It is this last consideration that emphasizes the practical danger of allowing an inductive circuit to be opened too rapidly. When the direct current in the highly inductive field circuit of a large generator is interrupted suddenly, the induced voltage may easily be several thousand volts. If the normal voltage on the field is only 125 volts, this overvoltage will be dangerous to the insulation of the winding, and a rapidly opened circuit may readily result in puncture of the insulation between leads, between turns, or between the field winding and its iron core.

To avoid damage of this sort, it is standard practice to use a "field-discharge resistor." A second contact point is placed on the field switch, as shown in Fig. 7b, and to it is connected the discharge resistor R_2. The switch is built so that when it is opening, the blade will make contact with the resistor contact-point before contact is lost with the exciter contact-point. By this means, the switch may be moved from the closed position to the resistor contact-point without interrupting the current through the inductance, and the field current will then gradually die away as the energy stored in the inductance is used up as heat in the resistances R_1 and R_2. Equation (6) was written for a circuit of this kind:

$$Ri + L\frac{di}{dt} = 0 \tag{6}$$

and in the field-discharge circuit

$$R = R_1 + R_2$$

In complying with the four rules for the solution of Eq. (6), we find **first** that the applied voltage is zero and no substitution is needed. The solution of (6) gives

$$i = K\epsilon^{-\frac{R}{L}t} \tag{11}$$

For the **second** and **third** rules, there is no steady-state current, owing to the lack of applied voltage, so Eq. (11) expresses the whole current. The **fourth** rule requires that we evaluate K from the known boundary condition that when time is zero, current equals E/R_1; substituting these values in (11) gives

$$\frac{E}{R_1} = K$$

so that finally

$$i = \frac{E}{R_1}\epsilon^{-\frac{R}{L}t} = \frac{E}{R_1}\epsilon^{-\frac{R_1+R_2}{L}t} \tag{43}$$

Equation (43) may be compared with (14), a solution of the same type of circuit. In (14) the resistance R appears in the coefficient of the exponential, and the same value of R is in the exponent. The coefficient in each equation is the initial current, while the exponent determines the rate of decay of the current. But in the field circuit of Fig. 7b, only R_1 limits the initial current, so it alone appears in the coefficient, whereas the discharge current flows through both R_1 and R_2. Since the total resistance is effective in diminishing the current, $R_1 + R_2$ appears in the exponent of Eq. (43). This shows how the same circuit equation may have different solutions, depending on the boundary conditions, but the solution in each case is obtained by application of the four rules of Sec. 10.

Figure 4 gives a picture of the decay of current in the field circuit, except that Fig. 4 was drawn to satisfy different boundary conditions. Hence the initial current and the initial slope of Fig. 4 must be changed for the field-circuit case. The current in the field circuit, when time is zero, is E/R_1. The initial slope may be found by differentiating Eq. (43) and then making $t = 0$.

$$\frac{di}{dt} = \frac{E}{R_1}\left(-\frac{R}{L}\right)\epsilon^{-\frac{R}{L}t}$$ (44)

and

$$\frac{di_0}{dt} = -\frac{ER}{LR_1}$$ (45)

The discharge of energy from the field circuit is an excellent illustration of the importance of the energy stored in an inductive circuit. The current cannot be stopped until the electromagnetic energy of the highly inductive field circuit is completely exhausted; if a field-discharge resistor is used, the energy will be changed to heat in a safe and orderly manner, whereas, if the circuit is broken without the resistor, the field-circuit energy will be largely dissipated as heat and light in an arc through air— the time of discharge of energy in the arc will be short, and the violence of action may be almost explosive. It might be possible to prevent an arc at the switch terminals by immersing them in oil and by extremely rapid opening of the switch; in such a case the electromagnetic energy has no choice but to expend itself in puncturing the insulation of the field circuit, and it is to avoid this danger that the discharge resistor is supplied.

The value of resistance to be used in the practical application of the field-discharge resistor may vary within wide limits. If the resistance is too high, it will not be very effective in reducing the induced voltage, for the entire absence of a discharge resistor is merely the limiting case as the resistance is increased to infinity. It is helpful to remember that at the instant of opening the switch the entire steady-state field current must flow momentarily through the discharge resistor, and when time is zero, current is E/R_1. The voltage across the discharge resistor will be greatest at this instant of greatest current and will be equal to the product of current and resistance:

$$\frac{E}{R_1}R_2.$$

Too high a value of R_2, the discharge resistance, would give an excessive induced voltage. As the normal applied voltage is E, it is possible to secure complete safety by making R_2 equal R_1; if this is done, the induced voltage can not exceed the applied voltage. But a higher voltage than this may be perfectly safe, and a value of R_2 equal to several times R_1 is usually not objectionable. A low resistance, on the other hand, has distinct disadvantages. While the switch is being opened, the switch blade makes contact with both exciter circuit and discharge resistor circuit for a moment, placing the full voltage of the exciter across R_2. With a low resistance, a large current will flow, and although this does no harm in normal operation, it may burn out the resistor if the switch is accidentally left for some time in the mid-position. A compromise value of resistance is used therefore on all modern machines.

14. Other Illustrations. It is easy to find illustrations of transient currents in circuits containing inductance and resistance. The only really important way in which an electric current can do anything useful, except heating and lighting, is by exerting a magnetic force—as in a motor, a doorbell, a telegraph, an ammeter or voltmeter, or even a telephone. The magnetic force involves inductance in fairly large amount. So we need only look around to find innumerable examples of transient currents in inductive circuits.

Circuits illustrating transient currents in capacitance and resistance are rare, but they are none the less interesting or vital on that account.

Problems

1. Connect a coil, a resistor, a battery, and a switch to give the circuit of Fig. 1. By means of an oscillograph, record the current that flows in the circuit when the switch is closed. Make three records with the same value of inductance and voltage, but different resistances. Use a coil that does not have an iron core, for there are losses in iron that are not included in the circuit's resistance. Measure the circuit parameters.

Transfer the experimentally determined curves from the oscillogram to a sheet of cross-section paper, plotting current as a function of time. On the same sheet, plot the corresponding curves as computed from the circuit parameters. Discuss the reasons for any differences that may appear between the observed and computed curves.

If it is not convenient to make an oscillographic record, that which is reproduced as oscillogram 1 may be used. This is an unaltered photographic record exactly as it came from the oscillograph. The lines on the record are, from top to bottom:

a. A line for calibration purposes, produced by a steady current of 2.50 amp. in the circuit. This gives the vertical scale of the oscillogram.

b. The transient current with low resistance.

c. The transient current with medium resistance.

d. The transient current with high resistance.

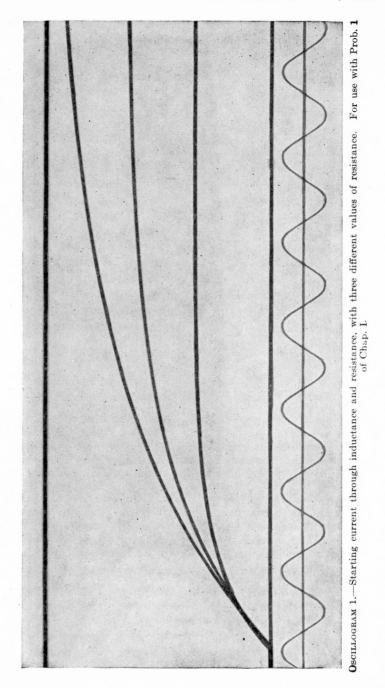

Oscillogram 1.—Starting current through inductance and resistance, with three different values of resistance. For use with Prob. 1 of Chap. I.

e. A line recorded with no current flowing.

f. A wave recorded by 60-cycle voltage, which plays no part in the transient behaviour but serves to calibrate the time scale of the oscillogram. With it is its zero line.

The measured parameters and voltage are:

$E = 67.2$ volts.   Low resistance = 26.82 ohms.
$L = 1.37$ henrys.   Medium resistance = 41.38 ohms.
      High resistance = 78.40 ohms.

It will be seen that three records are superposed on one oscillogram. Usually this is not desirable, for the timing wave can be simultaneous with only one of them (in this case with the low resistance record). It was done in this case to show that the initial slopes of all three curves are identical.

2. A six-pole 300-kw. 1200 r.p.m. 275-volt direct-current generator is designed to carry a main gap flux of 0.072 webers (7,200,000 maxwells). Leakage is 15 per cent of this. Each field spool contains 620 turns, the coils in series measure 7.1 ohms total resistance, and carry a normal current of 15 amp.

a. What is the self-inductance of the field circuit?

b. If 125 volts is applied to the field terminals what field-rheostat resistance is required to allow normal current to flow, and what percentage of the total voltage is the voltage across the rheostat?

c. What time must elapse before the field current has risen to 0.4 strength?, 0.9 strength?

d. With full field what is the energy stored in the magnetic field?

e. What must be the value of the field-discharge resistor to limit the voltage across the field to 1500 volts upon opening this circuit? What difference, if any, does it make if the resistor is placed inside rather than outside the field rheostat?

f. How much energy will the discharge resistor have to dissipate? Would the question of heating be of much importance in its design?

g. Why not make this resistor of zero resistance, or as low as possible, so as to reduce the induced field voltage?

State whatever assumptions you make in any of the steps of the problem.

3. A battery is suddenly connected to a circuit of inductance and resistance. At what value of current is the magnetic field receiving energy at the maximum rate?

4. The primary circuit of the spark coil of an automobile ignition system is shown in the diagram. A spark is produced (by the spark-coil secondary winding which is not shown) each time the cam allows the timer switch to open. What fraction of steady-state current is interrupted by the timer when it is producing sparks at the rate of 10,000 per min.? The inductance of the coil is 6.34 millihenrys and the resistance is 2.2 ohms. Assume that the cam operates so that the timer switch is open during the same length of time that it is closed.

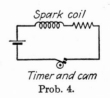

Spark coil

Timer and cam
Prob. 4.

CHAPTER II

THE BEHAVIOR OF CONDENSERS

1. Capacitance. In the early days of electricity, the condenser was named because of its ability to receive and contain what the pioneers were accustomed to call "the electric fluid." It is not, however, like a tank for water that will hold a definite volume of liquid, and is then full; but rather it is like a tank of air whose content is limited only by the pressure that can be applied. By increasing the "electric pressure" a greater amount of the "electric fluid" can be forced into the condenser, and if the analogy is still good the fluid will be "condensed."

We have in this century a different picture of the operation of a condenser, because we have a different concept of electricity, but externally the "condenser" idea is perfectly valid and in modern terms we say that the charge on a condenser is proportional to the terminal voltage. C, the condenser's capacitance, is defined as the factor of proportionality, so that the charge $q = Ce$. Hence the condenser voltage is

$$e = \frac{1}{C} q \tag{46}$$

Since charge is the accumulation of current, it is possible to find the charge on a condenser at any moment by integrating the current that has entered the condenser. Conversely, current is the flow of charge, and the condenser current is the rate of change of the condenser's charge. Interpreting charge as the integral of current, in Eq. (46), gives

$$e = \frac{1}{C} \int i \, dt \tag{47}$$

2. Charging a Condenser. When a battery is suddenly connected to a condenser and a resistance in series, as in Fig. 8, the condenser will be charged by current flowing through the resistance. It will not be charged all at once, however, but there will be a surge of current that will diminish gradually as charge accumulates on the condenser. The shape of the current surge is shown in Fig. 9b.

The circuit equation in which the applied voltage is equated to the sum of the resistance voltage and the condenser voltage, is

$$E = Ri + \frac{1}{C}\int i \, dt \qquad (48)$$

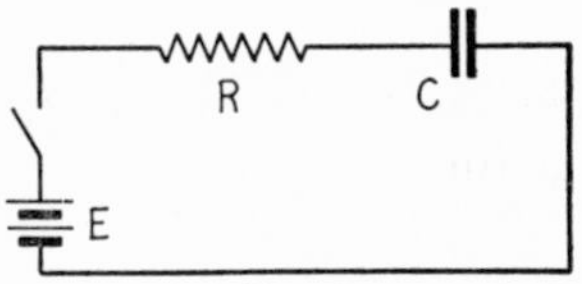

FIG. 8.

Until the switch is closed there will be no charge on the condenser, and there will be no voltage across it; so just at the instant of closing the switch the entire battery voltage E will be applied to the resistance, and the current will be E/R. This initial value of current can also be found from Eq. (48), for when time is zero the integral term must be zero, there having been no lapse of time in which current might flow and charge accumulate, and if the initial current is called i_0,

$$i_0 = \frac{E}{R} \qquad (49)$$

In Fig. 9a we wish to plot voltage as a function of time. The initial resistance voltage, e_{R0}, is equal to the applied voltage E;

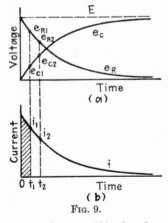

FIG. 9.

and the initial condenser voltage, e_{C0}, is zero. But current will flow through the resistance into the condenser, and as charge accumulates on the condenser there will appear a voltage corresponding to the integral term in Eq. (48). At some time t_1, shortly after closing the switch, the condenser voltage will have grown to e_{C1}; and since the applied voltage remains constant it follows that the resistance voltage must have decreased. There will have been a decrease of current, and the resistance voltage will be less by exactly the amount that the condenser voltage has increased. So at t_1, in Fig. 9a, we locate e_{C1} and e_{R1} in such a way that their sum is E. The value of e_{C1} is obtained from Eq. (47); it is proportional to the integral of current. To find the integral of current, a curve of current is drawn in Fig. 9b, with the initial current, i_0, equal to E/R. At every instant the voltage across the resistance is proportional to the current, and

$$e_R = Ri \tag{2}$$

So the current at time t_1 can be found from the resistance voltage at time t_1:

$$i_1 = \frac{e_{R1}}{R}$$

Charge on the condenser is the integral of current, so it is equal to the shaded area under the current curve, between zero time and t_1. Finally, this charge divided by capacitance gives condenser voltage e_{C1}, which we plot in Fig. 9a.

It is clear, of course, that this system is not well adapted to computation, because you cannot find e_{C1} unless you know e_{R1}, and you do not know e_{R1} until you have found e_{C1}; so a trial-and-error method is the only way that numerical values could be found. But when t_1 is a differential time instead of a finite interval, the error is an infinitesimal of second order, and may be neglected, and so the methods of calculus will readily determine current at every instant.

The area under the current curve as far as i_2 determines the value of e_{C2}, because it represents the charge on the condenser at time t_2, and voltage at any time can be found in the same way. But the difference between e_{C2} and e_{C1} is less than the difference between e_{C1} and e_{C0} because the area under the current curve is less during the second time interval than during the first. And so the voltage curves continue; in each succeeding interval of time the current is less, so during each interval the condenser gains less charge than in the previous one; as a result, the condenser voltage increases always more slowly, and the resistance voltage together with the flow of current will die away more and more gradually. The current will approach zero, as shown in Fig. 9b, and the condenser will gradually reach its steady charge and voltage as the current ceases.

Before proceeding with the formal solution, one feature of circuit operation that has been accepted in the discussion must be written into the symbolism; that is the limit of integration of current to obtain charge. Since current cannot flow until the switch is closed, and hence charge cannot begin to accumulate, there is no need to begin integrating until the instant of closing the switch, so the lower time limit is zero. The upper time limit may be any value of time at which we wish to determine conditions; it may be, for instance, t_1 or t_2 as in Fig. 9, or any other value. To be entirely general we will let the upper limit be any time t. The circuit equation then is

$$E = Ri + \frac{1}{C}\int_0^t i\, dt \qquad (50)$$

The current curve in Fig. 9 seems to have the same general shape as the curve of Fig. 4, which showed the dying out of current after the driving voltage was removed from an inductive circuit. To show that the similarity is more than superficial, we may determine the analytic form of condenser current from Eq. (50). To put this equation into a form similar to one we have already solved, we differentiate both sides with respect to time, giving

$$0 = R\frac{di}{dt} + \frac{1}{C}i \qquad (51)$$

which may be written

$$\frac{1}{C}i + R\frac{di}{dt} = 0 \qquad (52)$$

This is the differential equation of the circuit and its solution may be found by integration. The variables i and t of Eq. (52) may be separated, and the method of solution is the same that was used for Eq. (6):

$$\frac{1}{i}di = -\frac{1}{RC}dt$$

$$\int \frac{di}{i} = -\frac{1}{RC}\int dt$$

$$\ln i = -\frac{1}{RC}t + A$$

$$i = K\epsilon^{-\frac{1}{RC}t} \qquad (53)$$

It is interesting to compare Eq. (52) with (6), which is

$$Ri + L\frac{di}{dt} = 0 \tag{6}$$

It will be seen that Eqs. (6) and (52) are of the same form and differ only in coefficients. The solution of (6) is

$$i = K\epsilon^{-\frac{R}{L}t} \tag{10}$$

and the solution of (52) is exactly parallel and could have been deduced from (6) and (10). Referring again to the four rules for solution, we find that we have followed the first of them: Eq. (52), the differential equation, has no constant term to be set equal to zero, and its solution was found and is given in Eq. (53). In applying the second rule, we see from the circuit that there is no steady-state current, for the condenser blocks any continuous flow of direct current; therefore the steady-state term is zero. It remains, then, only to evaluate by boundary conditions the unknown coefficient K of Eq. (53); at the moment of closing the switch the current is E/R, as is given in Eq. (49), and when this is substituted in (53) with $t = 0$ the result is

$$\frac{E}{R} = K$$

so that finally

$$i = \frac{E}{R}\epsilon^{-\frac{1}{RC}t} \tag{54}$$

and this is the analytical form of the current plotted in Fig. 9b.

To remove any possible doubt that this is the correct expression for current, introduce it into the circuit equation (50).

$$E = R\left(\frac{E}{R}\epsilon^{-\frac{1}{RC}t}\right) + \frac{1}{C}\int_0^t \frac{E}{R}\epsilon^{-\frac{1}{RC}t}dt$$

$$= E\epsilon^{-\frac{1}{RC}t} - E(\epsilon^{-\frac{1}{RC}t} - 1) \equiv E \tag{55}$$

The reduction of the equation to an identity gives final proof.

While the condenser is being charged it is storing energy in electrostatic form. Energy comes from the battery; some of it is transferred to the condenser as current flows in opposition to the condenser voltage, and the rest is changed to heat in the resistance. Energy flows rapidly from the battery as soon as the switch is closed, for the battery supplies power in proportion to the current; at the first instant, however, it is all lost in heat, for the first small bit of charge flows into the condenser without opposition. Then, as the condenser becomes partly charged, the condenser voltage rises, and the flow of energy into the condenser increases. But the current, meanwhile, is diminishing, and the rate of storage of energy passes a maximum and then decreases.

The power, or rate of flow of energy, supplied to the condenser at each instant is found by multiplying the condenser voltage by the circuit current. This may be done graphically by multiplying the curve of e_C in Fig. 9a by the curve of i in Fig. 9b, or it may be done analytically by multiplying the corresponding equations. Reference to the curves of Fig. 9 shows that power will be zero at the first instant, for e_C is then zero, and it will again be zero in the steady state when i is zero. The rate of dissipation of electric energy in the resistance is given by the product of e_R and i. Total energy may be found by integration of the power, and the energy stored in the condenser at any instant may also be computed from $\frac{1}{2}Ce^2$.

It is interesting to notice that the amount of energy lost in the resistance of the circuit of Fig. 8 while charging the condenser is exactly equal to the amount of energy stored in the condenser. The battery, therefore, is called upon to supply double the quantity of energy stored. When the transient period is over, and current has ceased to flow, the condenser voltage is equal to the battery voltage and the condenser energy has attained a value of $\frac{1}{2}CE^2$—E being the battery voltage.

To compute the energy dissipated in the resistance while the condenser is being charged, we integrate the power the resistance consumes over the entire time from zero to infinity. The power is of course i^2R, and the energy lost in the resistance is therefore

$$\int_0^\infty i^2R \, dt = \int_0^\infty \left(\frac{E}{R} \epsilon^{-\frac{1}{RC}t} \right)^2 R \, dt$$

$$= \frac{E^2}{R} \int_0^\infty \epsilon^{-\frac{2}{RC}t} dt = \frac{1}{2}CE^2$$

This is equal to the amount of energy stored in the condenser, and it is independent of the magnitude of the resistance.

3. Discharging a Condenser. A lightning cloud is in some ways like one plate of a condenser; the other plate may be another cloud, or it may be the ground below. This atmospheric condenser is gradually charged by rain and currents of air until a very high voltage exists between cloud and ground; then suddenly a lightning flash results and the plates of the condenser are connected together (through the lightning) and the condenser is discharged.

On a smaller scale, the same thing happens whenever a charged condenser has its plates connected together: the condenser discharges, and its stored energy is lost as heat in the circuit. If the condenser in Fig. 10 is initially charged, for example, and then the switch S is closed, there will be a surge of current through the resistance, which will gradually die out, leaving the condenser discharged. The circuit equation for this circuit is similar to Eq. (50), but there is no impressed voltage, and the condenser starts with an initial charge. If the initial charge is q_0, the initial condenser voltage will be

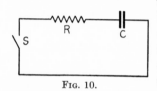

Fig. 10.

$$e_{c0} = \frac{q_0}{C} \tag{56}$$

and the initial charge must be added to the accumulated charge to get the total charge (and hence the condenser voltage) at any instant. On removing the applied voltage term and introducing the initial charge q_0, the circuit equation becomes

$$Ri + \frac{1}{C}\left(q_0 + \int_0^t i\,dt\right) = 0 \tag{57}$$

It is interesting to note that in this equation we have already introduced a boundary condition: that the initial charge on the condenser is q_0. But in rewriting (57) as a differential equation, in (58), this information regarding the boundary condition is lost from the mathematics and must be introduced again later. There is a way to avoid this complication, but for the present we will follow the four rules for solution, and differentiate Eq. (57) to obtain, as the differential equation of the circuit

$$R\frac{di}{dt} + \frac{1}{C}i = 0 \tag{58}$$

Since this is the same equation as (52), it has the same form of solution,

$$i = K\epsilon^{-\frac{1}{RC}t} \qquad (59)$$

In following rule 2, we find that again there is no steady-state current because there is no impressed voltage, so (59) is the complete current. To evaluate K it is necessary to consider the initial condition of the circuit: at the instant when the switch is closed there is a charge q_0 on the condenser, and this produces a voltage between condenser terminals equal to q_0/C [as was stated in Eq. (56)]; this voltage will be connected to the resistance by the closing of the switch, and will produce an instantaneous current of

$$i_0 = \frac{q_0}{C}\frac{1}{R} \qquad (60)$$

The current will of course diminish rapidly as the condenser loses its charge, but Eq. (60) gives the value of current when time is zero. Substituting i_0 for i, and zero for t, in Eq. (59) gives

$$K = \frac{q_0}{CR} \qquad (61)$$

so that

$$i = \frac{q_0}{CR}\epsilon^{-\frac{1}{RC}t} \qquad (62)$$

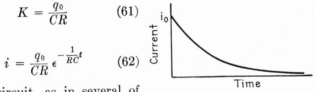

FIG. 11.

In this circuit, as in several of the others, the coefficient of the exponential is the initial current, and (62) may be written

$$i = i_0\epsilon^{-\frac{1}{RC}t} \qquad (63)$$

Current is plotted as a function of time in Fig. 11.

4. Operational Notation. The use of operational calculus in the solution of equations involving transient electrical phenomena has proved so powerful, and at the same time so convenient, that its adoption has been practically universal. Nevertheless, a thorough understanding of the classic solutions of fundamental circuits is indispensable before the operational method can be handled expediently. The classic method involves obtaining a solution of the differential equation of a circuit and then evaluating its arbitrary constants by means of known boundary conditions. The operational method accomplishes the solution in one step by assuming that the circuit has initially no stored energy; although if this is not the case the equations may be correspondingly altered. With simple circuits the classic method offers the simplest solution; but the operational method has evolved a notation that is a sort of shorthand way of writing differential equations, and it is always helpful to use operational symbols.

First, there is p, an abbreviation for $\dfrac{d}{dt}$, so that the meaning is the same whether we write Eq. (1) as

$$e_L = L \frac{di}{dt} \tag{1}$$

or as

$$e_L = Lpi \tag{64}$$

In other words, p is a *derivative operator*, and this is all the definition of it that is needed just now. It operates, as the symbol $\dfrac{d}{dt}$ does, on the function of time that is written to the right of it; and if there is ever any question concerning the use of p, the difficulty can be removed by writing $\dfrac{d}{dt}$ instead.

With this notation the circuit equation for the inductive circuit can be changed from

$$E = Ri + L \frac{di}{dt} \tag{3}$$

to the operational form

$$E = Ri + Lpi \tag{65}$$

and the differential equation of the condenser circuit, Eq. (58), becomes

$$\frac{1}{C}i + Rpi = 0 \tag{66}$$

The current to be operated upon by p in Eq. (65) (to be, in other words, differentiated with respect to time) is given in Eq. (19) as

$$i = \frac{E}{R}(1 - \epsilon^{-\frac{R}{L}t}) \tag{19}$$

and the curve of this current as a function of time is shown in Fig. 2. The quantity pi is merely the derivative, or slope, of the curve.

The solution for current in Eq. (66) is given by (63) as

$$i = i_0\epsilon^{-\frac{1}{RC}t} \tag{63}$$

This is the current, and its derivative is

$$pi = -\frac{i_0}{RC}\epsilon^{-\frac{1}{RC}t} \tag{67}$$

(for all positive values of time).

The slope of the current curve in Fig. 11, then, is given by Eq. (67) during the time when the switch is closed.

Another operational symbol is $1/p$, and it is an integrating operator. Since p is a derivative operator and $1/p$ is an integrating operator, the application of p will remove the effect of applying $1/p$ to a current. It is best to define $1/p$ as a definite integral with limits 0 and t, so that

$$\frac{1}{p}i = \int_0^t i\, dt \tag{68}$$

This has the advantage of avoiding a constant of integration that is essential to the indefinite integral. Of course, with $1/p$ defined in this way, and with p defined as the inverse operator, there will sometimes be trouble in interpreting p as a simple time derivative; but in much of our work no such conflict will arise, and when it does it will be pointed out and studied further.

With the operational symbol of integration we can write Eq. (50) as

$$E = Ri + \frac{1}{C}\frac{1}{p}i$$

and for convenience this is often written

$$E = Ri + \frac{1}{Cp}i \tag{69}$$

or even

$$E = \left(R + \frac{1}{Cp}\right)i$$

In the same notation, Eq. (57) becomes

$$Ri + \frac{q_0}{C} + \frac{1}{Cp}i = 0 \tag{70}$$

Since p is defined as an operator that cancels an operation by $\frac{1}{p}$, it follows that $p\frac{1}{p}i$ is just equal to i, and the two operations together have no effect. So

$$p\frac{1}{p}i = i \tag{71}$$

This fact can be used in deriving Eq. (51) from (50). Equation (50) has been written in operational notation as Eq. (69). To differentiate each side of (69), we operate by p, giving

$$pE = p\left(Ri + \frac{1}{Cp}i\right) = pRi + \frac{p}{Cp}i \tag{72}$$

but E is not a function of time so pE is zero, R is merely a constant, and p/p designates two operations that taken together produce no result. So Eq. (72) becomes

$$0 = Rpi + \frac{1}{C}i \tag{73}$$

and this is equivalent to Eq. (51).

The relation of Eq. (71) and the use made of it in the rest of the paragraph give the first indication of one of the chief values of operational notation. When differentiation is indicated by p and integration by $1/p$ (or as it is often written, p^{-1}) these operational symbols can be used to multiply and divide each other just as though they were algebraic quantities. In getting Eq. (73), for example, the left-hand member of (72) is differentiated and the two terms of the right-hand member are *operated on* by p according to the same rules as if it were *multiplication* by p. There is one thing that must be carefully remembered, however.

Any operator, whether written p or $\frac{d}{dt}$, or as an integral, operates only on a function of time which is written to the right of it in the equation. In Eq. (73), Rpi means resistance times the derivative of current with respect to time, and pRi would mean the same thing because R is a constant, but Rip is just as meaningless a thing to write as $Ri\dfrac{d}{dt}$.

The second derivative of current is the derivative of the derivative, so

$$\frac{d^2i}{dt^2} = p(pi)$$

and this commonly written

$$\frac{d^2i}{dt^2} = p^2i \tag{74}$$

In this way the notation can be extended to include any order of derivative; while p^{-2}, and so on, will indicate higher orders of integration.

But the essential feature of the operational method is that *it is correct to make algebraic transformations among operators applied to a time function*, for they obey the associative, commutative, and distributive laws, and much of calculus becomes merely algebra.

5. Applications of Condensers. There are three general uses for condensers in which the characteristics of their transient currents are of value. One is as a storage place for electrical energy until it is needed; this application is seen in many rectifiers in which a condenser is charged by the crest of the rectified alternating voltage wave, and the stored energy then flows from the condenser into the direct-current system between the half-cycles of alternating current, and power is supplied by the rectifier to the load even during the times when it can receive none from the incoming line. The use of the condenser makes it possible to obtain a nearly constant flow of power in the direct-current output system, although the rectifier is supplied with power in pulses that come from a 60-cycle system at the rate of 120 per second. In a modulation meter for radio measurements, a similar principle is used to charge a condenser to the crest voltage of the modulated wave, and the charge leaks off through a resistance at a rate that must be known.

Frequently, too, a condenser is used to receive energy—not for future use, however, but just to get rid of it.   If a condenser had been used in the field-discharge circuit of Fig. 7*b*, instead of the resistance R_2, the inductance of the field circuit could have poured its energy into the condenser and an arc at the switch would have been avoided just as well as with a resistance.   In the case of a generator field the size of condenser required would make such application too expensive, and a resistance is better adapted to the use.   But a similar circuit in which a condenser is used is in the ignition system of an automobile; to prevent sparking at the timer points, the timer switch is shunted by a condenser that takes the first rush of current from the coil when the timer switch opens.

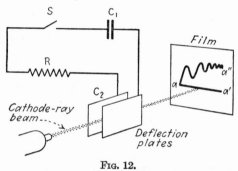

FIG. 12.

A third application of condensers makes use of the known rate of discharge of a condenser for timing purposes.   In a cathode-ray tube, for instance, a cathode-ray beam is deflected by an electric field between two parallel metal plates.   The cathode-ray beam, after deflection, passes on to strike against a fluorescent screen or, in some applications, a photographic film.   By proper control of the electric field, the cathode-ray beam can be made to sweep across the screen at a known rate.   It is commonly desirable to have the rate of travel of the beam across the screen constant, so that distance on the screen bears a linear relation to time.   Such cathode-ray tubes are used in oscilloscopes and for viewing tubes of television and radar sets.

6. The Oscillograph Sweep Circuit.   In Fig. 12 the essential elements of the sweep circuit are shown.   The cathode ray is projected between deflection plates onto a film or screen.   The "beam," or stream of electrons, is deflected by a field between the plates, and, when the deflecting field is increased, the beam is swept across the film from the point a to the point a'. As it goes it leaves a trace on the film that becomes visible when the film is developed, just as if the electron beam were a beam of light. When the beam is moved across the photographic film by the deflection plates acting alone, the record is a straight line, aa', and it is the time axis of the oscillogram. Transient voltages are recorded on the film by another set of deflection plates, set at right angles to the sweep plates, that produce a vertical deflection on the film so that the electron jet traces a line (illustrated by aa'') as a record of the transient voltage.

Before the oscillograph is to be operated, a condenser, C_1 in Fig. 12, is charged to some voltage E. It will receive a charge q_0 equal to EC_1. When the operator desires to have the electron beam begin sweeping across the film, the switch S is closed, and charge flows from the condenser onto the deflection plates producing a voltage between the plates of C_2 and a current in the resistance R.

Since the sum of the voltages around the circuit must be zero, the circuit equation is (in operational notation)

$$\left(\frac{q_0}{C_1} + \frac{1}{C_1 p}i\right) + \frac{1}{C_2 p}i + Ri = 0 \tag{75}$$

The first term of this equation expresses the initial condenser voltage due to the charge q_0; and since the second term gives the change of the condenser voltage as discharge occurs, the total condenser voltage at any instant is the sum of the first two terms. The third term is the voltage that appears between the deflection plates as current flows, and the last term of the left-hand member is the resistance voltage.

When the switch is closed, the condenser C_1 will start to discharge through the resistance; since at the first moment there will be no charge on the deflection plates they will not oppose the flow of current, and the initial current will be the initial condenser voltage divided by the resistance:

$$i_0 = -\frac{q_0}{C_1}\frac{1}{R} \tag{76}$$

But as charge accumulates on the deflection plates C_2, an opposing voltage will result and the current will rapidly become smaller; at the same time the voltage of the condenser C_1 will have grown less than its initial value as the initial charge flows away. So the voltage between the deflection plates will become greater and the condenser voltage will become less, and as the two opposed voltages approach equality the current will die away to zero. That is a qualitative picture of the transient current.

In Eqs. (75) and (76) there is a question of algebraic sign that needs further discussion. All of the terms of Eq. (75) were written with the positive sign, and justification for doing so is needed. First, one direction around the circuit must be chosen as the positive direction, and a current flowing in such direction is a positive current; the choice is entirely arbitrary, but it is customary to designate a current flowing in a clockwise direction as positive. In Fig. 13 the arrow indicates the positive direction of current. A counterclockwise current is negative. Next, an increase of a positive current produces a positive rate-of-change of current, for that interpretation is essential to the idea of rate of change.

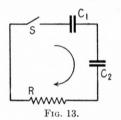

FIG. 13.

Finally, a positive current flowing into a condenser will place a positive charge on the condenser, and the integral of a positive current is a positive charge.

In applying these matters of definition to Eq. (75), we must consider which of the quantities in the equation will be negative. If the current is to flow in a positive or clockwise direction, the initial charge q_0 must have been negative, for it must have originally been placed on the condenser by a current flowing in a counterclockwise direction—a negative current—and a negative current will build up a negative charge. So q_0 is negative, and a positive current flows after the switch is closed, making the charge less and less negative. All the other terms will be positive. On the other hand, if q_0 had been placed on the condenser as a positive charge, the current i would have been negative, and so of course would all the terms which contain the current.

In Eq. (76), the initial charge is negative and the initial current is positive, so to make the right-hand member containing q_0 come out positive it must be written with a negative sign.

It is important to notice that Eq. (76), a boundary condition, can be obtained from Eq. (75), the circuit equation, when the proper information is worked into the mathematics of (75). As is always the case, all physical information must be put into mathematical form before the problem can be solved, for the mathematics will not supply ideas; but in this example we can change the form of our information from knowledge about initial charge (which we have) to knowledge about initial current (which we want) by means of algebra. We know that there is no initial charge except the charge q_0 on the condenser, so that the integral of circuit current is zero when time is zero. That is, when

$$t = 0, \qquad \frac{1}{p}i = 0 \tag{77}$$

When $\frac{1}{p}i$ is made zero in Eq. (75) the equation reduces to Eq. (76). Although in this case the initial current can be written directly by inspection of the circuit, it will often be valuable to be able to determine unknown initial conditions by introducing known conditions into the circuit equation.

The solution of Eq. (75) is begun by differentiating all its terms; this gives

$$\left(\frac{1}{C_1} + \frac{1}{C_2}\right)i + Rpi = 0 \tag{78}$$

The expression for current that will satisfy this equation has the familiar form

$$i = K\epsilon^{\lambda t} \tag{79}$$

where

$$\lambda = -\frac{1}{R}\frac{C_1 + C_2}{C_1 C_2} \tag{80}$$

Next, the boundary condition of Eq. (76) is introduced into Eq. (79), time being zero, and

$$i_0 = -\frac{q_0}{RC_1} = K \tag{81}$$

Having this value of K, we may now finally write the current

$$i = -\frac{q_0}{RC_1}\epsilon^{\lambda t} \tag{82}$$

But in this problem the desired result is not the current, but the voltage on the deflection plates C_2. The required voltage e_d is found from the integral of current:

$$e_d = \frac{1}{C_2 p} i = \frac{1}{C_2} \frac{1}{p} K \epsilon^{\lambda t} = \frac{1}{C_2} \left(\frac{1}{\lambda} K \epsilon^{\lambda t} \right)_0^t$$

$$= -\frac{K}{C_2 \lambda} \left(1 - \epsilon^{\lambda t} \right) = \frac{-q_0}{C_1 + C_2} \left(1 - \epsilon^{\lambda t} \right) \qquad (83)$$

Since the cathode ray is deflected by the electric field, the distance that it will have traveled in a horizontal direction across the film at a time t is proportional to e_d of Eq. (83); the beam will not be swept across at constant speed but will start fast and go slower and slower as the deflection-plate voltage approaches its steady-state value. The transient voltage recorded on the oscillogram is given as a function of time, but the time scale is not uniform, and the transient record is spread out at the start, near the point a in Fig. 12, whereas toward the finish, near a'', it is cramped with a vanishingly small time scale. A maximum deflection will be reached when time is infinite and $\epsilon^{\lambda t}$ becomes zero.

It is clear both from the nature of the circuit and from Eq. (83) that the charge on the deflection plates will be of opposite sign from the initial charge on the condenser, for part of the initial charge will flow out of the condenser onto the deflection plates. It will usually be only a small part of the initial charge that goes onto the deflection plates, for the capacitance of the deflection plates is small compared to the capacitance of the condenser, and in the end the charge will be divided in proportion to the capacitances.

The flow of energy in the circuit of the oscillograph deflection plates is of particular interest. In the first place, the condenser C_1 is initially charged and so is able to furnish energy for the transient current. Of course, the energy does not originate with the condenser but is supplied to it from a circuit not shown in Fig. 12; it is usual to charge the condenser through a high resistance and a rectifier, the energy being drawn from an alternating-current circuit. So the condenser acts as a reservoir of energy; it is filled slowly by the rectifier circuit, and discharges rapidly when the transient current flows. But it does not lose all of its energy in the discharge, for the outrush of current is stopped as the deflection plates become charged. The deflection plates, as a condenser, take some of the energy; some is lost in the resistance; but most will remain on C_1. The energy that remains stored in the two condensers after the transient current has ceased will be divided between them in direct proportion to their capacitances, for their voltages will be equal.

An unusual aspect of the cathode-ray oscillograph circuit is that a small amount of energy is changed from electrical to mechanical form by the action of the electrostatic field of the deflection plates on the jet of electrons. As the deflection plates become charged, the electrons that are in the space between the plates are attracted toward the positive plate. Although they do not reach the plate, they are deflected toward it and their speed is somewhat increased; the corresponding increase in kinetic energy is supplied from the electric circuit, for an apparent increase in the capacitance of the deflection plates results from the deflection of the electron jet. Kinetic energy is merely lent to the electron jet, however, for as the deflection plates are allowed to discharge, they regain all the electrostatic energy that was given to the jet while their charge was increasing. If, however, any of the electrons of the jet actually reach the positive plate, instead of passing on away from its influence, they will remove electrostatic energy from the circuit that can never be returned.

For some purposes it is highly desirable to have a time scale that is linear, for which the rate of sweep of the cathode-ray beam must be constant. An inch on the film, then, will represent so many microseconds whether it is measured near the start of travel or near the end. The same circuit as that of Fig. 12 can be used to give a practically linear time scale by use of the proper method. The initial voltage on C_1 and the value of R are increased in the same proportion; they are increased to several times their previous values. Then, after switch S is closed, the voltage on the deflection plates will rise to several times the value that it previously attained, but with the same initial rate of rise. Since, however, the smaller voltage was enough to deflect the beam across the entire width of the film, the higher voltage will give complete deflection in the early part of the transient period while the rate of change of charge is practically constant. By this means the rate of deflection is also made practically constant.

The linearity of cathode-ray sweep circuits can be improved by various other means also. Replacing the single condenser of Fig. 12 by a series-parallel combination of R and C will give better linearity, as in Prob. 10, page 184. Permitting the condenser to discharge (or to charge) through a constant-current electron tube is another solution.[1] Linear sweeps are essential in television and radar tubes as well as in the laboratory type of cathode-ray oscilloscope.

Example 1. The sensitivity of a cathode-ray oscillograph is such that 300 volts on the deflection plates will sweep the cathode beam completely across the film, which is 5 in. wide. The sweep circuit used is that of Fig. 12; the condenser capacitance C_1 is 15 $\mu\mu f$ and the deflection plates have a capacitance C_2 of 1 $\mu\mu f$. The resistance in the circuit is 1 megohm, but it can be changed. Data concerning the time scale are needed.

a. Find the voltage to which the condenser must be initially charged in order to give full scale (5-in.) deflection as time becomes infinite.

b. With voltage as determined in *a*, and with 1 megohm resistance, plot time as a function of beam deflection.

c. With the condenser initially charged to 1000 volts, and with the same initial rate of sweep as in *b*, plot time as a function of deflection.

Solution: a. From

$$e_d = -\frac{q_0}{C_1 + C_2}(1 - \epsilon^{\lambda t}) \qquad (83)$$

when $t = \infty$

$$300 = -\frac{q_0}{C_1}\frac{C_1}{C_1 + C_2} = -e_{c_0}\frac{15}{15 + 1}$$

$$e_{c_0} = -\tfrac{16}{15}\, 300 = -320 \text{ volts.}$$

b. Deflection $= 5(1 - \epsilon^{\lambda t})$

$$\lambda = -\frac{1}{R}\frac{C_1 + C_2}{C_1 C_2} \qquad (80)$$

$$= -\frac{16 \times 10^{-12}}{10^6(15 \times 10^{-24})} = -1.07 \times 10^6$$

Time, microsec.	λt	$\epsilon^{\lambda t}$	$1 - \epsilon^{\lambda t}$	Deflection, in.
0	0	1.00	0	0
0.5	−0.53	0.59	0.41	2.05
1.0	−1.07	0.34	0.66	3.3
1.5	−1.60	0.20	0.80	4.0
2.0	−2.13	0.12	0.88	4.4
2.5	−2.66	0.07	0.93	4.65
3.0	−3.20	0.04	0.96	4.8
3.5	−3.73	0.02	0.98	4.9

[1] Regarding these and others, see S. Seely, "Electron-tube Circuits," McGraw-Hill Book Company, Inc., New York, 1950.

c. The initial sweep is proportional to the initial rate of change of deflection-plate voltage e_d, and the rate of change of e_d is

$$pe_d = p\frac{1}{C_2 p}i = \frac{1}{C_2}i$$

The *initial* rate of change of e_d is found from this equation by substituting i_0 for i, giving

$$\frac{1}{C_2}i_0 = -\frac{e_{C0}}{RC_2}$$

So to keep the initial sweep unchanged when e_{C0} is raised from 320 to 1000 volts, R must be increased in proportion and becomes

$$R = \tfrac{1000}{320}(1 \times 10^6) = 3.12 \times 10^6 \text{ ohms}$$

The maximum deflection of the beam will be increased in proportion to the

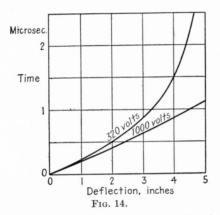

FIG. 14.

increased voltage, so if it were allowed to sweep undisturbed to its steady position it would travel $\tfrac{1000}{320}$ of 5 in.   This gives an equation for sweep:

$$\text{Deflection} = 5\tfrac{1000}{320}(1 - \epsilon^{\lambda t})$$
$$= 15.6(1 - \epsilon^{\lambda t})$$

and

$$\lambda = -\frac{1}{3.12 \times 10^6}\frac{16 \times 10^{-12}}{15 \times 10^{-24}}$$
$$= -0.342 \times 10^6$$

Time, microsec.	λt	$\epsilon^{\lambda t}$	$1 - \epsilon^{\lambda t}$	Deflection, in.
0	0	1.00	0	0
0.20	−0.068	0.934	0.064	1.0
0.40	−0.137	0.872	0.128	2.0
0.62	−0.214	0.808	0.192	3.0
0.86	−0.296	0.744	0.256	4.0
1.13	−0.386	0.680	0.320	5.0

Figure 14 shows that when the higher voltage is used, the useful part of the sweep is practically linear, with deflection always within a few per cent of being proportional to time.

Problems

1. Connect a condenser and resistance in series, with the necessary switching apparatus, to charge the condenser to a known voltage and then allow it to discharge through the resistance. Record on an oscillograph the current that flows as the condenser discharges. Make three records with the same capacitance and voltage but with different resistances.

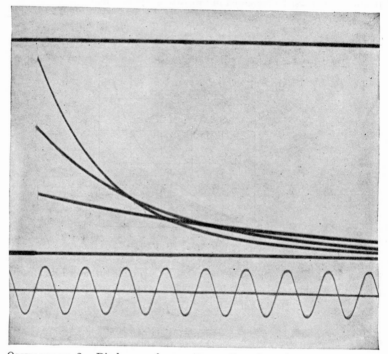

Oscillogram 2.—Discharge of capacitance through resistance, with three different values of resistance. For use with Prob. 1 of Chap. II.

Transfer the experimentally determined curves from the oscillogram to a sheet of semilogarithmic cross-section paper, plotting current (or deflection) on the logarithmic scale and time on the linear scale. Since the current varies exponentially with time, the plot on the semilogarithmic paper will be a straight line. (If a paper condenser is used, the points which correspond to very low values of current may lie above the straight line; if so, disregard them.)

The **time constant** of this circuit, the reciprocal of the coefficient of the exponent, is RC. It is the time required for current to diminish to 0.368

of its initial value. Locate this value, and the corresponding time, on each line on the semilogarithmic plot.

From the initial values of current, find the three values of resistance used and from the time constants find the value of capacitance. (Three values for capacitance will be obtained, which should agree.) The circuit parameters will thereby be obtained from transient behaviour alone.

If it is not convenient to record the transient currents, oscillogram 2 may be used. This is a reproduction of such an oscillogram with the following dimensions: the calibration line at the top of the sheet shows the deflection produced by 0.493 amp. in the circuit, and the timing wave at the bottom has 60 cycles per sec. The initial voltage on the condenser, in making these records, was 129.0. The dielectric material of the condenser was paper.

2. Show that the time constant of a circuit of capacitance and resistance (defined as RC, the reciprocal of the coefficient of the exponent) is the time required for current to diminish to 36.8 per cent of its initial value. Show also that if the initial rate of change of current were maintained, the current would become zero when the elapsed time equaled the time constant.

3. Returning to the data of Prob. 1 of Chap. I, plot on semilogarithmic cross-section paper the transient component of current for each value of resistance. The transient component is found as the difference between the circuit current and the steady-state current. This will give three straight lines. The time constant of an inductive circuit is L/R, this being the reciprocal of the coefficient of the exponent. Find the three time constants graphically, as the time required for the transient component of current to diminish to 0.368 of its initial value, and compare with time constants found from measured circuit parameters.

4. The following circuit is used in determining the moisture content of wood.[1] A source of constant voltage charges a condenser through a sample of the wood to be tested; the wood sample has high electrical resistance and the amount of resistance is a known function of the moisture content. The time of charging the condenser is determined by the wood's resistance. When a certain ionizing voltage is reached, the neon tube suddenly becomes conducting and dis-

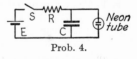

Prob. 4.

charges the condenser until the voltage across the tube falls to the de-ionizing value. Then the tube will not carry current until voltage rises again to the ionizing value. Flashes of the tube are timed to determine resistance of the wood.

In a given test-set the applied voltage is 180 volts, the ionizing voltage of the tube is 110 volts, and the de-ionizing voltage is 69 volts. Capacitance is 0.5 μf. Sketch the battery current for the first three flashes after the switch is closed. Assume no time is required to discharge the condenser through the neon tube. What is the steady rate of flashing?

5. A power transformer is heated by electrical losses when it is in operation. If I is heat generated per unit time, G is heat radiated per unit time per degree temperature rise, and C is heat stored in the transformer per

---

[1] Suits and Dunlap, *Gen. Elec. Rev.*, **34**, 706, 1931.

degree temperature rise, derive an expression for temperature at any time after the transformer is put into service.   To what electrical problem is this analogous?

6. The application of the voltage regulator to exciters having high magnetic speeds involves the breaking of relatively high currents by means of vibrating contacts.   An analysis of contact operation has resulted in the following conclusion: if the contacts can be opened so fast that the voltage between them is always less than that required to cause dielectric breakdown, no sparking will occur.   To make this possible, a condenser is placed across the contactor, as shown in the figure. L is field inductance, R is external field resistance of 400 ohms, C is condenser of 4.6 μf capacitance, and I is field current of 10 amp. at the instant of separating the contacts.   If the potential gradient required to cause dielectric breakdown of the gap is 10,000 volts per cm. (a merely approximate value), with what velocity must the contacts be opened to prevent sparking?   Assume L to be infinite (and current, therefore, to be constant) as this will give the worst condition of operation.

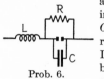

Prob. 6.

7. A relay will operate when the current through its holding coil falls below 5 per cent of normal current.   A condenser of 30 μf is connected across the terminals of the holding coil.   Resistance of the holding coil is 90 ohms.   If normal current is flowing through the holding coil, and then the supply line is suddenly opened, how long will current from the condenser hold the relay from operating?

8. A charged condenser, $C = 70$ μf, is used as an emergency supply of energy for the plate circuit of a crystal-controlled standard time clock. The condenser is charged initially to 300 volts.   It supplies a load of constant resistance.   Its voltage must not drop more than 10 per cent.   What current can it be counted on to supply for 0.6 sec?

9. In Fig. 52, two "integrating circuits" are shown in the second row of the figure.   For the R-C circuit, $R = 4130$ ohms, $C = 9.5 \times 10^{-9}$ farad. Plot condenser voltage as a function of time after a constant voltage of 1 volt is applied to "input" terminals for the first (a) 300 micro-sec., (b) 100 microsec., and (c) 8 microsec.   (These are approximately the curves of Fig. 52d, e, and f.)

10. For the R-C circuit of Prob. 9, plot resistor voltage during the first (a) 800 microsec., (b) 80 microsec., and (c) 25 microsec.   (These are approximately the curves of Fig. 52g, h, and i.)

11. It is sometimes specified that, for safety, a capacitor must be shunted by a discharge resistor that will reduce the capacitor voltage to a safe value in a certain time.   If the safe voltage is specified as 50 volts, and the time is 30 sec., find the necessary value of resistance for the following capacitors: (a) $C = 75$ μf, rated voltage $= 1000$ volts; (b) $C = 0.25$ μf, rated voltage $= 100,000$ volts.   Also, find the time constant for each of the shunted capacitors, and find the power that each resistor must be able to dissipate.

CHAPTER III

THE CIRCUIT EQUATIONS

1. Linear Differential Equations. Circuit equations for networks that have constant parameters are of the kind that the mathematician calls linear differential equations with constant coefficients. For all those circuits so far studied, and for most others in which the inductor is not wound on an iron core, the determination of the transient current requires the solution of this type of differential equation. Familiarity with the mathematics of linear differential equations will greatly aid in the solution of more complex networks and at the same time will help organize the ideas set forth in the two preceding chapters.

2. First Order. The linear equation of the *first order* with constant coefficients has the general form

$$A \frac{di}{dt} + Bi = f(t) \qquad (84)$$

where i and t are any variables. (In the study of transient electric currents the variables are most often current and time, so even the general form of the differential equation is here written with symbols i and t. Mathematicians would use the more customary symbols x and y, but the meaning would be the same.) A and B are any constants, and $f(t)$ indicates some function of the variable t. The symbol $f(t)$ (which is read "function of t" or simply "f of t") is often used in this manner, and it signifies some expression containing the variable t but not containing any other variable. It is possible for $f(t)$ to be merely a constant, as it often is in our work, and even zero; its only limitation is this: it must not contain any other variable than t.

Equation (84) is an equation of the first order. By definition, the order of a differential equation is the same as that of the highest order derivative appearing in the equation; Eq. (84) contains a first derivative and therefore is a first-order equation. Equation (104), page 66, is an example of a second-order equation, for it contains a second derivative.

Equation (84) is called a linear equation because its terms are all of first degree. The current, and the derivatives of current, are not squared or cubed, or of any power except the first. Almost all the equations of this book are linear, and this is fundamentally due to the fact that the voltages in ordinary circuits are proportional to the *first power* of charge, or current, or the derivative of current.

Equation (84) is a simple equation, but becomes even simpler in the special form in which $f(t)$ is zero. For that special case

$$A \frac{di}{dt} + Bi = 0 \tag{85}$$

The solution of this special case is readily found. Finding a "solution" of any differential equation means finding an equation that relates the variables and yet does not contain any derivative or integral terms. When such a relation between the variables is resubstituted in the differential equation it must reduce the differential equation to an identity, and its ability to do so is proof of the correctness of the solution. A correct solution, however, is not necessarily a complete solution; the complete solution must be the *most general* relation between the variables that will satisfy the differential equation. As an example of this statement, it will be seen that a solution of Eq. (85) is $i = 0$; but while this solution is correct, it is incomplete and, in this case, trivial.

The complete solution of Eq. (85) can be found by integration after separation of the variables. Write it as

$$\frac{di}{i} = -\frac{B}{A}dt \tag{86}$$

Let

$$-\frac{B}{A} = \lambda$$

Then, integrating,

$$\int \frac{di}{i} = \int \lambda \, dt$$

and

$$\text{in } i = \lambda t + C \text{ (constant of integration)}$$

The natural logarithm is related to the exponential, so

$$i = \epsilon^{\lambda t + C}$$

and if

$$\epsilon^C = K$$
$$i = K\epsilon^{\lambda t} \tag{87}$$

Since the constant of integration C can have any value whatever without damaging the validity of the solution, it follows that K can also have any value.

When the value of current found in Eq. (87) is substituted in Eq. (85) it reduces that equation to an identity,

$$\frac{di}{dt} - \lambda i = 0$$
$$\lambda K\epsilon^{\lambda t} - \lambda K\epsilon^{\lambda t} \equiv 0 \tag{88}$$

and this is proof that the solution is correct.

When the more general form of the first-order equation, as given in Eq. (84), is to be solved, it is impossible to separate the variables. A direct solution is possible by rather artificial strategy, but it will be best for us to state the solution of the equation

$$A\frac{di}{dt} + Bi = f(t) \tag{84}$$

as

$$i = K\epsilon^{\lambda t} + \frac{1}{A}\epsilon^{\lambda t}\int \epsilon^{-\lambda t}f(t)dt \tag{89}$$

where, as before

$$\lambda = -\frac{B}{A}$$

To prove that (89) is the correct solution, expand the terms of Eq. (84) by use of Eq. (89):

$$A\frac{di}{dt} = A\lambda K\epsilon^{\lambda t} + \lambda\epsilon^{\lambda t}\int \epsilon^{-\lambda t}f(t)dt + \epsilon^{\lambda t}\epsilon^{-\lambda t}f(t) \tag{90}$$

and

$$Bi = -A\lambda i = -A\lambda K\epsilon^{\lambda t} - \lambda\epsilon^{\lambda t}\int \epsilon^{-\lambda t}f(t)dt \tag{91}$$

Addition of (90) and (91) then gives the left-hand member of Eq. (84), but since addition leaves only a term that reduces to $f(t)$ the equation has become the identity

$$\epsilon^{\lambda t}\epsilon^{-\lambda t}f(t) = f(t) \equiv f(t) \tag{92}$$

and (89) is thereby proved to be the solution of (84).

The expression for current, Eq. (89), is the sum of two terms. In mathematical terminology, $K\epsilon^{\lambda t}$ is the **complementary function** and $\dfrac{1}{A}\,\epsilon^{\lambda t}\displaystyle\int \epsilon^{-\lambda t}f(t)dt$ is the **particular integral.** We shall show that in electric circuit analysis the *complementary function gives the transient component* of current while the *particular integral gives the steady-state component.*

3. An Example. As an example of the use of the general form of solution of the first-order differential equation in a circuit problem, consider the application of battery voltage to a circuit consisting of inductance and resistance as is illustrated in Fig. 1. The circuit equation is

$$Ri + L\frac{di}{dt} = E \tag{3}$$

This equation is identical in form with Eq. (84). The solution of Eq. (84), then, is also the solution of Eq. (3), and it is given in most general terms in Eq. (89). To identify Eq. (84) with its special form as Eq. (3), let $A = L$ and $B = R$; λ therefore is $-R/L$; $f(t)$ is the constant quantity E. Substituting these values in (89) gives

$$i = K\epsilon^{-\frac{R}{L}t} + \frac{1}{L}\,\epsilon^{\lambda t}\int \epsilon^{-\lambda t}E\,dt \tag{93}$$

E is not a function of time, and the integration indicated in the particular integral gives

$$\frac{1}{L}\,\epsilon^{\lambda t}\int \epsilon^{-\lambda t}E\,dt = \frac{E}{L}\,\epsilon^{\lambda t}\left(-\frac{1}{\lambda}\,\epsilon^{-\lambda t}\right)$$
$$= -\frac{E}{L\lambda} = \frac{E}{R} \tag{94}$$

So the purely mathematical solution of the differential equation gives

$$i = K\epsilon^{-\frac{R}{L}t} + \frac{E}{R} \tag{95}$$

This is Eq. (17), which was used without full explanation in Chap. I.

It is interesting to note that evaluation of the particular integral does not require a constant of integration. Equation (89) may be rewritten

$$i = \epsilon^{\lambda t}\left(\int \frac{1}{A}\,\epsilon^{-\lambda t}f(t)dt + K\right)$$

and in this form K is recognized as being itself the constant of integration. The integration, therefore, is made *complete* by the *complementary function;* and it is from this that the complementary function derives its name.

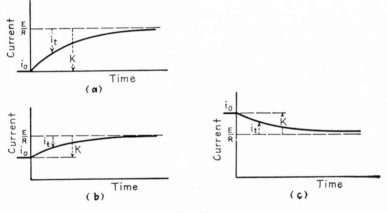

FIG. 15.

4. The Need for a Transient Component. The part played by an initial condition in determining the magnitude of the transient component of current is well illustrated by this same circuit. The purpose of the transient component of current is to provide a gradual transition from the initial current to the steady-state current; a transition that takes place in such a way that the differential equation of the circuit will always be satisfied. The steady-state current in a circuit containing resistance and inductance is E/R, and in Fig. 15 this value is shown by a dash line. In Fig. 15a the current is shown increasing from its initial value of zero to its final value of E/R; the transient component of current is i_t, for this is the amount that must be added to E/R to get the actual current at any instant. From Eq. (95) the transient component is seen to be $K\epsilon^{-\frac{R}{L}t}$, and the necessary value of K is seen in Fig. 15a to be the difference between the *initial* current and the steady-state current.

Sometimes a circuit is arranged in such a way that there is an initial current in the inductance. The voltage regulator gives an example of such a circuit in Chap. I, page 22. Figure 15b shows the transition from the initial current i_0 to the final current E/R, made possible by the transient component of current.

Just as in Fig. 15a, the transient component of current is $K\epsilon^{-\frac{R}{L}t}$, but the value of K is decreased from its former value because the transition is not so great, and therefore a smaller transient component of current is needed. The *shape* of the transient component is unchanged, however, for that is determined by the circuit.

The role of the transient component of current is still the same even if the initial current is greater than the steady-state current. The transition in such a case is shown in Fig. 15c. Again, the transient component at $t = 0$ is just large enough to close the gap between the initial and final values of current, and K is equal to the width of that gap. K is positive in Fig. 15c and is negative in Fig. 15a and b.

5. Complementary Function and Transient Component. It has been stated that the complementary function gives the transient component of current, whereas the particular integral gives the steady-state component, and it is important that this be proved. As a matter of definition, the transient component is that part of the current that diminishes to zero as time increases without limit, while the steady-state component will continue to flow, unchanged in value, as long as voltage is applied to the circuit.

The complementary function is, from Eq. (89),

$$K\epsilon^{\lambda t}$$

If λ is a negative quantity the complementary function will diminish to zero as time becomes infinite. If λ is positive the complementary function will increase without limit, but this is physically impossible in a stable circuit as it implies infinite current and infinite power. If λ is zero the complementary function is constant, but λ is zero only in a circuit without resistance. In any ordinary dissipative circuit, therefore, the complementary function describes a purely transient current that diminishes, in time, to zero.

6. Particular Integral and Steady-state Component. The particular integral is

$$\frac{1}{A}\epsilon^{\lambda t}\int \epsilon^{-\lambda t}f(t)dt \qquad (96)$$

where $f(t)$ is either the voltage or a time derivative of the voltage. There are various ways of showing that this quantity leads to a purely steady-state current, but the simplest—although not the most direct—starts by analyzing $f(t)$ into the sinusoidal terms of a Fourier series. Assuming that the applied voltage is either constant or periodic, as is almost invariably the case, $f(t)$ can be expanded into one or more terms of a Fourier series:

$$f(t) = \tfrac{1}{2}a_0 + a_1 \cos \omega_1 t + a_2 \cos 2\omega_1 t + \cdots$$
$$+ b_1 \sin \omega_1 t + b_2 \sin 2\omega_1 t + \cdots$$

Of course, $f(t)$ may be zero, in which case all coefficients in the series disappear; $f(t)$ may be constant, in which case all coefficients except a_0 disappear; or $f(t)$ may be sinusoidal, in which case all except a_1 and b_1 disappear. But in the general case, all coefficients will exist, and it must be shown that when the series is substituted for $f(t)$ in the particular integral, the result of integration will consist entirely of steady-state terms. When such substitution is made, the integral of Eq. (96) will contain terms of three general forms:

$$\epsilon^{-\lambda t} \qquad (97)$$
$$\epsilon^{-\lambda t} \cos \omega t \qquad (98)$$
$$\epsilon^{-\lambda t} \sin \omega t \qquad (99)$$

and since we wish to integrate the sum of terms of these forms, we can integrate term by term and obtain from the three general forms, respectively

$$-\frac{1}{\lambda}\epsilon^{-\lambda t} \qquad (100)$$

$$\frac{\epsilon^{-\lambda t}}{\lambda^2 + \omega^2} \, (\lambda \cos \omega t - \omega \sin \omega t) \tag{101}$$

$$\frac{\epsilon^{-\lambda t}}{\lambda^2 + \omega^2} \, (\lambda \sin \omega t + \omega \cos \omega t) \tag{102}$$

The particular integral becomes, after integration, a series of terms like those of (100), (101), and (102), added together, and each to be multiplied by a coefficient and by $\frac{1}{A} \epsilon^{\lambda t}$. Multiplication of any of the terms by $\epsilon^{\lambda t}$ results in the disappearance of the exponential $\epsilon^{-\lambda t}$, so that in its final form the particular integral appears as the sum of a constant term and a series of sinusoidal terms. None of the terms of the particular integral diminishes with time; for the constant term is simply constant, and the sines and cosines continue to oscillate with the same amplitude indefinitely. So the particular integral can describe only a steady-state current, and all the transient component is in the complementary function.

7. Discussion of Rules for Solution. Having now determined the *general* solution [Eq. (89)] of the first-order linear differential equation with constant coefficients, we are able to find the current in any circuit whose action is described by that sort of an equation. This includes all of the circuits of Chaps. I and II, for all the circuit equations there considered are of the type of Eq. (84) or else can be reduced to that type by differentiating both sides of the circuit equation in order to remove an integral sign. The four rules for the solution for transient current, given in Sec. 10 of Chap. I, can now be explained in terms of the mathematics that has just been reviewed.

The first rule said, "Solve for the form of the transient component. To do this, write the differential equation of the circuit, with zero substituted for the applied voltage, and solve for current." This step is only to determine the transient term, and the form of the transient component is independent of the applied voltage. The form is the same whether the applied voltage is zero, the direct voltage of a battery, or the alternating voltage of a generator. That this is true may be seen in Eq. (89), for $f(t)$ does not appear at all in the transient-current term, but appears only in the term for steady-state current. Equation (87), moreover, shows that when $f(t) = 0$ there is no steady-state current, and the complete solution for the special case in which

$f(t) = 0$ is precisely the transient component of the general case of Eq. (89). So the easiest way to determine the form of the transient component of current is to write zero in place of the applied voltage, and solve.

According to the second rule, one should "by any convenient method, find the steady-state current." This is for the purpose of evaluating the second term of Eq. (89), the particular integral. It may be done, as in the example of Sec. 3, by actually substituting the value of $f(t)$ in Eq. (89) and integrating; but it can often be done more simply by some other and more familiar means. Whether the voltage is direct or alternating, the steady-state current may usually be found by inspection or else by a simple computation of series and parallel impedances. In all circuits thus far considered, the value of steady-state current has been obvious.

To get the total current, as in Eq. (89), the transient and steady-state terms are added. This is rule 3. There is still, however, the undetermined constant K, appearing as coefficient of the transient term; it can be evaluated only from boundary conditions, such as initial current, charge, and voltage, and its evaluation is called for in rule 4. This completes the solution.

There are many other ways of proceeding to solve the differential equation of a circuit, but the use of the four rules gives a simple and reliable approach to any transient-current problem.

All the preceding discussion of the use and interpretation of the general solution of equations has been referred to circuits whose equations are of the first order. This has been merely for convenience, for the statements made have been general and will be seen to apply equally well to circuits with second-order equations.

8. Second Order. A circuit whose voltage equation is a differential equation of the second order is shown in Fig. 16. The equation is formed in the usual manner, by equating the applied voltage to the sum of the voltages around the circuit. Adding the voltages across resistance, inductance, and condenser gives

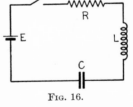

FIG. 16.

$$Ri + L\frac{di}{dt} + \frac{1}{C}\int_0^t i\,dt = E \tag{103}$$

If each side of the equation is now differentiated with respect to time:

$$R\frac{di}{dt} + L\frac{d^2i}{dt^2} + \frac{1}{C}i = 0 \tag{104}$$

This is a differential equation of the second order, because it contains a second derivative of current. Its solution may be found by an extension of the solution of the first-order equation.

It is easiest, in finding the general solution of a second-order equation, to use certain operational methods. In operational notation the first order equation (84) is written

$$Api + Bi = f(t) \tag{105}$$

or

$$(Ap + B)i = f(t) \tag{106}$$

$(Ap + B)$ is an *operator*, which, operating on i, gives $f(t)$. In this case the operator can be interpreted term by term, the first term of the operator requiring differentiation and the second merely multiplication; this was done in several examples in Chap. II. But sometimes Eq. (106) is written

$$i = \frac{1}{Ap + B}f(t) \tag{107}$$

and $\frac{1}{Ap + B}$ is an operator, which, operating on $f(t)$, gives i.

This is simply the definition of the operator $\frac{1}{Ap + B}$, for it can-not be interpreted term by term as was done with $(Ap + B)$; and all that Eq. (107) says is that the solution of Eq. (105), when it is found, may be written as equal to $\frac{1}{Ap + B}f(t)$. In other words, we can combine Eq. (107) and (89) and write

$$i = \frac{1}{Ap + B}f(t) = K\epsilon^{\lambda t} + \frac{1}{A}\epsilon^{\lambda t}\int \epsilon^{-\lambda t}f(t)dt$$

Multiplication by A gives

$$\frac{1}{(p - \lambda)}f(t) = K'\epsilon^{\lambda t} + \epsilon^{\lambda t}\int \epsilon^{-\lambda t}f(t)dt \tag{108}$$

Equation (104) is a second-order equation, and it may be written in operational terminology as

$$Lp^2i + Rpi + \frac{1}{C}i = 0 \tag{109}$$

or

$$\left(Lp^2 + Rp + \frac{1}{C}\right)i = 0 \tag{110}$$

The quantity in parentheses is the operator. This is the equation for a specific circuit—that of Fig. 16—and the most general form of second-order linear differential equation is

$$p^2i + Mpi + Ni = f(t) \tag{111}$$

where M and N are any constant coefficients. This may be written

$$(p^2 + Mp + N)i = f(t) \tag{112}$$

It is mentioned in Chap. II that algebraic changes can be made in an operator, so let us factor the operator of Eq. (112) and write it:

$$(p - \lambda_1)(p - \lambda_2)i = f(t) \tag{113}$$

where λ_1 and λ_2 are constants so selected that

$$(p - \lambda_1)(p - \lambda_2) = p^2 + Mp + N \tag{114}$$

It is clear that this is just ordinary factoring, and is done by finding λ_1 and λ_2 as the roots of the auxiliary equation:

$$\lambda^2 + M\lambda + N = 0 \tag{115}$$

Equation (113) tells us that i is to be operated on by $(p - \lambda_2)$, and that the result of the first operation is to be operated on by $(p - \lambda_1)$; the final result of the two operations will be $f(t)$. If the first operator is transposed to the other side of the equation (which may be done by operating on both sides of the equation by $\dfrac{1}{p - \lambda_1}$) the result is

$$(p - \lambda_2)i = \frac{1}{(p - \lambda_1)}f(t) \tag{116}$$

But Eq. (108) makes it possible to evaluate the right-hand member of this equation, and

$$(p - \lambda_2)i = \frac{1}{(p - \lambda_1)}f(t) = K'\epsilon^{\lambda_1 t} + \epsilon^{\lambda_1 t}\int \epsilon^{-\lambda_1 t}f(t)dt \quad (117)$$

The right-hand member is thus a function of time, and since the only variable it contains is time, it may be indicated by the conventional expression $F(t)$, where

$$F(t) = K'\epsilon^{\lambda_1 t} + \epsilon^{\lambda_1 t}\int \epsilon^{-\lambda_1 t}f(t)dt \quad\quad (118)$$

Then

$$(p - \lambda_2)i = F(t)$$

or

$$i = \frac{1}{(p - \lambda_2)}F(t) \quad\quad (119)$$

This in turn, may be identified, from Eq. (108), as

$$i = K_2\epsilon^{\lambda_2 t} + \epsilon^{\lambda_2 t}\int \epsilon^{-\lambda_2 t}F(t)dt \quad\quad (120)$$

When Eq. (120) is fully expanded by introducing the value of $F(t)$ from Eq. (118), the result is

$$i = K_2\epsilon^{\lambda_2 t} + \epsilon^{\lambda_2 t}\int [K'\epsilon^{\lambda_1 t}\epsilon^{-\lambda_2 t} + \epsilon^{\lambda_1 t}\epsilon^{-\lambda_2 t}\int \epsilon^{-\lambda_1 t}f(t)dt]dt \quad (121)$$

It is now possible to integrate the first term in the integral, for it does not contain $f(t)$. But the result will depend on whether or not λ_1 is equal to λ_2. If $\lambda_1 \neq \lambda_2$, Eq. (121) becomes

$$i = K_2\epsilon^{\lambda_2 t} + K_1\epsilon^{\lambda_1 t} + \epsilon^{\lambda_2 t}\int [\epsilon^{(\lambda_1 - \lambda_2)t}\int \epsilon^{-\lambda_1 t}f(t)dt]dt \quad (122)$$

This is obtained by writing

$$\epsilon^{\lambda_2 t}\int K'\epsilon^{(\lambda_1 - \lambda_2)t}dt = \epsilon^{\lambda_2 t}\frac{K'}{\lambda_1 - \lambda_2}\epsilon^{(\lambda_1 - \lambda_2)t} = \frac{K'}{\lambda_1 - \lambda_2}\epsilon^{\lambda_1 t}$$

and letting

$$\frac{K'}{\lambda_1 - \lambda_2} = K_1$$

Equation (122) is the general solution of the second-order differential equation, and corresponds to the general solution of the first-order differential equation which is given in Eq. (89).

When i is current in a stable, dissipative electric circuit, with λ_1 and λ_2 negative, the complementary function (which is composed of the first two terms of the right-hand member) will disappear as time increases, and

$$\text{Transient component of } i = K_1\epsilon^{\lambda_1 t} + K_2\epsilon^{\lambda_2 t} \qquad (123)$$

It can be shown, by the same method employed in Sec. 5 of this chapter, that the particular integral will not disappear as time increases, and

$$\text{Steady-state component of } i = \epsilon^{\lambda_2 t}\int[\epsilon^{(\lambda_1-\lambda_2)t}\int\epsilon^{-\lambda_1 t}f(t)dt]dt \qquad (124)$$

But since there is usually an easier way of determining the steady-state current than actually carrying out the integrations of (124), it results in practice that Eq. (123) is used frequently and Eq. (124) rarely.

As a simple illustration of the application of this general solution, consider Eq. (110), which describes the current in a circuit consisting of inductance, resistance, and capacitance in series.

$$\left(Lp^2 + Rp + \frac{1}{C}\right)i = 0 \qquad (110)$$

In order to factor the operator, write, from the operator, an auxiliary equation:

$$L\lambda^2 + R\lambda + \frac{1}{C} = 0 \qquad (125)$$

The roots of (125) are obtained as

$$\left.\begin{aligned}\lambda_1 &= -\frac{R}{2L} + \sqrt{\frac{R^2}{4L^2} - \frac{1}{LC}} \\ \lambda_2 &= -\frac{R}{2L} - \sqrt{\frac{R^2}{4L^2} - \frac{1}{LC}}\end{aligned}\right\} \qquad (126)$$

These values of λ_1 and λ_2 are then substituted in Eq. (123) to find the transient component of current. That the steady-state current is zero can be seen from the circuit, for there can be no steady current from a battery through a condenser. The same conclusion is reached by substituting zero for $f(t)$ in Eq. (124), whereupon the whole expression for steady-state component becomes zero. This circuit is discussed in detail in Chap. IV.

The general solution of the second-order equation when the roots λ_1 and λ_2 are equal, has not yet been given. But it can easily be found by returning to Eq. (121) and simplifying it by writing λ_m for both λ_1 and λ_2. It becomes

$$i = K_2 \epsilon^{\lambda_m t} + \epsilon^{\lambda_m t} \int [K' + \int \epsilon^{-\lambda_m t} f(t) dt] dt \qquad (127)$$

Integration of the K' term in the first integral then gives

$$i = K_2 \epsilon^{\lambda_m t} + K' t \epsilon^{\lambda_m t} + \epsilon^{\lambda_m t} \int \int \epsilon^{-\lambda_m t} f(t) dt \, dt \qquad (128)$$

and this is the general solution when the roots are equal. The steady-state current is given by the last term, which is the particular integral, and the transient component is the complementary function:

$$K_2 \epsilon^{\lambda_m t} + K' t \epsilon^{\lambda_m t} \qquad (129)$$

It is common, in circuit analysis, for the first of the transient terms to disappear because of K_2 being zero, but since this term it sometimes needed it must not be forgotten.

9. Determination of the Operator. It has been seen that fundamentally the operator is determined from the differential equation of the circuit. In the example in the preceding paragraph, for instance, the operator of Eq. (110) was found by writing Eq. (103) in which the sum of the voltage drops was equated to the applied voltage.

But there is an alternative method that can be used if desired, and it is often much simpler. It develops the operator from the ordinary alternating-current impedance of the circuit, instead of from the differential equation. A moment's thought shows that there is a very close relation between the alternating-current impedance of a circuit and its differential equation: the differential equation is a statement of the general principle that the sum of all the voltages around a closed circuit must be equal to zero *under all circumstances*, while the impedance equation says the same thing for that special case in which current and voltage are sinusoidal. The similar relations that exist are clearly shown by tabulating the voltages across the three electrical parameters in the general and special cases.

Voltage	In general	For sine wave
Across resistance....................	$R \cdot i$	$R \cdot I$
Across inductance..................	$L \cdot pi$	$L \cdot j\omega I *$
Across capacitance................	$\dfrac{1}{C} \cdot \dfrac{1}{p} i$	$\dfrac{1}{C} \cdot \dfrac{1}{j\omega} I *$

* ω is $2\pi f$, where f is alternating-current frequency.

It is true in all cases that if the alternating-current impedance of a network is written, and then p is substituted wherever $j\omega$ appears, the result will be the operator that must operate on any current to give the corresponding voltage.

As an illustration, let us refer again to Fig. 16 and write the impedance of that circuit.   It is

$$Z = R + j\omega L + \frac{1}{j\omega C} \qquad (130)$$

On making the substitution of p for $j\omega$ this becomes the operator

$$R + pL + \frac{1}{pC} \qquad (131)$$

which, operating on i, gives Eq. (103).

To find the transient component of current from the operator we can write the auxiliary equation

$$R + \lambda L + \frac{1}{\lambda C} = 0 \qquad (132)$$

by substituting λ for p.   In fact, we could have written the auxiliary equation without writing the operator at all, by substituting λ for $j\omega$ in the impedance expression of (130).   The roots of Eq. (132) are

$$\lambda_1, \lambda_2 = -\frac{R}{2L} \pm \sqrt{\frac{R^2}{4L^2} - \frac{1}{LC}} \qquad (133)$$

which give the transient component of current (in this case, the total current) when substituted in

$$i = K_1 \epsilon^{\lambda_1 t} + K_2 \epsilon^{\lambda_2 t} \qquad (134)$$

So, finally, a method is made available for finding the roots of the operator, and hence the exponents of the terms for transient current, without needing actually to write the differential equations. The first of the four rules given in Sec. 10, Chap. I, for solution of transient current problems may now be expanded to read:

1. Solve for the form of the transient component. To do this, either

a. Write the differential equation of the circuit, with zero substituted for the applied voltage, and solve for the current, or

b. Write the impedance of the circuit to alternating current; wherever $j\omega$ appears substitute λ; set equal to zero and solve for the roots λ_1, λ_2, etc. The transient current will then be $K_1 \epsilon^{\lambda_1 t} + K_2 \epsilon^{\lambda_2 t} + \cdots$

10. The General Linear Equation. It is implied in this statement of the rule that there can be more than two roots, and consequently more than two values of λ. Such is indeed the case when the network being studied consists of more than a single circuit, for the differential equation may be of some order higher than the second. The solution of the second-order equation is found by factoring the second-order operator; the operational factors are then applied one at a time, and the second-order solution is obtained by the successive solution of two first-order equations. This same method can be extended to give the solution of an equation of any order.

It appears in Eq. (89) that the transient component of current in a circuit with a first-order differential equation is

$$K\epsilon^{\lambda t} \tag{135}$$

In a circuit with a second-order differential equation, it is shown by Eq. (121) to be

$$K_1 \epsilon^{\lambda_1 t} + K_2 \epsilon^{\lambda_2 t} \tag{136}$$

In general, the number of exponential terms in the transient-current expression is equal to the order of the differential equation, and for an nth-order equation there are n exponential terms:

$$K_1 \epsilon^{\lambda_1 t} + K_2 \epsilon^{\lambda_2 t} + \cdots + K_n \epsilon^{\lambda_n t} \tag{137}$$

The general linear differential equation is

$$(A_0 + A_1 p + A_2 p^2 + \cdots + p^n)i = f(t) \qquad (138)$$

When (138) is the voltage equation of a network, the A's are coefficients that may be evaluated from the network parameters. Expression (137) is the complementary function of the solution of this equation, and it therefore expresses the transient component of current. The auxiliary equation derived from the differential equation (138) will be an algebraic equation of the nth degree:

$$A_0 + A_1 \lambda + A_2 \lambda^2 + \cdots + \lambda^n = 0 \qquad (139)$$

It will therefore have n roots, $\lambda_1, \lambda_2, \ldots \lambda_n$; and these will be the coefficients of the exponents of the n exponential terms of (137).

This discussion of the general equation has assumed that all n roots are distinct. It is found in considering the second-order equation that when the two roots are equal a special form of complementary function is needed, and a similar provision must be made for the general equation. If two or more of the roots of Eq. (139) are equal, so that λ_m appears s times, then s of the exponential terms of Eq. (137) are omitted and the following s terms are used instead:

$$k_1 \epsilon^{\lambda_m t} + k_2 t \epsilon^{\lambda_m t} + \cdots + k_s t^{s-1} \epsilon^{\lambda_m t} \qquad (140)$$

The second-order equation with equal roots is merely a special case of this more general statement, where λ_m appears two times so that $s = 2$, and the first two terms of (140) give expression (129).

The particular integral for the general equation is an n-fold multiple integral of the form

$$\epsilon^{\lambda_n t} \int \epsilon^{(\lambda_{n-1} - \lambda_n)t} \cdots \int \epsilon^{(\lambda_1 - \lambda_2)t} \int \epsilon^{-\lambda_1 t} f(t)(dt)^n \qquad (141)$$

This gives the steady-state component of current, but, as in the special cases, it is usually easier to find the steady-state current by other means.

The sum of expressions (137) and (141) (including (140) if necessary) is the complete solution of the *general linear differential equation with constant coefficients.*

11. A Revised Rule for Solution.   The four rules for solution for transient current, first stated in Sec. 10 of Chap. I, may be looked upon as a summary of the chapter just concluding. They reduce to methods the mathematical principles that are here discussed.   But the first of those rules may now be restated, as in Sec. 9, with more specific instructions for procedure that have been made possible by the determination of the general mathematical solution:

1. Solve for the form of the transient component of current. To do this most readily, write the impedance of the circuit to alternating current; substitute λ for $j\omega$, and set equal to zero; solve for the roots, λ_1, λ_2, etc.   If the roots are all distinct, the transient current will be $K_1\epsilon^{\lambda_1 t} + K_2\epsilon^{\lambda_2 t} + \cdots$.   If there are equal roots, use expression (140).

Problems

1. When alternating voltage is applied to a circuit of inductance and resistance the voltage equation of the circuit is $L\dfrac{di}{dt} + Ri = E \sin \omega t$. Find, by the equations of this chapter, the steady-state current in the circuit with this voltage applied and show that the reactance of the inductance is ωL.   (Reactance, by definition, is the ratio of the amplitude of voltage across the inductance to the amplitude of the current through it.)

2. When alternating voltage is applied to a circuit of capacitance and resistance, find the steady-state current in the circuit (using the equations of this chapter).   Find also the reactance of the capacitance.   (For definition, see Prob. 1.)   Note that these problems illustrate the generality of the solution by differential equations, and show its relation to elementary steady-state analysis.

3. Show that an alternative form of equation (124) is

$$i_s = \frac{1}{\lambda_1 - \lambda_2}[\epsilon^{\lambda_1 t}\int \epsilon^{-\lambda_1 t}f(t)dt - \epsilon^{\lambda_2 t}\int \epsilon^{-\lambda_2 t}f(t)dt]$$

4. Solve the following differential equations:

a. $4.5\dfrac{di}{dt} + 20i = 150$

b. $10\dfrac{di}{dt} + 30i = 0$

c. $8\dfrac{di}{dt} + 15i = \epsilon^{-3t}$

d. $7\dfrac{di}{dt} + 6\dfrac{d^2i}{dt^2} + 0.1i = 0$

e. $50\dfrac{di}{dt} + 3\dfrac{d^2i}{dt^2} + 0.1i = 0$

f. $0.6\dfrac{di}{dt} + 10i = 5\epsilon^{j377t}$

CHAPTER IV

THE COMPLETE SINGLE CIRCUIT

1. Forms of Solution. When all three of the electrical parameters—resistance, inductance, and capacitance—are present in a circuit, the transient current that flows when voltage is applied may be a single surge or it may be a train of oscillations that gradually dies away. It is the amount of resistance in the circuit, relative to the inductance and capacitance, that determines which form the current will take.

In Chap. III the circuit of Fig. 16 was considered, in which voltage is suddenly applied to resistance, inductance, and capacitance in series. From the impedance, Eq. (132) was written

$$R + \lambda L + \frac{1}{\lambda C} = 0 \tag{132}$$

and the roots of (132) were obtained as

$$\lambda_1 = -\frac{R}{2L} + \sqrt{\frac{R^2}{4L^2} - \frac{1}{LC}} \qquad \lambda_2 = -\frac{R}{2L} - \sqrt{\frac{R^2}{4L^2} - \frac{1}{LC}} \tag{133}$$

Finding that there were two values of λ, and knowing that steady-state current could not flow, we wrote

$$i = K_1 \epsilon^{\lambda_1 t} + K_2 \epsilon^{\lambda_2 t} \tag{134}$$

It is possible for the values of λ to be complex quantities as well as real numbers. They will be complex if the quantity under the radical in Eq. (133) is negative; the square root of the negative quantity will give an imaginary component to each λ. When the values of the circuit parameters are such that the roots are complex, the current is oscillatory; if the roots are real, the current is a single surge. The current is described by Eq. (134) in either case but, since it is difficult to compute numerical values for an exponential with a complex exponent, it is convenient to transform the exponential expression for current into a sinusoidal form when the current is oscillatory.   There is so marked a difference in the form of the current, both mathematical and physical, when it is oscillatory that it will be discussed separately, in Sec. 9.

The roots are real if the quantity under the radical of Eq. (133) is positive; that is, if

$$\frac{R^2}{4L^2} > \frac{1}{LC} \tag{142}$$

They are complex if

$$\frac{R^2}{4L^2} < \frac{1}{LC} \tag{143}$$

The change of form takes place when

$$\frac{R^2}{4L^2} = \frac{1}{LC}$$

or

$$R = 2\sqrt{\frac{L}{C}} \tag{144}$$

This is called the critical value of resistance.   Of course, there is fundamentally no reason for selecting resistance as the parameter which determines whether or not a circuit will allow current to oscillate.   A critical value of capacitance can be stated just as correctly in terms of inductance and resistance.   But, for practical use, resistance is commonly the determining factor, and its critical value is therefore the criterion most often used to determine whether or not the transient current will oscillate.

In addition to the so-called "oscillatory" and "overdamped" conditions there is also to be considered the special case in which resistance in the circuit has exactly the critical value so that $1/LC$ is just equal to $R^2/4L^2$; the radical then disappears entirely and both roots are equal to $-\dfrac{R}{2L}$.   This corresponds to the mathematical solution of the differential equation with equal roots which is considered in Chap. III, and its solution takes the form of expression (129).

2. Real Roots.   When the roots of Eq. (132) are real, the current is expressed, as in Eq. (134), as the sum of two exponential quantities with different exponents. Each exponential term of the form $K\epsilon^{\lambda t}$ is called a **normal mode** of the network, and each value of λ is called a **generalized natural angular velocity.** Equation (133) shows that when the roots are real both must be negative; this is physically necessary also, for otherwise the current would increase without limit as t becomes larger.

To describe completely the current it is necessary to follow the fourth rule of Sec. 10 of Chap. I and determine from the initial conditions of the circuit the values of the coefficients K_1 and K_2 in Eq. (134).

The first obvious initial condition is that, until the switch is closed, current cannot flow. Moreover, because of inductance in the circuit, current will still be zero at the instant of closing the switch, even though it has started to increase at a finite rate. This makes it possible to write, as an initial condition, that when

$$t = 0, \quad i = 0 \tag{145}$$

We specified in writing the circuit equation as

$$Ri + L\frac{di}{dt} + \frac{1}{C}\int_0^t i\,dt = E \tag{103}$$

that there was no initial charge on the condenser, for the condenser voltage was expressed by the term

$$e_c = \frac{1}{C}\int_0^t i\,dt$$

Since this integral becomes zero when $t = 0$, it follows that when

$$t = 0, \quad e_c = \frac{1}{Cp}i = 0 \tag{146}$$

3. Determination of Coefficients. Coefficients are evaluated by substitution of initial conditions into the current equation. The general principle is well illustrated by the circuit under consideration, whose voltage equation is

$$Lpi + Ri + \frac{1}{Cp}i = E \tag{147}$$

Formal solution of this equation has given us as an expression for current, with undetermined coefficients,

$$i = K_1\epsilon^{\lambda_1 t} + K_2\epsilon^{\lambda_2 t} \tag{134}$$

Two initial conditions for the circuit have been determined: when

$$t = 0, \qquad i = 0 \qquad\qquad (145)$$

and also when

$$t = 0, \qquad \frac{1}{p}i = 0 \qquad\qquad (146)$$

From these and the circuit equation the initial rate of change of current may be deduced. By substituting the initial conditions of (145) and (146) into the circuit equation (147) we find that when

$$t = 0, \qquad Lpi + 0 + 0 = E$$

and hence

$$pi = \frac{E}{L}$$

This gives a third initial condition. This value for the initial rate of change of current could have been determined in this simple case by an inspection of the circuit, by noting that there can be neither current in the resistance nor charge on the condenser at zero time; it follows that at the initial instant the entire applied voltage is available to produce an increase of current through the inductance, and the above value of pi results. But the mental process involved is exactly equivalent to the mathematical substitution used above, and when in more complex cases it is difficult to obtain a value by inspection, the mathematical method will be requisite.

Two equations involving K_1 and K_2 can now be written, and they may be solved simultaneously to obtain the values of the coefficients. The zero value of current at the initial instant is equated to the expression obtained by making $t = 0$ in the formal current equation (134),

$$0 = K_1 + K_2$$

Then Eq. (134) is differentiated to give

$$pi = K_1\lambda_1 e^{\lambda_1 t} + K_2\lambda_2 e^{\lambda_2 t}$$

From this expression we know that the initial value of pi, when $t = 0$, is $K_1\lambda_1 + K_2\lambda_2$, but we also know that the initial value is E/L, so

$$\frac{E}{L} = K_1\lambda_1 + K_2\lambda_2$$

We now have two equations which contain only K_1 and K_2. They are

$$K_1 + K_2 = 0$$

$$K_1\lambda_1 + K_2\lambda_2 = \frac{E}{L}$$

Simultaneous solution gives

$$K_1 = \frac{E}{L}\frac{1}{\lambda_1 - \lambda_2}$$

and

$$K_2 = -K_1 = \frac{E}{L}\frac{1}{\lambda_2 - \lambda_1}$$

Expressions for λ_1 and λ_2 are known, from Eq. (133), to be

$$\lambda_1 = -\frac{R}{2L} + \sqrt{\frac{R^2}{4L^2} - \frac{1}{LC}} \qquad \lambda_2 = -\frac{R}{2L} - \sqrt{\frac{R^2}{4L^2} - \frac{1}{LC}} \quad (133)$$

and it only remains to substitute numerical values for circuit parameters.

4. The Surge of Current. The analytical determination of the current in the circuit which contains resistance, inductance, and capacitance is now complete, and it is interesting to consider the physical nature of the current surge. Figures 17 and 18 show some of the shapes that the surge of current in such a circuit may have. The current surges from lightning strokes will have such shapes. So will the transient currents in many parts of radio circuits. Test circuits that supply either large currents or high voltages for a short time are frequently designed to give such surges.

The analytical form of the current is given in Eq. (134). It is made up of two normal modes, or exponential terms. In case the initial current in the circuit is zero, the two normal modes must have initial values that are equal and opposite, so they will add to zero. This has been formally stated by writing $K_1 + K_2 = 0$, and the current equation may correspondingly be written

$$i = K_1(\epsilon^{\lambda_1 t} - \epsilon^{\lambda_2 t}) \qquad (148)$$

Figure 17 shows the physical nature of a typical current surge of this form.

The two component normal modes are shown in Fig. 17, as well as the total current. λ_1 and λ_2 are both negative numbers, as they must always be, so each normal mode is a component that diminishes exponentially. Note that if either λ were a positive number the current would increase with time at a continually greater rate until it had increased beyond all limit, a conclusion that is physically not allowable because of the law of conservation of energy. The normal modes will diminish at different rates, depending on the generalized angular velocities, and if λ_2 has a larger negative value than λ_1 it follows that $\epsilon^{\lambda_2 t}$ will diminish more

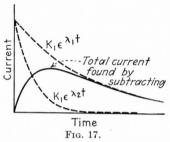

FIG. 17.

rapidly than $\epsilon^{\lambda_1 t}$. One normal mode is smaller than the other at all times except the initial instant, and the difference between them is the value of current in the circuit. As shown in Fig. 17, the current is found by subtracting one exponential curve from the other.

The shape of the current curve may vary widely as the values of the angular velocities are changed. If λ_2 is very large, for instance, the current will be very nearly equal to the upper exponential curve except during the first few moments as it rises steeply from zero. This is illustrated in Fig. 18a; physically, it is the result of having low inductance in the circuit.

In Chap. II the surge of current into a condenser through a resistance is considered. That circuit may be thought of as a special case of the more general circuit with all three parameters (resistance, capacitance, and inductance) in which the value of inductance is vanishingly small. The similarity of Fig. 18a and Fig. 9 is apparent, and, if inductance is further reduced, the curve of Fig. 18a becomes more and more like that of Fig. 9. Since it is impossible to have a circuit without at least a small amount of inductance, it is physically impossible for current in a circuit to rise instantly from zero in the manner suggested by Fig. 9. Strictly, the current must be represented by a curve of the nature of that in Fig. 18a. However, the ideal shape of Fig. 9

is approached very closely when the inductance of the circuit is extremely small, and in many cases the rise of current is so sudden that an oscillograph will record it as being quite instantaneous. (See, for instance, oscillogram 2, at the end of Chap. II.) So for practical purposes it is best to neglect inductance in a circuit in which it is negligibly small (compared to the resistance and capacitance) and to use the simple solutions of Chap. II.

The circuit of Fig. 1, Chap. I, containing only resistance and inductance, may also be looked upon as a special case of the circuit containing all three parameters, with the capacitance of

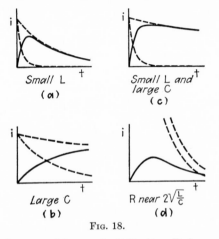

FIG. 18.

the condenser increased beyond all limit. It is apparent that a circuit without inductance is the limiting case of a circuit in which the inductance is decreased toward zero, because as the inductance becomes small the voltage across it disappears. A circuit without capacitance, on the contrary, is the limiting case of a circuit in which the capacitance is increased toward infinity, for the voltage across a condenser disappears as the capacitance is greatly increased, and an infinitely large condenser is equivalent to a short-circuit. So in order to consider a circuit in which the condenser has little effect, the capacitance must be made very large; and a circuit of resistance and inductance only is equivalent to a circuit of resistance, inductance, and capacitance in which the capacitance is infinite. As C becomes very large in the generalized angular velocities of Eq. (133), the value of the radical approaches $R/2L$; consequently λ_1 becomes very small. One normal mode therefore decays very gradually as shown in Fig. 18b, and the first part of the surge of current is not unlike that of Fig. 2.

It is interesting to consider the mathematical result of carrying these parameters to their limits. We have found that in general the current in a circuit is

$$i = K_1(\epsilon^{\lambda_1 t} - \epsilon^{\lambda_2 t}) \qquad (148)$$

where

$$\lambda_1 = -\frac{R}{2L} + \sqrt{\frac{R^2}{4L^2} - \frac{1}{LC}} \qquad \lambda_2 = -\frac{R}{2L} - \sqrt{\frac{R^2}{4L^2} - \frac{1}{LC}} \qquad (133)$$

We have found that

$$K_1 = \frac{E}{L}\frac{1}{\lambda_1 - \lambda_2}$$

and substitution of the above values of λ gives

$$K_1 = \frac{E}{L}\frac{1}{2\sqrt{\dfrac{R^2}{4L^2} - \dfrac{1}{LC}}} = \frac{E}{\sqrt{R^2 - \dfrac{4L}{C}}} \qquad (149)$$

Now if C is made to approach infinity, so that the circuit becomes equivalent to a circuit without a condenser, λ_1 becomes zero, λ_2 becomes $-\dfrac{R}{L}$, and K_1 becomes $\dfrac{E}{R}$. In such a case, Eq. (148) may be written

$$i = \frac{E}{R}(\epsilon^0 - \epsilon^{-\frac{R}{L}t}) \qquad (150)$$

and, since ϵ with the exponent 0 is always 1, this is identical with Eq. (19) which was derived for the circuit containing resistance and inductance only:

$$i = \frac{E}{R}(1 - \epsilon^{-\frac{R}{L}t}) \qquad (19)$$

In a similar manner, although not quite so simply, Eq. (148) will also reduce to the solution of a circuit of resistance and capacitance only. To show this, let L approach zero. This makes each term of Eq. (133) approach infinity. But we may rewrite the values of λ as

$$\lambda_1 = \frac{-R + \sqrt{R^2 - \frac{4L}{C}}}{2L} \qquad \lambda_2 = \frac{-R - \sqrt{R^2 - \frac{4L}{C}}}{2L} \qquad (151)$$

The limit of λ_2 as L approaches 0 is clearly $-\infty$. The limit of λ_1 is not apparent, for if L were allowed to decrease without limit in Eq. (151), λ_1 would be of the form $0/0$. However, if both numerator and denominator of Eq. (151) are multiplied by $(-R - \sqrt{R^2 - 4L/C})$, the limit becomes clear, as follows:

$$\lim_{L \to 0} \lambda_1 = \lim_{L \to 0} \frac{2/C}{-R - \sqrt{R^2 - \frac{4L}{C}}} = -\frac{1}{RC} \qquad (152)$$

The value of K_1 is E/R as is at once evident from Eq. (149). So for this special case the current is

$$i = \frac{E}{R}(\epsilon^{-\frac{1}{RC}t} - \epsilon^{-\infty t}) \qquad (153)$$

Since, for all positive values of time, the exponential $\epsilon^{-\infty t}$ will be zero, this equation is identical with Eq. (54) which was derived in Chap. II for a circuit of resistance and capacitance:

$$i = \frac{E}{R} \epsilon^{-\frac{1}{RC}t} \qquad (54)$$

Another interesting condition that can arise in a circuit with the three parameters appears when the inductance is small and the capacitance large. Resistance is then the dominant factor in controlling the flow of current. The nature of the current surge is shown in Fig. 18c. One normal mode diminishes very rapidly and the other very slowly, with the result that the current surge rises quickly and then remains almost constant for a relatively long time. The sudden rise of current is possible because of the small inductance of the circuit, and its slow subsidence is due to the fact that a long time is required to charge the large condenser. Of course, current must eventually cease as the condenser becomes fully charged.

The limit of this type of surge appears when inductance is zero and capacitance infinite. As soon as the switch in such a circuit is closed the current will rise to a value of E/R, and that value will be maintained thereafter. Since resistance is the only parameter remaining in the circuit across which voltage can appear, it is natural that

$$i = \frac{E}{R} \tag{154}$$

This value for current is derived mathematically when L in Eq. (150) is zero, or when C in Eq. (153) is infinite. Figure 18c illustrates the similarity of the actual surge of current to the limiting rectangular surge, for although the front of the actual surge is somewhat rounded, and although the current must eventually cease, the surge may nevertheless be made as nearly rectangular as is desired.

When resistance is small, relative to inductance and capacitance, the current surge will be rounded as in Fig. 18d. Of course, resistance must not be less than the critical value of $2\sqrt{L/C}$, for we wish at present to speak only of currents whose normal modes are purely real. But when resistance is only slightly greater than the critical value, the radicals of Eq. (133) become very small, for $R^2/4L^2$ is very nearly the same size as $1/LC$. As a result, λ_1 and λ_2 are nearly equal, one being slightly larger and the other slightly smaller than $-\dfrac{R}{2L}$. Also, as may be seen in Eq. (149), a small value of the radical makes K_1 very great. The components of current are therefore as shown in Fig. 18d; each normal mode is very large because of the high value of K_1, but the difference between them is never very great because of their similarity of shape.

5. The Critically Damped Surge. In the limiting case, in which the resistance has its critical value and the two values of λ are identical, the mathematical form of current becomes indeterminate. The current in Eq. (148), for instance, appears as the product of an infinite K_1 and a zero difference of exponentials. But this contingency has already been provided for; in Sec. 8 of Chap. III it was pointed out that when the two values of λ are equal the useful form of current equation is altered. It becomes

$$i = \frac{E}{L} t \epsilon^{-\frac{R}{2L}t} \qquad (155)$$

Derivation of this equation will appear below.

The distinction between a circuit with critical resistance and a circuit with resistance slightly greater than the critical is very clear in the *mathematical* solution, but there is no such clear distinction between the *physical* natures of the surges of current in the two cases. If a series of oscillograms of the current surges in a circuit in which the resistance was decreased by small steps toward the critical value were recorded, there would be no distinguishing characteristic to identify the oscillogram which corresponded to the critical value of resistance. The critical value of resistance is merely the lowest value that will permit the current to appear as a single, unidirectional surge.

The solution of the critically damped circuit is not important because of any probability that such a circuit may be encountered in practice. In fact, it is highly improbable that a circuit would ever have *exactly* the critical resistance. Even if a circuit were specially designed to have resistance equal to the critical value, it is to be expected that careful measurement would always be able to find a slight difference from the theoretical value. But the form of solution that is given in Eq. (155) for a critically damped circuit is often the best form to use for computation of current surges in circuits whose resistance is quite close to the critical value. This is due to the extreme difficulty of computing from Eq. (148) in such a case.

The current appears in Eq. (148) as the small difference between two large and nearly equal exponential terms; and the exponent of each of the normal modes is itself a small difference between two nearly equal terms. The denominator of K_1 in Eq. (149) also appears as a small difference between the terms of the radical. Slight inaccuracy in the processes of computation will be magnified. If resistance is within 1 per cent of the critical value, it is not satisfactory to depend on slide-rule calculation of current, as an error of 5 per cent in the current may result from an error of 0.1 per cent in manipulation. So when the current is quite close to the critical value it may often be found more easily, and yet with sufficient accuracy, by assuming that the resistance has exactly the critical value. The computation is then made from Eq. (155).

The usual derivation of Eq. (155) makes use of Eq. (128), which is the general solution of the second-order linear differential equation when the two roots of the auxiliary equation are equal. The general solution contains two transient terms and a steady-state component:

$$i = K_2\epsilon^{\lambda_m t} + K'te^{\lambda_m t} + \epsilon^{\lambda_m t}\int\int\epsilon^{-\lambda_m t}f(t)dt\, dt \qquad (128)$$

Since there can be no steady-state current in the circuit under discussion, the particular integral is zero. This can be seen analytically also, because $f(t)$ is zero as in Eq. (104).

The value of λ_m is very simple in the critically damped circuit. In general,

$$\lambda_1 = -\frac{R}{2L} + \sqrt{\frac{R^2}{4L^2} - \frac{1}{LC}} \qquad \lambda_2 = -\frac{R}{2L} - \sqrt{\frac{R^2}{4L^2} - \frac{1}{LC}} \quad (133)$$

With critical damping, however,

$$\frac{R^2}{4L^2} = \frac{1}{LC}$$

and the value of the radical becomes zero. Both λ_1 and λ_2 are then equal to $-\dfrac{R}{2L}$. This, of course, is λ_m and

$$\lambda_m = -\frac{R}{2L} \qquad (156)$$

The two coefficients of the transient terms are evaluated by means of initial conditions, and two initial conditions have already been determined for the circuit: when

$$t = 0, \qquad i = 0 \qquad (145)$$

and when

$$t = 0, \qquad pi = \frac{E}{L}$$

Substitution of (145) in (128) gives $0 = K_2 + 0$, showing that $K_2 = 0$, and

$$i = K'te^{\lambda_m t} \tag{157}$$

Finally, Eq. (157) is differentiated:

$$pi = K'\epsilon^{\lambda_m t} + \lambda_m K'te^{\lambda_m t} \tag{158}$$

and since the value of the derivative at zero time is known to be E/L, we substitute $t = 0$ in Eq. (158) and write

$$\frac{E}{L} = K' + 0 \tag{159}$$

When the different parts of the solution are combined in the form of Eq. (157) it appears that the current in a critically damped circuit, in case there is no initial current in the circuit and no initial charge on the condenser, is

$$i = \frac{E}{L}te^{-\frac{R}{2L}t} \tag{160}$$

6. Other Initial Conditions. Little has been said about circuits in which current is flowing prior to the application of the voltage that produces the transient current, because such circuits are rare. The method of solution is unchanged; however, in evaluating the coefficients in the overdamped case, it is no longer found that $K_2 = -K_1$, and, in the critically damped case, there is a value other than zero for K_2. Initial charge on the condenser will likewise alter only the coefficients, much as was discussed in Sec. 4 of Chap. III.

7. A General Method of Solution for Coefficients. Evaluation of coefficients is usually the most difficult part of transient-current solutions. It is highly desirable, therefore, to make their determination as systematic as possible. In Sec. 3 we found values for K_1 and K_2 from initial conditions by means of two simultaneous equations. There are only two coefficients in Eq. (134), and hence only two simultaneous equations are needed to determine them. But by an extension of the method used it is possible to obtain further equations involving the coefficients, and any number of coefficients may thereby be evaluated. The importance of the general method is great enough to justify a repetition of the solution for K_1 and K_2 with a broadening of method that will adapt it to more complex networks.

The circuit equation is written below as (162), and with it are grouped a number of equations which are derived from it.

$$Li + R\frac{1}{p}i + \frac{1}{Cp^2}i = Et \tag{161}$$

$$Lpi + Ri + \frac{1}{Cp}i = E \tag{162}$$

$$Lp^2i + Rpi + \frac{1}{C}i = 0 \tag{163}$$

$$Lp^3i + Rp^2i + \frac{1}{C}pi = 0 \tag{164}$$

Equation (161) is obtained from (162) by integration; (163) results from differentiation of (162), and (164) from differentiation of (163). Further successive integrations or differentiations will extend this group of equations to any desired extent.

The known initial conditions are
when

$$t = 0, \qquad \frac{1}{p}i = 0 \tag{165}$$

and when

$$t = 0, \qquad i = 0 \tag{166}$$

From these two known conditions the value of any initial derivative of current may be found: Eqs. (165) and (166) are used in conjunction with the group of Eqs. (161) to (164). Substitute (165) and (166) in (162):
when $t = 0$

$$Lpi + 0 + 0 = E \qquad pi = \frac{E}{L} \tag{167}$$

thereby obtaining the first derivative. Substitute (166) and (167) in (163):
when $t = 0$

$$Lp^2i + R\frac{E}{L} + 0 = 0 \qquad p^2i = -\frac{ER}{L^2} \tag{168}$$

and the second derivative results. Substitute (167) and (168) in (164):
when $t = 0$

$$Lp^3i - R\frac{ER}{L^2} + \frac{1}{C}\frac{E}{L} = 0 \qquad p^3i = \frac{E}{L}\left(\frac{R^2}{L^2} - \frac{1}{LC}\right) \quad (169)$$

and this is the third derivative. Equations (165) to (169) all express initial conditions, and this list of initial derivatives of current can be lengthened indefinitely by continued substitution in the manner illustrated.

Initial derivatives have been determined in order that they may be equated to expressions, obtained from the current equation, containing K_1 and K_2.

From Eq. (134), which is rewritten as Eq. (170), differentiation gives

$$i = K_1\epsilon^{\lambda_1 t} + K_2\epsilon^{\lambda_2 t} \tag{170}$$
$$pi = K_1\lambda_1\epsilon^{\lambda_1 t} + K_2\lambda_2\epsilon^{\lambda_2 t} \tag{171}$$
$$p^2i = K_1\lambda_1^2\epsilon^{\lambda_1 t} + K_2\lambda_2^2\epsilon^{\lambda_2 t} \tag{172}$$
$$p^3i = K_1\lambda_1^3\epsilon^{\lambda_1 t} + K_2\lambda_2^3\epsilon^{\lambda_2 t} \tag{173}$$

Values of current and its derivatives are known when $t = 0$, from Eqs. (166) to (169), so that by making $t = 0$ in Eqs. (170) to (173) it is possible to equate them as follows.
From (170) and (166):

$$0 = K_1 + K_2 \tag{174}$$

From (171) and (167):

$$\frac{E}{L} = K_1\lambda_1 + K_2\lambda_2 \tag{175}$$

From (172) and (168):

$$-\frac{ER}{L^2} = K_1\lambda_1^2 + K_2\lambda_2^2 \tag{176}$$

From (173) and (169):

$$\frac{E}{L}\left(\frac{R^2}{L^2} - \frac{1}{LC}\right) = K_1\lambda_1^3 + K_2\lambda_2^3 \tag{177}$$

Simultaneous solution of these equations will evaluate coefficients. Any two of these equations may be solved for K_1 and K_2, making use of the known values of λ. From Eq. (133)

$$\lambda_1 = -\frac{R}{2L} + \sqrt{\frac{R^2}{4L^2} - \frac{1}{LC}} \qquad \lambda_2 = -\frac{R}{2L} - \sqrt{\frac{R^2}{4L^2} - \frac{1}{LC}} \quad (178)$$

It is obvious that the easiest pair to solve is (174) and (175), for

$$K_2 = -K_1 \tag{179}$$

and

$$\frac{E}{L} = K_1(\lambda_1 - \lambda_2) \tag{180}$$

so that

$$K_1 = \frac{E}{L}\frac{1}{\lambda_1 - \lambda_2} \tag{181}$$

and

$$K_2 = -K_1 = \frac{E}{L}\frac{1}{\lambda_2 - \lambda_1} \tag{182}$$

This completes the solution for the coefficients of Eq. (170), and it will be seen that many of the equations of the groups (161) to (164), (165) to (169), and (170) to (173) were not used. They are not needed in this simple case, but they were written so that the method employed would be available in those more complex networks for which more than two coefficients must be evaluated; if there had been four values of K in Eq. (170) instead of just two, they could all have been found from Eqs. (174) to (177). The method can be extended indefinitely, although at the expense of considerable algebraic complexity.

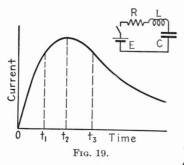

FIG. 19.

To recapitulate: *Express the initial values of current and its derivatives in terms of circuit parameters, making use of any known initial conditions and substituting in the differential equation or its derivatives; also express the initial values of current and its derivatives in terms of the unknown coefficients, which may be done by letting $t = 0$ in the formal current equation; equate corresponding expressions of initial values, and solve the resulting equations simultaneously for the unknown coefficients.*

8. Action of the Circuit. Figure 19, like Fig. 18*d*, illustrates an example of the single surge of current, for which resistance is near the critical value.   It is interesting to formulate a mental picture of the physical action that takes place within the circuit after the switch is closed.

Just at first there will be no current and the entire applied voltage will be across the inductance.   Because of this the current will have a rapid rate of increase.   But as current grows there will appear a proportional voltage across the resistance of the circuit; less than the whole applied voltage will then be across the inductance, and the rate of increase of current will be correspondingly lessened.   When time is t_1 the slope of the current curve of Fig. 19 has decreased considerably from its initial value. But still there is voltage available to increase the current, although at a diminished rate.   In the mean time, during the time interval from zero to t_1, charge has been accumulating on the condenser in the circuit and it, as well as the resistance, is now exerting a voltage that opposes the flow of current.   Condenser, resistance, and inductance are all working against the applied battery voltage.   The condenser voltage builds up slowly, because it can not be effective until charge has had time to accumulate, and at t_1 it is less than either the inductance voltage or the resistance voltage.   Voltages across the resistance and condenser continue to increase, and voltage across the inductance diminishes, until the maximum value of current is reached.

The instant of maximum current is marked t_2.   The slope of the current curve is zero at this point, for the current has ceased increasing; that is because there is no longer any voltage available for the inductance—it is all being used to maintain current in the resistance and charge on the condenser.   But such a condition cannot last, for charge is constantly accumulating on the condenser, and to maintain a proper balance the current must decline from its maximum value.   A decrease of current, however, means a negative rate of change, and at t_3 we find that the voltage across the inductance is negative and the energy stored in the inductance is actually helping the battery to force current through the circuit.   This is of course entirely consistent with the idea that inductance always acts to prevent a change of current.   At t_3 the sum of the condenser voltage and the resistance voltage is greater than the applied voltage, and the difference is made up by the inductance.   As time passes beyond t_3, the resistance voltage decreases as the current becomes less.

the condenser voltage increases in proportion to the area under the current curve, and the inductance voltage becomes first more strongly negative and then finally diminishes as the curve flattens out toward the axis. Voltage on the condenser gradually approaches its steady-state value, which is equal to the applied voltage.

The flow of energy in the circuit of Fig. 19 is somewhat similar to its flow in the circuit of capacitance and resistance only. The inductance receives energy during the time of increase of the transient current, but as the current diminishes it returns all of its energy to the circuit, for it can retain no electromagnetic energy when the current has died away. The condenser, on the other hand, receives energy continuously during the life of the transient current, for charge is constantly flowing into the condenser and never escaping. The rate of flow of energy to the condenser is greatest at a somewhat later time than the instant of maximum current, for the condenser voltage is constantly increasing, and power to the condenser is the product of current and voltage. The total stored energy in the condenser is a maximum when the transient period is over and is plainly $\frac{1}{2}CE^2$.

Because the circuit contains resistance in excess of the critical value, the transient current in the circuit is but a single unidirectional surge. If resistance were less, the current would oscillate, being alternately positive and negative. If a pendulum is pulled to one side and released it will swing back and forth for a long time before finally coming to rest in its central position. But if the pendulum is hung in thick oil instead of air it will move slowly, when released, to its central position and will stop there. The pointer on a voltmeter or an ammeter, or the speedometer of an automobile, will usually move too far in response to a sudden change, and will swing back and forth a few times before settling down at the correct point. Some meters, however, are intentionally made to come to rest without any oscillation; this is done by damping the motion of the moving parts.

In the same way the transient response of an electric circuit may be either oscillatory or overdamped. Resistance produces the damping, and if there is little resistance in a circuit its transient current will oscillate freely.

9. The Oscillatory Current. When the switch is first closed in a circuit having resistance, inductance, and capacitance, the current *begins* to increase at a rate determined by the inductance alone. If the resistance is small, there is little opposition to the flow of current until a charge has accumulated on the condenser, so the rate of increase of current does not diminish as rapidly as it does when resistance is an important factor in the circuit. Figure 20 shows the current in an oscillatory circuit. The initial slope of the current curve is determined by the inductance alone, for none of the applied voltage is used across either the resistance or the condenser until the flow of current has begun. At a later time t_1 on the front of the first current wave, while the current is still increasing, the applied voltage is divided practically between the inductance and the condenser, the resistance taking only a small part of the applied voltage. At the crest of the current wave at time t_2, the condenser and resistance together

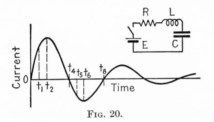

FIG. 20.

have attained a voltage equal to the applied voltage, and since at time t_2 there is no voltage across the inductance $\left(\dfrac{di}{dt} = 0\right)$, the current cannot increase further. The current begins at once to diminish. The inductance voltage due to a negative rate of change of current will prevent the cessation of current flow, for the stored energy of the inductance will literally drive the current into the condenser, regardless of voltage, until the inductance energy, $\frac{1}{2}Li^2$, is exhausted. When the inductance energy is zero, the current also will be zero. As the condenser voltage was nearly equal to the applied voltage at t_2, the resistance voltage being small, the condenser will be overcharged at t_4, as the condenser has received energy from the inductance between t_2 and t_4.

It is characteristic of the oscillatory circuit that when the current first ceases—at t_4—the condenser is charged to a voltage greater than the applied voltage. The condenser must therefore discharge before equilibrium is reached. In fact, when the resistance is small, as in the circuit of Fig. 20, the condenser voltage at t_4 is almost twice the applied voltage. Then, since the applied voltage is not great enough to hold so much charge on the condenser, the charge will immediately begin to flow out of the condenser, and the result will be a negative current, as at t_5.

Let us consider in a little more detail the conditions at t_4. There is no current; there is a battery in the circuit with voltage E; there is a condenser that at this instant has an opposing voltage greater than E but less than $2E$. Since there is no current, the resistance takes no voltage, and the excess of condenser voltage over applied voltage will be used in producing a negative rate of change of current through the inductance. Hence a negative current will begin to flow, and this current will increase until the condenser voltage is no longer sufficiently in excess of the applied voltage to overcome the opposing voltages of both resistance and inductance. The maximum of negative current will then be reached, at t_6, but negative current will still flow, diminishing in value, once more being driven by the inductance. A second point of zero current then occurs, but the charge on the condenser has been decreased by negative current, and a positive wave of current will immediately begin to replace the charge. So the oscillation of current continues indefinitely, each wave being of smaller amplitude than the preceding wave, but with equilibrium never quite reached.

The flow and exchange of energy in such a circuit is somewhat involved. Let us consider first an ideal circuit without resistance. Such a circuit is physically impossible, but may be considered as a limiting case. A battery is connected to such a circuit, and current begins to flow, much as in Fig. 20. As long as the current is increasing, the battery supplies energy to the electromagnetic field of the inductance, and as long as current flows in the positive direction the condenser gains energy. However, from t_2 to t_4 the current is diminishing, and energy is transferred from the inductance to the condenser, so that when current becomes zero at t_4 the inductance has lost all its energy and the condenser has acquired all the energy that has been supplied to the circuit by the battery.

At time t_4 the condenser voltage is twice the battery voltage, and this causes current to flow around the circuit in a negative direction. While current is flowing in a negative direction, the condenser is returning energy to the battery. The condenser is also transferring energy to the inductance as long as the current is increasing toward a negative maximum, but, after the negative maximum is passed, the condenser and inductance both deliver energy to the battery. At t_8, when the current is again zero, there is no energy in either inductance or capacitance, and the battery has received back all that it supplied in the first half-cycle. (It should be emphasized that the resistance is zero.) Since all conditions at the end of the first cycle, at time t_8, are identical with initial conditions at time zero, a second cycle of current will be identical with the first cycle, a third with the second, and so on without limit.

During the half-cycle in which the condenser and inductance cause a current to flow through the battery against the battery voltage, energy is being delivered to the battery. It does not follow that such energy is being returned to the battery in the same chemical form in which it existed previously, or indeed in any useful form.

When resistance is present in the circuit, it receives energy that is dissipated as heat. Power to the resistance is always small, since the resistance itself must be small in a circuit in which the current is oscillatory; power to the resistance is maximum when the current is maximum, and becomes momentarily zero as the current passes through zero at times t_4, t_8, and so on. When resistance is present, it takes part of the energy that otherwise would have gone to the condenser, so that at the end of a half-cycle the condenser has received less energy than it would have received in the ideal case of no resistance. It is still sufficiently overcharged to reverse the current, however, though less vigorously, and at time t_8 the current again becomes zero without the condenser being fully discharged. The action continues until all excess energy has been transformed into heat in the resistance, and current ceases to flow; the condenser is then charged to the voltage E of the battery, and its stored energy is $\frac{1}{2}CE^2$.

Analogies to the oscillatory current in such a circuit are often proposed. But the purpose of an analogy is to compare an unfamiliar action with one that is accustomed, in order to clarify the mental picture of the new situation. But we have progressed so far in the knowledge of electricity that we have no need for such illustrations of the behaviour of simple circuits; rather, electric circuits will be found useful as simple analogues for problems in other fields.

10. The Sinusoidal Form of Equation. It is mathematically correct to describe an oscillatory current by Eq. (148),

$$i = K_1(\epsilon^{\lambda_1 t} - \epsilon^{\lambda_2 t}) \tag{148}$$

which was derived without reference to the relative values of the parameters. But computation from this equation is awkward when the current is oscillatory, because both exponents and coefficient are then complex numbers. For practical use, therefore it is much better to change the equation from exponential to trigonometric form. It will be remembered that Eq. (148) applies only when the initial current is zero, but, as this condition is quite common, it will serve as a good illustration. If the initial charge on the condenser is also zero, the value of K_1 is known from Eq. (149) to be

$$K_1 = \frac{E}{2L\sqrt{\dfrac{R^2}{4L^2} - \dfrac{1}{LC}}} \tag{183}$$

The values of λ_1 and λ_2 are given in Eq. (133) as

$$\lambda_1 = -\frac{R}{2L} + \sqrt{\frac{R^2}{4L^2} - \frac{1}{LC}} \qquad \lambda_2 = -\frac{R}{2L} - \sqrt{\frac{R^2}{4L^2} - \frac{1}{LC}} \tag{133}$$

When the current is oscillatory, the quantity beneath the radical is negative, and since this makes the radical imaginary, the equations may best be written:

$$\lambda_1 = -\frac{R}{2L} + j\sqrt{\frac{1}{LC} - \frac{R^2}{4L^2}} \qquad \lambda_2 = -\frac{R}{2L} - j\sqrt{\frac{1}{LC} - \frac{R^2}{4L^2}} \tag{184}$$

Merely for convenience it is desirable to abbreviate these equations to

$$\left.\begin{aligned} \lambda_1 &= -\alpha + j\omega \\ \lambda_2 &= -\alpha - j\omega \end{aligned}\right\} \tag{185}$$

in which it is evident that by definition

$$\alpha \equiv \frac{R}{2L} \qquad \omega \equiv \sqrt{\frac{1}{LC} - \frac{R^2}{4L^2}} \tag{186}$$

Although Eq. (148) is entirely correct as a description of the current, it is not customarily used for computation because of the difficulty of determining the numerical value of an exponential with a complex exponent. When λ_1 and λ_2 are real, it is easy to find the values of the exponentials in Eq. (148) from a table of exponentials or, what is equivalent, a table of natural logarithms. When λ_1 and λ_2 are complex, and the current is oscillatory, it is much easier to use a sinusoidal form of expression for the current, which may be derived from Eq. (148).

When the generalized natural angular velocities, as abbreviated in Eq. (185), are substituted in Eq. (148), the result is

$$
\begin{aligned}
i &= K_1(\epsilon^{-\alpha t}\epsilon^{j\omega t} - \epsilon^{-\alpha t}\epsilon^{-j\omega t}) \\
&= K_1\epsilon^{-\alpha t}(\epsilon^{j\omega t} - \epsilon^{-j\omega t})
\end{aligned}
\tag{187}
$$

Since it is known from mathematics that the sine function can be expressed in terms of exponentials as

$$
\sin x = \frac{1}{2j}(\epsilon^{jx} - \epsilon^{-jx})
$$

it is helpful to multiply and divide Eq. (187) by $2j$, giving

$$
i = 2jK_1\epsilon^{-\alpha t}\frac{1}{2j}(\epsilon^{j\omega t} - \epsilon^{-j\omega t})
$$

Then,

$$
i = 2jK_1\epsilon^{-\alpha t}\sin \omega t
\tag{188}
$$

Instead of leaving K_1 in the form in which it is given in Eq. (183), it is better to recognize that the quantity under the radical is negative and write

$$
K_1 = \frac{E}{2jL\sqrt{\dfrac{1}{LC} - \dfrac{R^2}{4L^2}}}
\tag{189}
$$

This value of K_1 is then substituted in Eq. (188) to give the final result:

$$
i = \frac{E}{L\sqrt{\dfrac{1}{LC} - \dfrac{R^2}{4L^2}}}\,\epsilon^{-\alpha t}\sin \omega t
\tag{190}
$$

It is easy to evaluate current from Eq. (190), for α and ω are both real numbers and the sine and exponential may readily be found in tables.

It is interesting to consider that Eq. (190) describes the current when overdamped as well as when oscillatory, although in the overdamped case ω is an imaginary quantity. Since the sine of an imaginary quantity is related to the hyperbolic sine of a real quantity, it is possible to compute numerically from Eq. (190) for the overdamped current, although it is not usual.

The form of current curve described by Eq. (190) is commonly called a damped sinusoid. If the exponential term $\epsilon^{-\alpha t}$ did not appear, there would be no damping, and sinusoidal current would continue to flow indefinitely and undiminished. It is for this reason that $\epsilon^{-\alpha t}$ is called the **damping factor** or **decrement factor.** When there is damping, the current curve still retains the general appearance of a sine wave, but (as in Fig. 20) each crest is lower than the one preceding. We can go farther than that, and say that the nature of the exponential function is

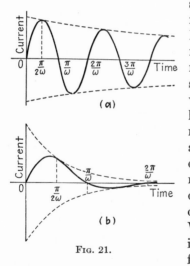

(a)

(b)

Fig. 21.

such that each crest is a certain fraction of the one just preceding. If the damping is slight, due to low resistance in the circuit, the diminution may be slow; Fig. 21*a* shows a wave in which each crest value is nine-tenths that of the half-cycle just preceding. If the resistance in the circuit is nearly as great as the critical value, the dying out of oscillation will be rapid, as in Fig. 21*b*, where each crest value is only one-tenth that of the half-cycle just preceding. With such rapid damping it is impossible to show a third crest, for it would be only $\frac{1}{100}$ of the first one. Although bearing in mind that *mathematically* no transient current *ever* becomes and remains zero, it would be true for most practical purposes to say that after the second half-cycle of Fig. 21*b* there is no significant current. The steady state has therefore been reached.

11. Natural Frequency. The sinusoidal part of the expression for current in (190) indicates that the current will surge back and forth in the circuit, and that it will be zero momentarily when ωt is equal to zero or to any multiple of π. Both curves of Fig. 21 illustrate this statement, although in *a* the curve retains the appearance of a sine wave while in *b* the typical shape has been greatly altered by rapid attenuation. In both, the current is zero when time is π/ω, $2\pi/\omega$, and so on. Figure 22 also shows the current wave passing through zero whenever ωt is a multiple of π. A period of time equal to $2\pi/\omega$ is customarily referred to as the duration of one cycle of the oscillatory current. Since the current is not truly cyclic, owing to damping, this use of the term "cycle" is not above question. But we will follow the custom and speak of the current between consecutive zero values as a half-cycle and the current during twice as long an interval as a cycle.

The frequency of the oscillating current is perhaps its most important characteristic from a practical point of view. Frequency is of particular importance in radio and other branches of communication work. But in any circuit, if transient oscillations are undesirable and must be suppressed, the essential characteristic that allows suppression is frequency; and, if transient oscillations are useful in the circuit, it is even more necessary to know their frequencies.

Frequency, by analogy to a steady-state cyclic current, is the number of cycles per second; ω is the **natural angular velocity** of the circuit, and $\omega/2\pi$ is the **natural frequency.** It is in accord with this terminology that λ, which is made up of the natural angular velocity ω and the **natural decrement** α, is called the *generalized* natural angular velocity.

We know from Eq. (186) that the natural angular velocity of a transient oscillation is

$$\omega = \sqrt{\frac{1}{LC} - \frac{R^2}{4L^2}}$$

Division by 2π will change angular velocity to frequency:

$$2\pi f = \omega = \sqrt{\frac{1}{LC} - \frac{R^2}{4L^2}}$$

$$f = \frac{1}{2\pi}\sqrt{\frac{1}{LC} - \frac{R^2}{4L^2}} \tag{191}$$

If the oscillation is but slightly damped, owing to resistance of the circuit being small, the second term under the radical will be small compared to the first.   In fact, the natural angular velocity of a highly oscillatory current can be determined to a good degree of approximation by neglecting the effect of resistance on frequency and writing

$$\omega \approx \sqrt{\frac{1}{LC}} \qquad (192)$$

This approximation is particularly satisfactory because resistance is squared in the complete expression for natural angular velocity and a low value of resistance, relative to the critical value, leads to an extremely low value for the quantity $R^2/4L^2$. If resistance is 0.1 the critical value, for instance, the error due to neglecting it entirely and using Eq. (192) for angular velocity is only 0.005.   Similarly, a good approximation to the natural frequency of a circuit can be obtained from (191):

$$f \approx \frac{1}{2\pi}\sqrt{\frac{1}{LC}} \qquad (193)$$

Natural frequency is largely dependent on the inductance and capacitance of a circuit.   If both are large, the frequency will be low, whereas if both are small the frequency will be high. Assuming low resistance, and therefore accepting Eq. (193), the product of inductance and capacitance determines the frequency.

If the natural frequency of current in a circuit is to be changed, it may be done by altering either the capacitance or the inductance.   If frequency is to be reduced, the condenser in the circuit can be removed, and a larger one substituted.   To reduce the frequency by one-half its value, the capacitance of the new condenser must be four times that of the one it replaces.   Or, if an increase of capacitance is not practicable, the frequency may be reduced by increasing the inductance, and, to reduce the frequency by one-half its value, the inductance must be increased to four times its previous value.   It is often distressing in the design of circuits to find how slowly the frequency is altered by changes of either inductance or capacitance alone, for the frequency changes only as the *square root* of their product.   On the other hand, a practical advantage of the slow change of frequency with inductance and capacitance is that it gives to the operation of the circuit a stability that is sometimes very desirable in maintaining constant frequency despite small but unavoidable changes of the circuit elements.

Although the natural frequency is little affected by small amounts of resistance in the circuit, it will be very materially reduced if the resistance is anywhere near the critical value. It is evident that the radical in Eq. (191) approaches zero as resistance approaches the critical value; and although the error, as already mentioned, is only 0.5 per cent when the resistance is 10 per cent of the critical, it becomes 13.4 per cent when the resistance is half the critical. A short tabulation will illustrate the effect of resistance on natural frequency:

Resistance, % of critical	Reduction of Frequency, % of undamped
0	0
10	0.5
30	4.6
50	13.4
70	28.6
90	56.4
100	100

12. Damping. Much more characteristic of resistance than its influence on frequency is the damping it causes. This effect of resistance is illustrated in Fig. 21; the two parts of this figure compare a slightly damped wave-train in a circuit of low resistance to strongly damped oscillations in a circuit whose resistance is not very much below the critical value. Figure 22 shows a wave with a degree of damping between these two extremes.

At each quarter-cycle point, when ωt is equal to some odd multiple of $\pi/2$, the factor $\sin \omega t$ in Eq. (190) is equal to either plus or minus one. The current at such instants therefore is simply

$$\pm \frac{E}{L\sqrt{\dfrac{1}{LC} - \dfrac{R^2}{4L^2}}} \epsilon^{-\alpha t} \tag{194}$$

Although this expression coincides with the value of current only at the quarter-cycle instants, it is useful to note that it describes a curve that is a simple exponential, as indicated by the dotted lines in Fig. 22 and in both parts of Fig. 21. For each case there

are two of these curves symmetrically above and below the
time axis, and corresponding to the plus and minus options of
expression (194).   The current curve is contained entirely within
these dotted lines, being tangent to them but never crossing, and
for that reason the exponential curves are frequently called the
envelope of the current wave.   Once more we must apologize to
the mathematicians, for the technical definition of "envelope"
does not quite cover such an application.   The curve must have
some name, however, and the practical applicability of the word
"envelope" is evident.

The idea of the oscillating wave being contained within the
exponential envelope is very convenient and useful.   It helps in
drafting a damped-sinusoid curve, for the points of tangency of
curve and envelope may readily be located, and the complete
curve can then be sketched by anyone who has had a little experience in drawing sine waves.   The accuracy of such a freehand
sketch is surprisingly good.

But of far greater importance than the use of the envelope in
actually drafting the curve is its help in gaining an effective
mental picture of the damping of an oscillating current.   The
alternating current is "modulated" (to use a word from communication engineering) by an exponential curve.   We may
assume as a first approximation that the frequency of oscillation
is determined by inductance and capacitance of the circuit, and
the initial amplitude of the oscillation [the coefficient of $\epsilon^{-\alpha t}$ in
(194)] is also determined mainly by inductance and capacitance.
Picture, then, an oscillating current with a certain frequency;
it has a certain initial amplitude, but the amplitude diminishes
as the wave-train of current is compressed within an envelope
of exponential form.   The circuit resistance governs the shape
of the envelope.   Low resistance allows the current to flow on,
relatively unimpeded and with only gradual damping as the wave-
train is constrained within the envelope; greater resistance
makes the envelope shrink rapidly and the oscillating current is
sharply constricted.   Just as the natural frequency of oscillation
characterizes the transient current in one way, the form of the
envelope characterizes it in another.

A third use for the concept of an envelope is found in estimat-
ing the magnitude of duration of a transient disturbance.   Such
information is often more readily obtained from a knowledge of

the envelope than from instantaneous values of the actual current wave. A certain time is required, for instance, for the envelope to diminish to a tenth of its initial value, and for some purposes that period of time may be considered the duration of the transient current. As an example, consider that lightning strikes near an electric power line and induces a transient current in some oscillatory circuit. Figure 22 is a record of the transient current. When ωt equals $5\pi/2$ the envelope of the wave-train has diminished to one-tenth its initial value, and thereafter the lightning-induced wave-train is too small to be troublesome. So from the point of view of the engineer wishing to protect the circuit against lightning disturbances, the effective duration of the transient current is $1\frac{1}{4}$ cycles.

But if an oscillogram were to be recorded, showing the same wave-train in full detail, it would be necessary to arrange to have the oscillograph continue in operation as long as the current could be detected. Let us specify that the record must continue until the envelope is reduced to 1 per cent of its initial value. Figure 22 does not extend far enough to help us find the length of time needed, but computation from Eq. (194) shows that the oscillogram must record $2\frac{1}{2}$ cycles of the current. So for the purpose of obtaining a complete record the duration of the transient current is $2\frac{1}{2}$ cycles. Under some other circumstances the effective duration might be more, or less, but a quick estimate of the magnitude of the disturbance at any time can conveniently be made from the shape of the envelope.

Expression (194) is used in making such estimates. It is a very simple expression: merely an exponential term with a coefficient. The coefficient is determined by the circuit characteristics and the applied voltage. If the current is but slightly damped, the coefficient is primarily determined by the inductance and capacitance of the circuit rather than by the resistance—as has been mentioned previously. Physically, this is true because the small amount of resistance that corresponds to slight damping plays a much less important role in limiting the waves of current than does the condenser; mathematically it is evident because resistance appears only in the coefficient of expression (194) as part of the radical

$$\sqrt{\frac{1}{LC} - \frac{R^2}{4L^2}}$$

whose value we already know is not much influenced by the resistance term when the resistance is small.

The exponent of the exponential term is

$$-\alpha t = -\frac{R}{2L}t \tag{195}$$

The rate of damping is governed by this exponent, and is therefore proportional to R/L. When the exponent is large, as would result from a large resistance, the exponential decrement factor $\epsilon^{-\alpha t}$ is small (at a given value of time) and attenuation of the wave-train is rapid. Specifically, the exponent contains the product of resistance and time, so that if resistance is increased the time of damping is decreased proportionately.

For purposes of this discussion, inductance has been assumed to remain constant, for a change of inductance will alter damping just as effectually as will a change of resistance. Large inductance will result in slow damping. The effect of inductance is indirect, for damping can only be due to loss of energy which takes place in the resistance. But an increase in inductance results in a decrease of current, and the rate of dissipation of energy in the resistance is thereby lowered. Since the total energy of the circuit is practically unchanged by the increase of inductance, the lessened rate of dissipation corresponds to a less rapid damping. It is interesting to notice that changing the capacitance of the circuit's condenser will not affect the decrement factor in any way. It will change the natural frequency of the current, and it will change the coefficient of the envelope, but the rate of damping is independent of the size of the condenser.

Another remarkable property of the circuit consisting of capacitance, inductance, and resistance is that the amount of energy lost in resistance during the life of the transient current is quite independent of the values of resistance and inductance. The energy changed to heat is equal to the energy stored in the condenser, being $\frac{1}{2}CE^2$. It is the same whether the current is oscillatory or a single surge. When resistance is small the rate of dissipation is low, but the current persists for a longer time, and vice versa. Proof that the loss of energy is equal to the energy stored in the condenser is easily obtained; the method is exactly parallel to that of a similar proof in Sec. 2 of Chap. II.

13. Crests of the Wave Train. In the section on natural frequency it is pointed out that although the expression for the transient oscillating current contains a sinusoidal factor, the current is not truly cyclic because of damping. Continuous attenuation of the wave train results in a lack of symmetry of each of those pulses of current that have been loosely called half-cycles; Fig. 21b shows very clearly the distortion that results, so also does Fig. 22, and the same effect exists, although to a small and almost unnoticeable extent, in Fig. 21a. One of the con-

sequences of the lack of symmetry is that the crest of the wave does not occur at a time half way between the instants of zero current—in other words, the maximum current does not appear at the quarter-cycle when ωt is an odd multiple of $\pi/2$. When ωt is $\pi/2$, $\sin \omega t$ is 1, and it is at this instant, as indicated at t_2 in Fig. 22, that the current curve is tangent to the envelope. The current maximum, however, occurs at an earlier moment t_1, and during the interval from t_1 to t_2 the current has diminished

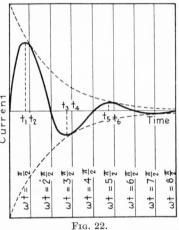

FIG. 22.

slightly. Although the value of $\sin \omega t$ is still rising during this interval, the value of $\epsilon^{-\alpha t}$ is falling at a more rapid rate than $\sin \omega t$ is rising, and the net result is that current [as expressed in Eq. (190)] is less at t_2 than at t_1.

Since the maximum current is often a point of great interest, it is important to determine the time at which it occurs. The points of tangency to the envelope occur at the odd quarter-cycles, when ωt equals $\pi/2$, $3\pi/2$, $5\pi/2$, and so on; or another and shorter way of describing the same points is to specify that at the points of tangency

$$\omega t = \tan^{-1} \infty \tag{196}$$

To find the times of maximum current we refer to Eq. (190). For our present purposes the coefficient of the current can be abbreviated as A, and the equation becomes

$$i = A\epsilon^{-\alpha t} \sin \omega t \qquad (197)$$

Differentiation of current with respect to time gives

$$\frac{di}{dt} = A(\omega\epsilon^{-\alpha t} \cos \omega t - \alpha\epsilon^{-\alpha t} \sin \omega t) \qquad (198)$$

Since maxima occur when $\dfrac{di}{dt}$ is zero, we let

$$\omega\epsilon^{-\alpha t} \cos \omega t - \alpha\epsilon^{-\alpha t} \sin \omega t = 0$$

from which

$$\tan \omega t = \frac{\omega}{\alpha}$$

and

$$\omega t = \tan^{-1}\frac{\omega}{\alpha} \qquad (199)$$

Equation (199) says that the current reaches a maximum, of either positive or negative sign, at every value of time which makes tan ωt equal to a certain constant quantity. This constant quantity, ω/α, can be written in terms of inductance, capacitance, and resistance of the circuit by reference to Eq. (186).

Comparison of Eqs. (199) and (196) is enlightening. If there is very little resistance in the circuit, with a correspondingly small value of α, the fraction ω/α is not very different from ∞; so if damping is very slight, the times of maximum current occur—like the times of tangency to the envelope—at the quarter-cycles. Another consideration will lead to the same conclusion: if the damping is very small, the current wave is practically a pure sine wave, and the maxima of a sine wave, of course, occur at the quarter-cycles.

But when α is large, and damping rapid, the maximum occurs earlier than the tangency. The ratio ω/α is a positive number, large unless damping is extremely rapid, and tan ωt becomes equal to it periodically as time increases. Since tan ωt is large and positive shortly before becoming infinite, the maximum current precedes the quarter-cycle. As an example, the ratio ω/α is 3.14 for Fig. 22, so the first current maximum is when ωt is 1.26 radians (tan 1.26 = 3.14), or 72 deg. The maximum therefore precedes the point of tangency by 18 deg., and this is the angular distance between t_1 and t_2.

The later instants at which current attains a maximum value are marked t_3, t_5, and so on. It will be seen from Eq. (199) that they are spaced just one half-cycle apart and that in Fig. 22 the values of ωt at t_1, t_3, t_5, and so on, are respectively (1.26), $(1.26 + \pi)$, $(1.26 + 2\pi)$, $(1.26 + 3\pi)$, and so on.

So it appears that among the peculiar characteristics of the damped sinusoid wave we should note particularly that maximum current is reached less than a quarter-cycle later than zero current, this lack of symmetry of the wave being due to damping; but that the times of maximum current are uniformly separated by the same interval that appears between the times of zero current, and that this remains true whether or not there is damping.

The maximum value of current at the crest of a wave can easily be found when the time of the maximum is known. It is only necessary to substitute the value of time determined from Eq. (199) in Eq. (190), and the result is the maximum current. This is frequently a quantity of great importance in transient analysis. Quick-acting relays will discriminate between transient impulses solely according to the height of the first current crest; their satisfactory operation therefore depends on a setting that is determined from the maximum of the current wave. The same thing is true of various electronic devices that are actuated instantaneously. In recording a transient current with an oscillograph it is clearly necessary to know the height of the highest crest in order to determine the desired sensitivity.

The effectiveness of an artificial-lightning generator is determined by the first crest of the transient current that it produces. A condenser that has previously been charged to a very high voltage is suddenly allowed to discharge through a resistance, in series with whatever inductance is unavoidable in the circuit. The voltage across the resistance is then used to simulate the voltage of lightning, and its maximum value is proportional to the maximum value of the current wave.

The spark that is used in automobile ignition is also a transient electric current, and its ability to ignite the explosive mixture of gases in the cylinder depends on the first maximum of the transient impulse. The circuit, however, is less simple, as it contains an inductance coil with two windings.

A term that was widely used in connection with spark transmitters for radiotelegraphy was **logarithmic decrement.** It is defined as the natural logarithm of the ratio of the maximum current during any given oscillation of a discharge to the slightly smaller maximum current during the next oscillation, one cycle later. In Fig. 22, for example, the logarithmic decrement may be found as the logarithm of the ratio of current at t_1 to current at t_5. It is readily shown that the logarithmic decrement is equal to the decrement factor α divided by the natural frequency: the proof follows.

The ratio of current at one instant t_1 to that at a latter instant t_5 can be written by use of Eq. (197) as

$$\frac{A\epsilon^{-\alpha t_1} \sin \omega t_1}{A\epsilon^{-\alpha t_5} \sin \omega t_5}$$

If t_1 and t_5 are exactly one cycle apart, so that

$$\omega t_5 = \omega t_1 + 2\pi$$

the sine in the numerator will equal the sine in the denominator, and the ratio becomes

$$\frac{\epsilon^{-\alpha t_1}}{\epsilon^{-\alpha t_5}}$$

The natural logarithm of this ratio is

$$\ln \epsilon^{-\alpha t_1} - \ln \epsilon^{-\alpha t_5} = -\alpha t_1 + \alpha t_5 = \alpha(t_5 - t_1)$$

The interval of time $t_5 - t_1$ is the duration of one cycle; it is therefore equal to the reciprocal of the natural frequency. The quantity $\alpha(t_5 - t_1)$ is therefore equal to α/f. Since the ratio of currents is computed for *any* values of current separated by a time interval of exactly one cycle, it will be the ratio of any current crest to the next crest of the same polarity [see Eq. (199)]. But the logarithm of this ratio is, by definition, the logarithmic decrement, so

$$\text{Logarithmic decrement} = \frac{\alpha}{f} = \frac{R}{2Lf}$$

14. The General Sinusoidal Equation. In Eq. (190) the current in a series circuit of condenser, inductance, and resistance is expressed in the form of a damped sinusoid with a coefficient.

The value of the coefficient is known in Eq. (190), because it is determined from the exponential expression of what is essentially the same equation, the exponential form from which it is derived being Eq. (148). But there is a specific initial condition implicitly contained in Eq. (148), and there is another in Eq. (183) which is also used in the derivation of the sinusoidal form, so that Eq. (190) is not general but is limited in application to a circuit with these particular initial conditions. This limitation is discussed in the first paragraph of Sec. 10, and the limiting conditions are stated: zero initial current in the inductance and zero initial charge on the condenser.

To avoid any limitation by initial conditions, let us return to the most general form of solution for current in the circuit of Fig. 16, which is first given as Eq. (134):

$$i = K_1 \epsilon^{\lambda_1 t} + K_2 \epsilon^{\lambda_2 t} \tag{134}$$

The real and imaginary parts of the exponents can then be separated by use of Eq. (185), giving

$$i = K_1 \epsilon^{-\alpha t} \epsilon^{j\omega t} + K_2 \epsilon^{-\alpha t} \epsilon^{-j\omega t}$$

and when the two exponentials with imaginary exponents are expanded into sinusoidal functions, the result is

$$\begin{aligned} i &= K_1 \epsilon^{-\alpha t}(\cos \omega t + j \sin \omega t) + K_2 \epsilon^{-\alpha t}(\cos \omega t - j \sin \omega t) \\ &= \epsilon^{-\alpha t}[(K_1 + K_2) \cos \omega t + j(K_1 - K_2) \sin \omega t] \end{aligned} \tag{200}$$

Simply for convenience, let

$$\begin{aligned} K_1 + K_2 &= M \\ j(K_1 - K_2) &= N \end{aligned}$$

and Eq. (200) becomes

$$\begin{aligned} i &= \epsilon^{-\alpha t}(M \cos \omega t + N \sin \omega t) \\ &= A\epsilon^{-\alpha t} \sin (\omega t + \phi) \end{aligned} \tag{201}$$

where

$$\begin{aligned} A &= \sqrt{M^2 + N^2} = 2\sqrt{K_1 K_2} \\ \phi &= \tan^{-1} \frac{M}{N} = \tan^{-1} \frac{K_1 + K_2}{j(K_1 - K_2)} \end{aligned}$$

Equation (201) is the general form of sinusoidal equation of current that will fit any possible initial conditions. It has two undetermined coefficients, A and ϕ, which are related to K_1 and K_2 as shown in the foregoing equations; and if K_1 and K_2 are known, A and ϕ may be found by that means. But Eq. (201) is just as truly a solution of the differential equation of the circuit as is Eq. (134), and the undetermined coefficients A and ϕ may be determined directly from the circuit's initial conditions without any reference whatever to K_1 and K_2. This is, in fact, the usual procedure and is often the more advantageous one.

15. An Example. As the first and simplest illustration, let us again assume that there is no initial charge on the condenser and no initial current. When

$$t = 0, \qquad i = 0$$

Therefore, from (201),

$$0 = A\epsilon^0 \sin (0 + \phi)$$

so that

$$\sin \phi = 0 \tag{202}$$

For this condition, then, Eq. (201) becomes

$$i = A\epsilon^{-\alpha t} \sin \omega t \tag{203}$$

To introduce the other initial condition, that when

$$t = 0, \qquad \frac{1}{p}i = 0$$

we follow the method of Sec. 7 of this chapter, and find that when

$$t = 0, \qquad pi = \frac{E}{L} \tag{167}$$

But, from Eq. (203),

$$pi = A(\omega\epsilon^{-\alpha t} \cos \omega t - \alpha\epsilon^{-\alpha t} \sin \omega t) \tag{204}$$

and when

$$t = 0, \qquad pi = A\omega = \frac{E}{L}$$

from which

$$A = \frac{E}{L\omega} = \frac{E}{L\sqrt{\dfrac{1}{LC} - \dfrac{R^2}{4L^2}}} \tag{205}$$

With this value of A substituted in Eq. (203) the complete expression for current appears:

$$i = \frac{E}{L\sqrt{\dfrac{1}{LC} - \dfrac{R^2}{4L^2}}}\epsilon^{-\alpha t} \sin \omega t \qquad (206)$$

Equation (206) is obtained from the general sinusoidal solution with undetermined coefficients by direct substitution of boundary conditions, and it is interesting to notice that it agrees, as of course it must, with Eq. (190), which was obtained indirectly from the exponential form of current expression.

16. Another Example. *Gas-engine Ignition.* An example in which the initial current in the circuit is not zero is furnished by the ignition system of a gasoline engine. In an automobile there is a spark coil with two windings: a high-voltage winding of many turns, which is connected to the spark plug by way of the distributor, and a low-voltage winding of relatively few turns, which is in series with a battery and a cam-operated switch called a timer. Across the timer switch is a condenser, for the purpose of preventing sparking at the switch. Figure 23 shows the low-voltage circuit: L and R are the inductance and resistance of the spark coil, S is the timer switch, C the condenser, and a voltage E is applied by the battery of the automobile. L' is the high-voltage winding, with which however we are not at present concerned.

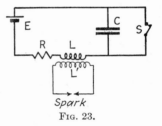

Fig. 23.

Shortly before a spark is needed, switch S is closed by its cam. Current then begins to flow through the coil but is interrupted when the switch is suddenly reopened. The high voltage that results from sudden interruption of the current is used to produce a spark in the cylinder of the engine. In studying the operation of the ignition system it is first necessary to determine the behaviour of current in the low-voltage circuit after the timer switch opens.

We will count as zero time the instant of opening of the switch. Let us assume that the switch has been closed long enough for current through the coil to have reached its steady-state value. This will be true in low-speed engines. At the initial instant, then, current is limited only by the resistance of the circuit and we have as one initial condition that when

$$t = 0, \qquad i = \frac{E}{R} \tag{207}$$

The other condition is that there is no charge on the condenser at the instant of opening the switch, and therefore no voltage across it.

The circuit that we are studying is that which exists after the switch S is opened and before a spark occurs, and its voltage equation is the same that has been written many times:

$$Lpi + Ri + \frac{1}{Cp}i = E \tag{208}$$

The high-voltage circuit does not affect this equation because there is no current in it until the spark occurs; at least we shall assume so, neglecting any small capacitance or leakage current. The left-hand member contains a term $\frac{1}{Cp}i$; this is the condenser voltage and is zero at zero time. From this, and from (207), we can say that, when time is zero, Eq. (208) becomes

$$Lpi + R\frac{E}{R} + 0 = E$$

from which, when

$$t = 0, \qquad pi = 0 \tag{209}$$

This equation is a mathematical statement of the fact that merely opening the switch does not affect the flow of current, and there is no change until a back-voltage has been built up by charge on the condenser. It is for this purpose that the condenser is used; it prevents sparking at the contacts of S.

The general solution of (208) is Eq. (201).

$$i = A\epsilon^{-\alpha t} \sin(\omega t + \phi) \tag{201}$$

When time is zero it becomes, with Eq. (207),

$$\frac{E}{R} = A \sin \phi \tag{210}$$

By differentiating (201), we obtain

$$pi = A[\omega\epsilon^{-\alpha t} \cos (\omega t + \phi) - \alpha\epsilon^{-\alpha t} \sin (\omega t + \phi)] \quad (211)$$

in which Eq. (209) is substituted to give

$$0 = \omega \cos \phi - \alpha \sin \phi$$

so that

$$\phi = \tan^{-1} \frac{\omega}{\alpha} \quad (212)$$

Since

$$\tan \phi = \frac{\omega}{\alpha}$$

it follows that

$$\sin \phi = \frac{\omega}{\sqrt{\omega^2 + \alpha^2}}$$

and, since α and ω have the values assigned by Eq. (186), this can be simplified to

$$\sin \phi = \omega\sqrt{LC} \quad (213)$$

Equation (213) can then be combined with Eq. (210) to give a value for A:

$$A = \frac{E}{\omega R\sqrt{LC}} \quad (214)$$

It is evident that the expression for A can be written in many different ways: ω can be expanded, ω and the radical can be combined, and so on; whichever is most convenient for computation, or whichever best displays some aspect of the nature of the coefficient may be used.

The solution for the current in the ignition system before the moment of the spark is now complete. It is expressed by Eq. (201), in which the values of A and ϕ are given by (214) and (212) respectively.

In the engineering study of the operation of such a device, the voltage at the spark plug would no doubt be one of the quantities to be determined. It is quite simply found from the current, for it is Mpi, where M is the mutual inductance between the two windings of the spark coil and pi is the derivative of current as determined in Eq. (211). The manner in which different circuits affect each other will be considered in the next chapter.

The condenser is placed across the terminals of the switch in the circuit of Fig. 23 to prevent undue sparking as the contact points separate. The useful life of the points is greatly increased by the condenser, but if the condenser is too large it will seriously reduce the voltage that must produce the spark. It will cushion the shock of opening the switch, and by reducing the rate of decrease of current it will correspondingly lessen the induced voltage. Equation (211) gives the rate of change of current; the first term within the brackets is far larger than the second because of ω being larger than α, and as a fair approximation

$$pi \approx A\omega\epsilon^{-\alpha t} \cos (\omega t + \phi)$$

The value of A is almost independent of the size of C, as may be seen by expanding Eq. (214), but ω is (nearly) inversely proportional to the square root of C. So a large condenser means a small ω and a correspondingly low induced voltage.

If no condenser were used, it would be impossible to interrupt the current without a spark as the switch contacts separated, and this fact is utilized in the so-called "low-tension" ignition systems in which there is but one winding in the coil, and the spark to ignite the explosive gases occurs at the switch points as they interrupt the current. The circuit is shown in Fig. 24; it is similar to the low-voltage circuit of Fig. 23, but the cam-operated contactor S is located within the cylinder of the engine. No condenser is used, for its

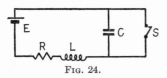

FIG. 24.

only effect would be to reduce the voltage of the spark, but some capacitance between leads and between switch points is unavoidable and this is designated by C. Low-tension ignition systems are now obsolescent, but remain in use on a few low-speed engines for which simplicity is of sufficient advantage to outweigh efficiency.

Since the circuit of the "low-tension" system is identical with that of the "high-tension" system, except for dimensions, the solution for current is given by Eqs. (201), (212), and (214). Only voltage needs be treated differently. The voltage across S in Fig. 24 is also the voltage across C, so to determine the

voltage available for sparking it is necessary to find the condenser
voltage.   Charge on the condenser may be found by integrating
current, and voltage is the ratio of charge to capacitance.   Integration of Eq. (201) will give charge on the condenser [see Eq.
(47)] and division by C will give voltage.   That is,

$$e_s = \frac{1}{C} \int_0^t A \epsilon^{-\alpha t} \sin (\omega t + \phi) dt$$

It is evident that our solutions for both current and voltage
apply only during the time between the opening of S and the
formation of a spark, for, if current is not limited to the circuit
consisting of inductance, resistance, and capacitance, the circuit
equation (208) does not apply.

The process of finding an expression for current in the ignition
circuit consists almost entirely of evaluating constants, for the
general form of the current is already known by Eq. (201).
Such is often the case, and it will be helpful to trace the method of
attack that is used, for it is essentially a method that can be
applied whenever needed.

To begin quite at the beginning, let us refer to the four rules
for solution which are formulated in Sec. 10 of Chap. I.   The
first of these rules is satisfied when Eq. (208) is written and (201)
is recognized as its solution; since there is no steady-state current
the second and third rules do not apply; the fourth rule, which
requires evaluation of the undetermined coefficients, is therefore
the major part of the solution.   Evaluation of constants from
initial conditions is discussed in Sec. 7 of this chapter, and the
outline which is given there is followed in this case.

First, two obvious initial conditions are taken from the circuit,
and to express them mathematically it is stated that when
$t = 0$, $i = \dfrac{E}{R}$ and $\dfrac{1}{p}i = 0$.   It is necessary, in order to evaluate
A and ϕ, to have two equations containing A and ϕ and not containing time or any function of time.   One such equation is
obtained from the general solution [Eq. (201)] which relates
current to time: since the actual current is known for one specific
time, $t = 0$, it is possible to determine the only value of the
coefficient [Eq. (210)] that is consistent with the known current
[Eq. (207)].   Since the resulting equation contains both A and
ϕ it cannot be solved until another equation has been derived

for simultaneous solution. Since $\frac{1}{p}i$ is known to be zero when time is zero, it would appear that integration of both sides of Eq. (201) would give a right-hand member that could be equated to zero; this is not satisfactory, however, for $1/p$ is a *definite* integral with limits 0 and t, so when t is set equal to zero the integrated equation reduced to the identity $0 \equiv 0$.

So instead of obtaining another equation by integration of (201) we may derive a new equation by differentiating (201); this is done in Eq. (211), and if the value of pi at any one instant can be found, a second equation containing A and ϕ will result. By the method of Sec. 7 it is possible to determine pi when time is zero from the circuit equation (208), for when time is zero all terms of Eq. (208) are known except the one containing pi. Hence it is found that the initial value of pi is zero [Eq. (209)], and this gives the necessary concurrent values to remove time functions from (211), resulting in Eq. (212). As (212) contains ϕ and does not contain A, it is unnecessary in this case to carry out a simultaneous solution, for, having an explicit value for ϕ in (212), it is only necessary to introduce it into Eq. (210) to complete the solution by expressing A as in Eq. (214).

17. Another Example. *A Radio Transmitter.* Another and final example of the resonant circuit is suggested by the oscillatory circuit of a spark transmitter for radiotelegraphy. Just as the "low-tension" ignition system is obsolescent for gasoline engines, the spark transmitter has disappeared from the field of radio. One of its chief limitations is its inability to produce a continuous high-frequency oscillation; instead, it gives a series of damped transient oscillations. The essential circuit is shown in Fig. 25a. A spark gap S acts as a switch in this circuit, and, when voltage across it is sufficient to make it spark, it will release the charge of the condenser. If the gap is of the type known as a rotary gap, its sparking is further controlled by the fact that the spark jumps between a fixed point and a moving point that projects from a rapidly rotating disc, and can occur only when the two points are opposite each other. The voltage supply circuit takes no part in the transient action (because of its relatively high inductance) and may be regarded as merely a means of charging the condenser. When there is no spark bridging the gap, charge will flow from the supply circuit onto the condenser by way of the inductance coil L. During the process of charging, the condenser voltage will practically equal the voltage across the gap, and a spark will jump when the condenser voltage reaches a value that we will designate by e_0. The time of formation of the spark will be the reference time $t = 0$. The circuit will consist of the condenser, the coil which has both inductance L and resistance R, and the spark whose resistance is considered to be negligible and which will therefore simply take the place of a switch. The circuit equation will be modified slightly from the form given in Eq. (208) because of the presence of initial charge on the condenser; just as in Chap. II it was necessary to include initial charge in Eq. (57), it is now necessary to introduce into the circuit equation a term for the initial voltage on the condenser. In Eq. (215) the familiar terms for inductance voltage and resistance voltage are followed by a parenthesis which expresses the condenser voltage; equate the sum to zero.

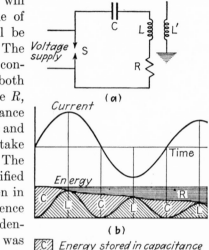

(a)

(b)

Energy stored in capacitance

Energy stored in inductance

Energy lost in resistance

FIG. 25.

$$Lpi + Ri + \left(e_0 + \frac{1}{Cp}i\right) = 0 \qquad (215)$$

An algebraic change in Eq. (215), however, shows that mathematically it is of the same form as (208), for it can be written

$$Lpi + Ri + \frac{1}{Cp}i = -e_0 \qquad (216)$$

The solution will therefore be similar in form to Eq. (201):

$$i = A\epsilon^{-\alpha t} \sin(\omega t + \phi) \qquad (217)$$

It is best to assume that the applied voltage has placed a *negative* initial charge on the condenser, so that e_0 is numerically a negative quantity and $-e_0$ is numerically positive. The advantage of this rather artificial assumption is that it leads to a positive sign for the resulting current, as is discussed in Sec. 6 of Chap. II. The parenthesis of Eq. (215) expresses the condenser voltage; its initial value is negative since e_0 is negative, but as current flows in the circuit in a positive direction the integral term becomes larger and the sum in the parenthesis becomes less negative—even becoming positive if the current is oscillatory.

To complete the solution for current, A and ϕ must be determined. The process is similar to previous examples, but the initial conditions are different. Neglecting any small charging current that may be flowing from the voltage supply circuit, the initial current must be zero because of the presence of inductance. So when

$$t = 0, \qquad i = 0$$

and substitution in Eq. (217) shows that ϕ is zero, giving

$$i = A\epsilon^{-\alpha t} \sin \omega t \qquad (218)$$

To determine A, pi must be found, and Eq. (215) offers the most ready means. The other known condition is that the condenser has an initial voltage e_0. The definite integral $\frac{1}{p}i$ is of course initially zero, because by definition [see Eq. (68)] as well as by usage [in Eq. (215)] this term is the integral of current in the circuit *after* $t = 0$, and does not take into account anything that happens before zero time. So the initial value of the parenthesis in (215) is e_0, and when

$$t = 0, \qquad Lpi + 0 + e_0 = 0$$

from which we find the initial derivative:

$$t = 0, \qquad pi = -\frac{e_0}{L} \qquad (219)$$

This gives a specific set of values for t and pi which may be used to determine A. Differentiate Eq. (218):

$$pi = A(\omega\epsilon^{-\alpha t} \cos \omega t - \alpha\epsilon^{-\alpha t} \sin \omega t)$$

Substitute (219):

$$-\frac{e_0}{L} = A\omega \qquad A = -\frac{e_0}{\omega L}$$

With this coefficient substituted in Eq. (218) the solution is complete. Note that, as stated, the current will have a positive coefficient if e_0 is negative. The first cycle of current is plotted in Fig. 25b.

In this circuit, in which no energy is supplied to the circuit from any battery or other external source during the transient period, transient current is maintained by a continual interchange of energy between the electrostatic field of the condenser and the electromagnetic field of the inductance. Finally, of course, the energy is all dissipated by the resistance of the circuit, and current dies away, but while current flows the energy alternates from one form to the other. The circuit's energy is initially electrostatic; as current flows the condenser loses charge and energy, but the growing current imparts energy to the electromagnetic field of the inductance.

Figure 25b illustrates the transfer of energy from the condenser to the inductance during the first quarter-cycle of current, and also shows the gradual loss of energy in the resistance. During the second quarter-cycle of current the condenser regains all of the remaining energy of the circuit, but delivers it again to the inductance in the third quarter-cycle. This continual transfer of energy takes place in all circuits which contain both inductance and capacitance. It is for this reason that transient phenomena in such circuits are sometimes called **double-energy** phenomena, to distinguish them from **single-energy** transient phenomena that appear in circuits that contain either inductance or capacitance, but not both. Single-energy phenomena are studied in Chaps. I and II. A single-energy circuit, in which there is only one kind of energy storage, always leads to a first-order differential equation; a double-energy circuit requires a second-order differential equation. It will be seen later (in Sec. 23 of Chap. V) that more complicated networks require higher order differential equations, but that the order of the differential equation is always equal to the number of energy storage possibilities of the network.

The energy diagram of Fig. 25b also shows that the change of electric energy into heat by the resistance does not occur at a constant rate. No energy is being changed into heat when the current is zero, and the loss is most rapid when the current is greatest.

When a radiotelegraph operates with a spark transmitter, the oscillatory circuit of Fig. 24 is coupled to the antenna circuit by means of mutual inductance between L and L'. Energy is transferred from the spark circuit to the antenna circuit at a rate that is determined by the closeness of coupling. In the analysis that has just been completed, coupling has been entirely neglected; the dying away of current in the oscillatory circuit is assumed to be due entirely to resistance, and no allowance is made for energy which passes to the antenna circuit. Since a radio transmitter in which no energy goes into the antenna is of no use, the solution must be modified before it can be applied to a practical installation. The presence of the antenna circuit changes the problem from one involving a simple oscillatory circuit to one involving a network, and its treatment will be considered in a later chapter. For the present it is enough to say that, with ordinary coefficients of coupling to the antenna circuit, A and ω in Eq. (218) will be substantially correct, but α will be of an entirely incorrect magnitude.

18. The Concept of Zero Impedance. There is one limiting condition of the oscillatory circuit that is of interest, not so much because of its own importance as because it serves as an introduction to a way of thinking about transient phenomena that is very illuminating.

Consider the circuit that is discussed in this chapter, and allow the circuit resistance to diminish so that it becomes zero. The circuit then consists of inductance and capacitance in series, together with a source of voltage. If voltage is applied when there is no energy stored in the circuit the resulting transient current is

$$i = A\epsilon^{-\alpha t} \sin \omega t \qquad (220)$$

Since $R = 0$,

$$A = \frac{E}{L\sqrt{\dfrac{1}{LC} - \dfrac{R^2}{4L^2}}} = E\sqrt{\frac{C}{L}}$$

$$\alpha = \frac{R}{2L} = 0$$

$$\omega = \sqrt{\frac{1}{LC} - \frac{R^2}{4L^2}} = \sqrt{\frac{1}{LC}}$$

Because resistance is zero, Eq. (220) is simplified to

$$i = E \sqrt{\frac{C}{L}} \sin \sqrt{\frac{1}{LC}} t \tag{221}$$

This is the "transient" current in the circuit, but it has the peculiarity of not being strictly transient, for since there is no damping it will continue to flow indefinitely. We know from steady-state theory that a circuit consisting of inductance and capacitance in series, without resistance, has zero impedance for a current of its natural frequency, and the same effect appears here. The current that flows is a form of current to which *the circuit offers no impedance*, and once started it will never stop. No external voltage is required to maintain it. The form of the current gives it the peculiar property of consuming no voltage.

An extension of this concept may be applied to other circuits, even though they contain resistance. In any circuit *the transient current is the particular form of current which, in that circuit, can flow without requiring any applied voltage.* Except in the purely hypothetical case just considered, in which there is no resistance, the current that can flow without voltage is a diminishing current that will grow smaller, but—mathematically, at least—it will never cease.

In the case of the three-parameter circuit, for instance, the current that will flow without encountering impedance is a damped sinusoid. In a circuit of capacitance and resistance, or inductance and resistance, it is a simple exponential. For example, in Sec. 6 of Chap. I no external voltage is required to maintain indefinitely, in a circuit of inductance and resistance, the current

$$i = K\epsilon^{-\frac{R}{L}t} \tag{10}$$

Let us refer to Fig. 15; the need for a transient component of current is discussed in connection with this figure, and two requirements are emphasized: the current must satisfy the differential equation during both transient and steady-state periods, and the current (and its derivatives) must have the correct initial value. In Fig. 15b, for instance, the correct initial value of current is i_0, and the differential equation, which is

$$Ri + Lpi = E$$

is satisfied during the transient period by

$$i = K\epsilon^{-\frac{R}{L}t} + \frac{E}{R} \tag{95}$$

and during the steady-state period by

$$i = \frac{E}{R} \tag{94}$$

Either (94) or (95) is a solution of the differential equation, as may be seen by substitution, although (94) is only a partial solution and will not ordinarily satisfy initial conditions.

Let us now look at the circuit from this point of view: as soon as the switch is closed the steady-state current begins to flow, and all the applied voltage is required to produce the steady-state current, E/R, through the resistance of the circuit. The differential equation is satisfied, which is the same as saying that the voltages around the entire closed circuit add to zero. This current is indicated by the dash line in the Fig. 15b. But it does not satisfy the condition that initial current must be i_0, so we must visualize a second current flowing in the circuit at the same time. There is no voltage left over to produce this additional current, so it must be the kind of current that can flow without requiring voltage; it must have the form

$$i = K\epsilon^{-\frac{R}{L}t} \tag{22}$$

This sort of a current can flow in any amount without disturbing the differential equation, for the sum of the voltages that it produces in the circuit is always zero, and this fact can be verified by substitution in the left-hand member of the differential equation. The amount of such current that will flow, in any case, is the amount that is required to bridge the gap between the initial current and the steady-state current. The three parts of Fig. 15 furnish an illustration of three different initial currents and the three corresponding transient currents that must flow. Finally, to get the current that actually exists in the circuit, the hypothetical steady-state current (which uses all the voltage) is added to the hypothetical transient current (which uses no voltage), and the total current satisfies both the voltage equation and the initial conditions.

The physical concept of a transient current that can flow without applied voltage is closely related to the mathematical method of solution for transient current in which the applied voltage is arbitrarily made equal to zero. In Sec. 10, Chap. I, we propose four rules for solution, and the first rule says, "Solve for the form of the transient component. To do this, write the differential equation of the circuit, with zero substituted for the applied voltage, and solve for current." The substitution of zero for the applied voltage is justified in Chap. III, Sec. 7, on mathematical grounds, and now it may be justified in another manner: the transient component is a current that encounters zero impedance, and hence will flow without voltage; therefore, *to determine the form of the transient component, merely solve for that current which can exist with zero voltage.*

Problems

1. Connect a coil and a condenser in series, with a switch and battery, as in Fig. 16. Measure the inductance of the coil and the capacitance of the condenser. Record on an oscillograph the current that flows when the switch is closed. Increase the resistance of the circuit to the critical value, and record the critically damped surge of current. Increase the resistance to two or three times the critical value, and record an overdamped surge of current. Measure the three resistances. Use a coil without an iron core, and a resistance that is practically noninductive.

Transfer the experimentally determined curves to sheets of cross-section paper, and on the same sheets plot curves of current computed from the circuit parameters. Compare the computed and experimental results, and discuss any differences that may appear.

If it is not convenient to record the current experimentally, oscillogram 3 may be used. It is a photographic record made according to the above instructions, with three transient current curves, a calibration line, a zero line, and a timing wave. The calibration line was produced by a steady current of 0.512 amp.; the timing wave was made by a 60-cycle voltage. The circuit parameters, including the three different values of resistance, were as follows:

E = 129.6 volts.   Low resistance = 38.6 ohms.
L = 1.68 henrys.   Medium resistance = 253   ohms.
C = 106.5 μf.   High resistance = 583   ohms.

Superposition of the three curves on the oscillogram shows that they all have the same initial slope.

2. A 60-cycle voltage $(80 + j60)$ volts causes a steady-state current $(2 + j5)$ amp. to flow in a circuit containing resistance, inductance, and capacitance. The amount of capacitance is 50 μf. Will transient current

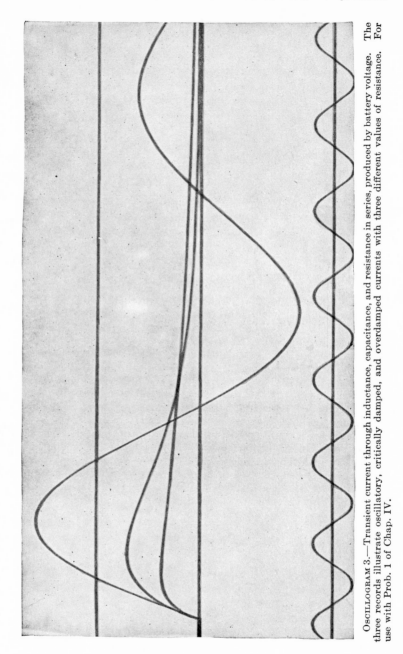

Oscillogram 3.—Transient current through inductance, capacitance, and resistance in series, produced by battery voltage. The three records illustrate oscillatory, critically damped, and overdamped currents with three different values of resistance. For use with Prob. 1 of Chap. IV.

in this circuit oscillate? If so, at what frequency? (Complex notation is used in stating this problem; the conventions of complex notation are familiar in steady-state electrical theory, although not used elsewhere in this book.)

3. The equivalent circuit of an impulse generator for testing electrical equipment is shown in the diagram.* The test specimen, which carries no current, is connected to the terminals of R_2. Given the following parameters, plot voltage across the test specimen (in terms of initial voltage on C_1) as a function of time.

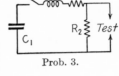

Prob. 3.

$$C_1 = 0.0125 \ \mu\text{f}.$$
$$L_1 = 900 \ \text{microhenrys}.$$
$$R_1 = 2000 \ \text{ohms}.$$
$$R_2 = 2900 \ \text{ohms}.$$

Repeat, using R_1 equal to 100 ohms.

4. Formulate the differential equation of motion of a ballistic galvanometer. Its moment of inertia is 1000 g. cm.²; the elastic restoring force of the suspension is 1 g. cm. per radian; the damping, proportional to velocity, is 2.5 g. cm. per radian per sec. Write an expression for the angular displacement of the moving coil following an initial impulsive disturbance.†

5. The successful operation of large oil circuit breakers is dependent upon their speed as compared to the rate of rise of the "recovery voltage" across them.‡ Alternating current becomes zero at the end of each half-cycle, and, in an oil circuit breaker that has started to open, current of the next half-cycle will not immediately commence to flow. High-frequency transient oscillations of voltage will appear across the circuit breaker, and flow of current will begin again only if the breaker is unable to withstand the voltage. If the transient voltage is not sufficient to initiate a new flow of current through the breaker, the circuit has been successfully opened. The two important factors are the maximum voltage of the oscillations and the rate of rise of voltage.

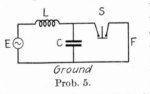

Prob. 5.

The simplest representation of the system connected to the circuit breaker is shown in the accompanying figure. While the circuit breaker S is closed, current flows freely through it to ground, presumably because of a fault at F. Then the circuit breaker opens; current continues to flow through the breaker, by arcing, with negligible voltage across the breaker, until current normally becomes zero at the end of a half-cycle. As current

* THOMASON, J. L., Impulse Generator Circuit Formulas, *Trans. A.I.E.E.*, **53**, 169, 1934.

† See LAWS, F. A., "Electrical Measurements," McGraw-Hill Book Company, Inc., New York, 1917.

‡ PARK and SKEATS, Circuit Breaker Recovery Voltages, *Trans. A.I.E.E.*, **50**, 204, March, 1931.

becomes zero, de-ionization of the arc channel commences, and the breaker is able to sustain a certain amount of voltage without allowing current to pass.   To predict whether the arc will form again it is necessary to know the transient voltage that will appear across the switch terminals.

The instantaneous value of the generated voltage E is maximum when current through the breaker becomes zero, and although it is an alternating voltage it will practically retain its maximum value during the time that is of importance in this problem.   It is this value of voltage, therefore, that may be considered to be suddenly applied to the distributed capacitance of the system C through the inductance L of the generator and other connected equipment.   At the initial instant (when the arc starts to de-ionize) current through L is zero and charge on C is zero.

Given the following data, find (a) the maximum voltage across the breaker, and (b) the average rate of rise of voltage up to the first crest of the oscillation.

Generator voltage, line to neutral, effective = 8400 volts.
Reactance of generator and connected system = 3.05 ohms, at 60 cycles.
Distributed capacitance to ground = 0.008 μf.

Resistance of the system is negligible.

6. The transient current in a circuit is known to be oscillatory; the values of inductance and capacitance are fixed, but resistance can be varied. Derive an expression to relate the amount of resistance to the values of time at which current becomes maximum.

7. Current in a circuit is critically damped.   Find the time at which current is maximum and compare it to the time that would be required to reach the first maximum of current if resistance were zero.   Find voltage across the capacitance, voltage across the inductance, and voltage across the resistance at the instant of maximum current in the critically damped circuit.   Compare voltages to the corresponding ones in the circuit with zero resistance.

8. A tuned circuit has $L = 0.13$ millihenry, $R = 1.3$ ohms, $C = 1.3$ μf. Excitation is suddenly removed from this circuit and the oscillating current diminishes gradually.   Find (a) the frequency of the oscillatory current and (b) the time T required for the amplitude of the oscillation to diminish to 0.368 times its initial value.   Plot the envelope of the current wave, and indicate roughly the oscillations of current within the envelope.

9. Repeat Prob. 8 with $L = 2.5$ millihenrys, $R = 2.8$ ohms, $C = 1000$ μμf.

10. Write the equation of the current of Prob. 8 using numerical values. What is the impedance of the circuit to this current?

11. In the ignition circuit of Fig. 23, $E = 6.0$ volts, $C = 0.1$ μf, $L = 7.5$ millihenrys, $R = 2.2$ ohms.   The switch opens at $t = 0$ after having been closed for a long time.   Assuming no spark, find the maximum voltage across L.   When does this maximum voltage occur?

CHAPTER V

NETWORKS

1. Interrelated Circuits. It is not often that a circuit is free to behave in an entirely independent manner. Practical examples in the previous chapters illustrate this, for in nearly every case it is necessary to disregard the influence of some other circuit. In the case of the radio transmitter, the effect of the antenna circuit on the spark circuit was so great that it could not be disregarded. Under such circumstances it becomes necessary to consider the action of the two circuits at the same time—or (using mathematical terminology) to solve them simultaneously.

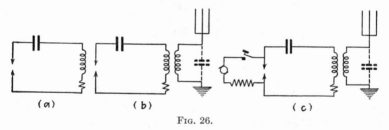

(a)   (b)   (c)

Fɪɢ. 26.

As a matter of definition, a circuit is a single closed path for current, while a network is a combination of several interrelated circuits. These definitions are not precise, for circuit studies are not limited to electric currents; water, heat, or sound may flow in a circuit instead of electricity; also many problems that have nothing to do with closed circuits may nevertheless be treated as circuit problems. But the definitions are sufficient to indicate that any network may be analysed into two or more circuits. For example, Fig. 26a is the spark circuit of a radio-telegraph transmitter, similar to that of Fig. 25. When the antenna circuit is considered, it is necessary to deal with the two-circuit network of Fig. 26b. Still another circuit supplies power to the spark, and if the source of electric power is a direct-current generator, the complete network is shown in Fig. 26c.

Two circuits are interrelated and form a network when voltage is induced in one by action taking place in the other. A change of current in either winding of a transformer, for example, will induce a voltage in the other winding; a voltage is induced in circuit 2 when there is a change of current in circuit 1, or vice versa. The relation between the circuits is magnetic and the parameter that is common to both circuits is the mutual inductance. Coupling of this sort is inductive coupling. The circuits of Fig. 26b are inductively coupled.

The circuits of Fig. 27a are also inductively coupled, for the mutual inductance L_{12} is the only common parameter. The network is not physically possible, however, for one cannot have

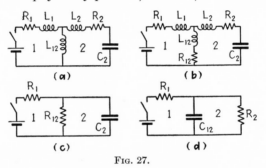

Fig. 27.

a coil of wire common to both circuits of Fig. 27a without having resistance in the coil. When the coil resistance is included in the diagram, Fig. 27b results; the two circuits of this network have a common coil of wire with inductance L_{12} and resistance R_{12}.

Practically pure resistance coupling is not only possible, but quite common; it is shown in Fig. 27c. Capacitance coupling is illustrated in Fig. 27d, in which the parameter that is common to both circuits is a condenser. It is interesting to notice that the networks of Fig. 27c and 27d are identical; in each case a resistance and a condenser are connected in parallel, and either one may be considered as the mutual element. Although the resistance may be thought of as a shunt across the condenser C_2, it is much more helpful in transient analysis to think of two circuits with a common parameter. Capacitance coupling is not limited to the case in which the plates of a condenser are common to two circuits; it is only necessary that the two circuits have a common electrostatic field. A very important illustration is furnished by the electrostatic coupling between a power line and a near-by telephone line, as shown in Fig. 28. Circuit 1 consists of the generator and the capacitance of the power line to ground; circuit 2 contains the capacitance of the telephone line to ground and the terminal resistance as indicated; the

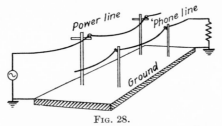

Power line		'phone line

Ground

Fig. 28.

circuits are coupled by mutual capacitance, and a sudden change of voltage on the power line is quite capable of producing dangerous voltage on the telephone line.

As illustrated in Fig. 27b, circuits may be coupled by more than one common parameter. Any two or all three parameters may be common to two circuits. A network, moreover, may consist of several circuits all interconnected in all possible ways. Figure 29 shows three circuits, each one coupled to both the other two. To avoid unnecessary complication in such networks, it is necessary to formulate a system of notation, for slovenly notation is perilous in network study.

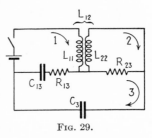

Fig. 29.

2. Notation. Circuits are arbitrarily numbered (as in Figs. 27, 29, and 30), and the current in each circuit bears as subscript the number of the circuit. The current in circuit 1, for example, is i_1. Each parameter is denoted by the number of the circuit in which it occurs; and mutual parameters have a double subscript, as in Fig. 27c, where R_{12} is a mutual resistance through which both i_1 and i_2 may flow. In Fig. 27b there are two resistances in circuit 1, one of which is mutual with circuit 2; they are called R_1 and R_{12}, as indicated in the diagram, and their sum is called R_{11}. By definition $R_{11} = R_1 + R_{12}$. Similarly, in circuit 2 of the same network R_{22} will include both R_2 and the mutual resistance. Thus, R_{11} is the total resistance of circuit 1; it is called the *self*-resistance; it is the resistance of circuit 1 if circuit 2 is entirely neglected; it is the resistance that will be measured in circuit 1 if circuit 2 is temporarily open. In the same manner, R_{22} is the self-resistance of circuit 2.

Similar notation is used for other parameters. In Fig. 27a there is mutual inductance L_{12} and self-inductance of each circuit, L_{11} and L_{22}. This network, in fact, will be recognized as the "equivalent network" of a transformer for which the self-inductances are L_{11} and L_{22}, the leakage inductances L_1 and L_2, and the mutual inductance L_{12}. It must be particularly remembered that when circuit 2 is open for measuring purposes, and the inductance of circuit 1 alone is measured, it will be L_{11}, the total inductance, and not merely L_1, the leakage inductance, that is determined. There is not much chance of trouble when the circuit is drawn as in Fig. 27a, but when there are two separate coils magnetically coupled (as in Fig. 26b or 29) it is easy to measure the inductances of each coil separately and write them incorrectly as L_1 and L_2 instead of L_{11} and L_{22}.

The same system is applied to self- and mutual capacitances, but with one obvious difference. The total or self-capacitance of a circuit such as circuit 3 of Fig. 29 is C_{33}, but it is not the sum of C_3 and C_{13}. Rather

$$\frac{1}{C_{33}} = \frac{1}{C_3} + \frac{1}{C_{13}}$$

A consistent electrical terminology would discuss, not capacitance, but the reciprocal of capacitance (often called elastance). However, the idea of capacitance is so much more familiar to most of us than the idea of elastance that it is generally advantageous to use the more common term and avoid unnecessary confusion.

3. A Network with Mutual Resistance. The heart of the mathematical analysis of transient behavior is the voltage equation of the circuit. We must always return to the voltage equation when some new condition is introduced that we do not yet understand. In solving for currents in the network of Fig. 30, there will be two voltage equations, one for each circuit. For circuit 1 we write all the voltages that can appear in the circuit owing to the current of circuit 1; they are $L_1 p i_1$, $R_1 i_1$, and $R_{12}i_1$. But there can be another voltage in circuit 1: voltage will appear across R_{12} when there is current in circuit 2 even though there is none in circuit 1. This additional voltage, which is produced in circuit 1 by a current in circuit 2, is $R_{12}i_2$. The voltage produced in R_{12} by a positive, or clockwise, current in circuit 2 will, however, be opposite in sense to that produced in R_{12} by a positive current in circuit 1. The voltage due to i_2 will

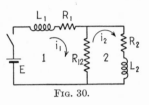

Fig. 30.

therefore have a negative sign and will be $-R_{12}i_2$. All the voltages in circuit 1 are now known, and since the sum of them is equal to the applied voltage we write

$$L_1 p i_1 + R_1 i_1 + R_{12}i_1 - R_{12}i_2 = E \tag{222}$$

This can be shortened, by using the definition of R_{11}, to

$$L_1 p i_1 + R_{11}i_1 - R_{12}i_2 = E \tag{223}$$

A voltage equation is also written for circuit 2. In circuit 2 there is voltage due to current in circuit 1 equal to $-R_{12}i_1$, and the voltage due to its own current is $R_{12}i_2 + R_2 i_2 + L_2 p i_2$. Since there is no applied voltage in circuit 2, the sum of all voltages must be zero, and

$$-R_{12}i_1 + R_{22}i_2 + L_2 p i_2 = 0 \tag{224}$$

4. Solution of Simultaneous Voltage Equations. Equations (223) and (224) are a pair of differential equations that must be solved simultaneously, as both contain i_1 and i_2. The solution is accomplished by following the same rules that are laid down in Chaps. I and III for the solution of a single differential equation. First, to find the transient component of current, substitute zero for E. This gives, from Eq. (223),

$$L_1 p i_1 + R_{11}i_1 - R_{12}i_2 = 0 \tag{225}$$

and, from this,

$$i_2 = \frac{L_1 p i_1 + R_{11}i_1}{R_{12}} \tag{226}$$

This value can then be substituted in Eq. (224) to eliminate i_2:

$$-R_{12}i_1 + R_{22}\frac{L_1 p i_1 + R_{11}i_1}{R_{12}} + L_2 p \left(\frac{L_1 p i_1 + R_{11}i_1}{R_{12}} \right) = 0 \tag{227}$$

The transformations to this point have been purely algebraic, for wherever a derivative term, such as pi_1, has occurred it has been treated as a unit and no operations have been performed on it. But in Eq. (227) the last term in the left-hand member is a somewhat complex operator which indicates that the quantity in parenthesis, which itself involves differentiation, is to be differentiated. However, if the nature of the operation is considered it will be seen that we are justified in expanding that term to

$$\frac{L_2 L_1}{R_{12}} p^2 i_1 + \frac{L_2 R_{11}}{R_{12}} p i_1$$

and the entire equation becomes

$$(L_1 L_2 p^2 + R_{22} L_1 p + R_{11} L_2 p + R_{11} R_{22} - R_{12}{}^2) i_1 = 0 \quad (228)$$

Equation (228) is a differential equation of second order, being similar to the formal Eq. (112), and we know that its solution will be

$$K_1 \epsilon^{\lambda_1 t} + K_2 \epsilon^{\lambda_2 t} \tag{229}$$

The values of λ are found from the auxiliary equation derived from Eq. (228) by writing λ in place of p:

$$L_1 L_2 \lambda^2 + (R_{22} L_1 + R_{11} L_2) \lambda + R_{11} R_{22} - R_{12}{}^2 = 0 \quad (230)$$

The roots of this equation, λ_1 and λ_2, are found to be

$$\lambda_1,\ \lambda_2 = -\frac{R_{22} L_1 + R_{11} L_2}{2 L_1 L_2} \pm$$

$$\sqrt{\left(\frac{R_{22} L_1 + R_{11} L_2}{2 L_1 L_2}\right)^2 - \frac{R_{11} R_{22} - R_{12}{}^2}{L_1 L_2}} \quad (231)$$

It is perfectly valid, and often more convenient, to write auxiliary equations from the differential equations of the network. With two circuits, there will be two auxiliary equations. In the present example, they would be derived from (224) and (225), and would be

$$-R_{12} i_1 + R_{22} i_2 + L_2 \lambda i_2 = 0$$
$$L_1 \lambda i_1 + R_{11} i_1 - R_{12} i_2 = 0$$

Their simultaneous solution would lead to Eq. (230). The only advantage of performing the simultaneous solution in this manner, with the auxiliary equations instead of the differential equations, is that the auxiliary equations are simply algebraic and require less care in making transformations.

But there is yet another method of obtaining the values of λ that is commonly the preferable one. It is the same that is discussed for single circuits in Chap. III; it utilizes the alternating-current impedance of the network. In fact, the rule of Sec. 11 of Chap. III is just as valid for networks of any kind as it is for single circuits. The rule is: *Write the impedance of the network to alternating current* (the impedance, that is, as viewed from the circuit in which voltage is applied); *substitute λ for $j\omega$, and set equal to zero; solve for the roots.* To show that this method of obtaining the roots is sometimes the easiest, let us apply it in the present problem. The steady-state alternating-current impedance is

$$j\omega L_1 + R_1 + \frac{R_{12}(R_2 + j\omega L_2)}{R_{12} + R_2 + j\omega L_2}$$

The last term is the impedance of both sides of circuit 2 in parallel, as they are when viewed from the battery E. Then, following, the rule,

$$L_1\lambda + R_1 + \frac{R_{12}(R_2 + L_2\lambda)}{R_{22} + L_2\lambda} = 0$$

and clearing of fractions gives

$$L_1L_2\lambda^2 + (R_{22}L_1 + R_{11}L_2)\lambda + R_1R_{22} + R_{12}R_2 = 0 \quad (232)$$

This equation is equivalent to Eq. (230),[1] and was much more easily and quickly obtained because of the extensive experience we have had with parallel and series combination. When there is any doubt about the proper procedure, it is best to fall back on the voltage equation of the circuits, but in ordinary problems the impedance rule will save time.

---

[1] To show that this equation is identical with (230) it is necessary to show that

$$R_1R_{22} + R_{12}R_2 = R_{11}R_{22} - R_{12}^2$$

Elimination of R_1 and R_2 gives

$$(R_{11} - R_{12})R_{22} + R_{12}(R_{22} - R_{12}) = R_{11}R_{22} - R_{12}R_{22} + R_{12}R_{22} - R_{12}^2$$

which is obviously equal to $R_{11}R_{22} - R_{12}^2$. Equations (230) and (232) are therefore the same.

Before completing the solution for i_1, it will be well to consider the form of current in the second circuit. The differential equation of circuit 2 is (224), and it was solved simultaneously with the differential equation of circuit 1, which is (225), to determine λ_1 and λ_2. The solution is therefore the solution of both equations; λ_1 and λ_2 satisfy both Eqs. (224) and (225), and expression (229) may be the transient component of current in either circuit 1 or circuit 2. The values of λ will be the same in both circuits, but the values of K will not be the same; so to distinguish between coefficients we introduce a double subscript notation and write

$$\text{Transient component of } i_1 = K_{11}e^{\lambda_1 t} + K_{12}e^{\lambda_2 t} \quad (233)$$
$$\text{Transient component of } i_2 = K_{21}e^{\lambda_1 t} + K_{22}e^{\lambda_2 t} \quad (234)$$

Note that the first subscript of each coefficient agrees with the number of the circuit to which it applies, and the second subscript agrees with the number of the normal mode. (This double subscript notation for the K's is not similar to that used to distinguish circuit parameters; in the latter, both subscripts signify circuit numbers.)

5. Steady-state Components of Current. Remembering the four rules for solution, from Chap. I, we now determine the steady-state currents to be added to the transient components. The steady-state current is limited only by resistance, and the total current from the battery (which is the current in circuit 1) is

Steady-state component of $i_1 =$

$$\frac{E}{R_1 + \dfrac{R_{12}R_2}{R_{22}}} = E \frac{R_{22}}{R_1 R_{22} + R_{12}R_2} \quad (235)$$

The part of this current that flows through R_2 is the steady-state component of i_2; it is found from the familiar rule that, in a parallel circuit, direct current divides in inverse proportion to the resistance. It is therefore less than the total current, which is the steady component of i_1, by the ratio of R_{12} to $(R_{12} + R_2)$:

$$\text{Steady-state component of } i_2 = E \frac{R_{22}}{R_1 R_{22} + R_{12}R_2} \cdot \frac{R_{12}}{R_{22}}$$
$$= E \frac{R_{12}}{R_1 R_{22} + R_{12}R_2} \quad (236)$$

It will help to simplify further algebra if we abbreviate these two equations to

$$\text{Steady-state component of } i_1 = \frac{E}{R'} \qquad (237)$$

$$\text{Steady-state component of } i_2 = \frac{E}{R''} \qquad (238)$$

6. Evaluation of Coefficients in Circuit 1. Addition of transient and steady-state components gives the expression for total current in circuit 1:

$$i_1 = K_{11}e^{\lambda_1 t} + K_{12}e^{\lambda_2 t} + \frac{E}{R'} \qquad (239)$$

where

$$R' = \frac{R_1 R_{22} + R_{12} R_2}{R_{22}} \qquad (240)$$

It now remains to evaluate the coefficients. These must be found, as coefficients always are, from initial conditions; we must therefore specify the initial conditions that we intend to consider before the solution can proceed. There are initial conditions in both circuits, and it will be found that any two are sufficient for our purpose as there are only two normal modes whose coefficients must be evaluated.

Let us assume that the network is initially at rest, there being no current in either inductance before the switch is closed. Because of inductance, it is impossible for finite current to flow instantly in either circuit, and two initial conditions are thereby very conveniently determined: when

$$t = 0, \qquad \begin{matrix} i_1 = 0 \\ i_2 = 0 \end{matrix} \Biggr\} \qquad (241)$$

Since we have assumed an initial condition of rest within the network, the following solution for coefficients will apply only to that condition; when other initial conditions are encountered it will be necessary to alter Eq. (241) to correspond, but the method of solution will be unchanged.

These initial conditions must now be used to derive two simultaneous equations which may be solved for K_{11} and K_{12}. The general method was outlined in Sec. 4 of Chap. IV. One of the necessary pair of equations may be obtained directly by substituting $t = 0$, $i_1 = 0$ in Eq. (239):

$$K_{11} + K_{12} + \frac{E}{R'} = 0 \qquad (242)$$

To derive another, differentiate Eq. (239) to find a general equation for pi_1.

$$pi_1 = K_{11}\lambda_1 \epsilon^{\lambda_1 t} + K_{12}\lambda_2 \epsilon^{\lambda_2 t}$$

The *initial* value of pi_1 is then found by substituting zero for t, giving

$$\text{Initial } pi_1 = K_{11}\lambda_1 + K_{12}\lambda_2 \qquad (243)$$

The *specific* value of the initial derivative is obtained by introducing the known initial conditions of Eqs. (241) into the circuit equation (223); since

$$L_1 pi_1 + 0 - 0 = E$$

it follows that

$$pi_1 = \frac{E}{L_1} \qquad (244)$$

In the relatively simple network of Fig. 30, the value of pi_1 could be written from inspection of the circuit without recourse to the differential equations. At the first instant there can be no current; consequently there can be no voltage across any resistance; therefore the whole applied voltage is across L_1, and Eq. (244) results. But it should be emphasized that the use of Eqs. (223) and (241) to evaluate pi_1 is nothing more than a mathematical statement of the facts expressed in the previous sentence, using symbols instead of words. The mathematical method is valuable because initial values are often very difficult to obtain by inspection. The *specific* initial value of rate of change of current from Eq. (244) is now equated to the *general* expression from Eq. (243):

$$\frac{E}{L_1} = K_{11}\lambda_1 + K_{12}\lambda_2 \qquad (245)$$

Equations (242) and (245) are the desired pair of simultaneous equations, for they contain no variable or unknown quantity except K_{11} and K_{12}, for which we proceed to solve. The solution is simple; the use of determinants is recommended, but it is by no means necessary, and the result is

$$K_{11} = E \frac{R' + L_1\lambda_2}{R'L_1(\lambda_1 - \lambda_2)} \left.\begin{array}{c} \\ \\ \\ \end{array}\right\}$$
$$K_{12} = -E \frac{R' + L_1\lambda_1}{R'L_1(\lambda_1 - \lambda_2)} \qquad (246)$$

The solution for i_1 is now complete. The form is given by Eq. (239), and numerical values of the coefficients may be substituted from Eqs. (231) and (246). An illustration of the general shape of the current curve is given in Fig. 31a.

7. Evaluation of Coefficients in Circuit 2. *Two Methods.* There are now two methods available for finding the coefficients of i_2. By adding the transient and steady-state components we have

$$i_2 = K_{21}\epsilon^{\lambda_1 t} + K_{22}\epsilon^{\lambda_2 t} + \frac{E}{R''} \qquad (247)$$

K_{21} and K_{22} can of course be found from initial conditions, and this is the first of the two methods; it is exactly parallel to the determination of K_{11} and K_{12}, and requires little discussion. From Eqs. (247) and (241),

$$K_{21} + K_{22} + \frac{E}{R''} = 0 \qquad (248)$$

where

$$R'' = \frac{R_1R_{22} + R_{12}R_2}{R_{12}} \qquad (249)$$

From (247):

$$pi_2 = K_{21}\lambda_1\epsilon^{\lambda_1 t} + K_{22}\lambda_2\epsilon^{\lambda_2 t} \qquad (250)$$

When (241) is substituted in equation (224):

$$0 + 0 + L_2 pi_2 = 0$$

so that when

$$t = 0, \qquad pi_2 = 0$$

and

$$K_{21}\lambda_1 + K_{22}\lambda_2 = 0 \qquad (251)$$

Simultaneous solution of Eqs. (248) and (251) gives

$$K_{21} = E \frac{\lambda_2}{R''(\lambda_1 - \lambda_2)} \left.\begin{array}{c} \\ \\ \\ \end{array}\right\}$$
$$K_{22} = -E \frac{\lambda_1}{R''(\lambda_1 - \lambda_2)} \qquad (252)$$

The alternative method of finding K_{21} and K_{22} does not carry us back as far as the initial circuit conditions. It makes use of the fact that K_{11} and K_{12} are derived from initial conditions, and therefore K_{21} and K_{22} can be derived from K_{11} and K_{12}. In carrying out such a derivation we need equations relating the coefficients of the current in one circuit to the coefficients of the current in the other; this relationship is given by either of the circuit equations (223) or (224).

Equation (224) relates circuit voltages in terms of i_1, i_2, and pi_2. These three quantities are expressed in Eqs. (239), (247), and (250) respectively, and substitution in equation (224) gives

$$-R_{12}\left(K_{11}\epsilon^{\lambda_1 t} + K_{12}\epsilon^{\lambda_2 t} + \frac{E}{R'}\right) + R_{22}\left(K_{21}\epsilon^{\lambda_1 t} + K_{22}\epsilon^{\lambda_2 t} + \frac{E}{R''}\right)$$
$$+ L_2(K_{21}\lambda_1\epsilon^{\lambda_1 t} + K_{22}\lambda_2\epsilon^{\lambda_2 t}) \equiv 0 \quad (253)$$

Collecting terms with like functions of time we obtain

$$\epsilon^{\lambda_1 t}(-K_{11}R_{12} + K_{21}R_{22} + K_{21}L_2\lambda_1)$$
$$+ \epsilon^{\lambda_2 t}(-K_{12}R_{12} + K_{22}R_{22} + K_{22}L_2\lambda_2)$$
$$+ \left(\frac{E}{R''}R_{22} - \frac{E}{R'}R_{12}\right) \equiv 0 \quad (254)$$

Equations (253) and (254) are *identities;* that is, they must be true for *all* values of time. There is only one possible way in which Eq. (254) can be true for all values of time, and that is that the groups of coefficients enclosed in parentheses must each be zero. So, as the only way that Eq. (253) can always be true, it is necessary that[1]

$$-K_{11}R_{12} + K_{21}R_{22} + K_{21}L_2\lambda_1 = 0 \quad (255)$$
$$-K_{12}R_{12} + K_{22}R_{22} + K_{22}L_2\lambda_2 = 0 \quad (256)$$

Solution of Eq. (255) gives

$$K_{21} = K_{11}\frac{R_{12}}{R_{22} + L_2\lambda_1} \quad (257)$$

and, from Eq. (256),

$$K_{22} = K_{12}\frac{R_{12}}{R_{22} + L_2\lambda_2} \quad (258)$$

[1] It is evident that the third parenthetical expression in Eq. (254), which contains none of the coefficients and no function of time, must be identically zero. Substitution of Eqs. (240) and (249) for R' and R'' proves that this is true, but there is no information to be gained from it.

From these equations it is simple, knowing the coefficients of i_1 to find the coefficients of i_2.

Since there are two possible methods of evaluating the second pair of coefficients,[1] it is necessary to consider which attack is preferable. We have tried both methods, and found little choice as to the time or effort needed—but that is because we applied the methods to a very simple network. The most lengthy part of the solution that begins with initial conditions is the simultaneous solution of equations that contain the coefficients of the normal modes. In our simple network there are only two normal modes and therefore only two equations to solve simultaneously, but even in a two-circuit network there can be four normal modes and hence four simultaneous equations. There is no doubt that in any but the simplest networks it is much quicker and easier to derive coefficients in terms of each other, as in Eqs. (257) and (258).

8. Discussion of Solution. Although Eqs. (239) and (247) are in themselves complete descriptions of currents in the network under all possible conditions (within limitations set by the fundamental assumptions of constant circuit parameters and somewhat idealized elements), it will nevertheless be helpful to discuss the nature of the currents under various circumstances.

The most apparent characteristic of i_1 is that it consists of two exponential terms and a constant steady-state term. If the exponents of the normal modes are real, the form of the current is similar to the curve of Fig. 31a. The three component parts of the current are shown in this figure, as well as the total current.

If in Eq. (231) the positive sign is taken to correspond to λ_1 and the negative to λ_2, it is evident that both λ's will be negative

---

[1] Since K_{21} and K_{22} when derived by one method are expressed in Eqs. (252), and when derived by another method are given as (257) and (258), these pairs of equations must be equivalent. By substituting K_{11}, from Eq. (246), in Eq. (257) we get

$$K_{21} = E \frac{R' + L_1\lambda_2}{R'L_1(\lambda_1 - \lambda_2)} \cdot \frac{R_{12}}{R_{22} + L_2\lambda_1} \tag{259}$$

and although this appears quite unlike the expression for K_{21} in Eq. (252), it is really equal to it, as can be shown by substituting for R' and λ_1 in (259) (it is unnecessary to substitute for λ_2 or for $(\lambda_1 - \lambda_2)$) and simplifying the resulting expression.

and that λ_2 will be numerically the larger. The normal mode containing λ_2 will therefore decay the more rapidly. Something about the magnitudes of the transient terms can be predicted from inspection of Eqs. (246). The denominator of these equations must always be positive, while the sign of the numerator will depend on whether the negative quantity $L_1\lambda$ is greater or less than the positive R'. But the values of λ_1 and λ_2 from Eq. (231) are such that the coefficients K_{11} and K_{12} both prove to be negative. Either of the coefficients may be the larger; if K_{12} is larger than K_{11} the exponential component curves of Fig. 31a will cross, while if it is smaller they will be as shown. The total current i_1 has something of the appearance of an exponential curve, but since it is really composed of two exponential quantities of different exponents it appears to be distorted, particularly near the origin. This is due to the initial slope being greater, in proportion to the rest of the curve, than it would be in a pure exponential curve.

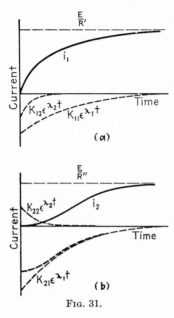

FIG. 31.

It is evident that circuit 1 and circuit 2 do not act independently, and it is not correct to say that one value of λ is due to one circuit and the other to the other circuit. As the coupling becomes smaller and smaller, however, as it would if R_{12} were reduced, the values of λ for the network become more and more nearly equal to those of the circuits individually. So it is not an entirely mistaken concept to associate the λ's with the individual circuits, especially if the circuits are "loosely" coupled, but it is an idea that must be used with care.

The current in circuit 2, like that of circuit 1, is composed of a steady-state term and two exponential terms, but they are combined in such a way that the appearance of the curve for i_2 in Fig. 31b is markedly different from the curve for i_1. Equations (252) show that, since both λ's are negative, K_{21} will be negative and K_{22} will be positive.   Moreover, since λ_2 is numerically larger than λ_1, K_{21} will be proportionately larger than K_{22}.   So we may collect this information and say that in Fig. 31b there will be, in addition to the steady-state component, two exponential components—one will be positive, small, and rapidly decaying; the other will be negative, large, and slowly decaying. The initial values of the three components must add to zero. The initial slope of one exponential component must be equal and opposite to that of the other.   A dash line is drawn in the figure to indicate the result of adding the exponential components to get $K_{21}\epsilon^{\lambda_1 t} + K_{22}\epsilon^{\lambda_2 t}$; when the dashed curve is displaced upward by being added to the steady-state component it becomes the total current.

The physical reason for there being no initial rate of increase of current in circuit 2 is of enough interest to be mentioned. It is simply due to there being no initial voltage in circuit 2. When the switch is closed in the network of Fig. 30 there can be no current at the first instant, because of inductance L_1; there will be no current through R_{12} and consequently no voltage across it; hence there can be no voltage across R_2 and L_2.   So until current is flowing in circuit 1, and a voltage appears across R_{12}, there is nothing to cause current to start to flow in circuit 2.

It has been assumed in discussion of this network that the values of λ are real.   If they are complex the current will be oscillatory.   It is necessary to determine, therefore, whether any possible combination of parameters can make the λ's complex.   From Eq. (231), they will be complex if the quantity under the radical is negative, which will happen if

$$\left(\frac{R_{22}L_1 + R_{11}L_2}{2L_1L_2}\right)^2 < \frac{R_{11}R_{22} - R_{12}{}^2}{L_1L_2} \qquad (260)$$

Expansion of the left-hand member of (260), and simplification of the result, lead to

$$\left(\frac{R_{22}L_1 - R_{11}L_2}{2L_1L_2}\right)^2 < -\frac{R_{12}{}^2}{L_1L_2} \qquad (261)$$

But the left-hand member of (261) is a square, and is therefore always positive, and cannot under any circumstances be absolutely less than the negative quantity in the right-hand member. Since the condition of (260) is therefore physically impossible, we are sure that there can be only real values of λ in this network, and the current can never be oscillatory.

9. A Network in Which the Current Can Be Oscillatory. If the inductance coil in the second circuit

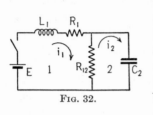

FIG. 32.

of Fig. 30 is replaced by a condenser, however, to give us the circuit of Fig. 32, we shall find that under certain conditions the current may be oscillatory. Under other conditions it will be a single surge. Let us carry out the solution.

First, we shall write the voltage equations, for they are the foundation of all our work.

$$(L_1p + R_{11})i_1 - R_{12}i_2 = E \qquad (262)$$

$$-R_{12}i_1 + \left(R_{12} + \frac{1}{C_2p}\right)i_2 = 0 \qquad (263)$$

We make no immediate use of them, however, as it is easier to find the values of λ from the circuit impedance. The steady-state alternating-current impedance is

$$j\omega L_1 + R_1 + \frac{R_{12}\dfrac{1}{j\omega C_2}}{R_{12} + \dfrac{1}{j\omega C_2}}$$

The last term is the impedance of R_{12} and C_2 in parallel. Then,

$$L_1\lambda + R_1 + \frac{R_{12}\dfrac{1}{\lambda C_2}}{R_{12} + \dfrac{1}{\lambda C_2}} = 0 \qquad (264)$$

and clearing of fractions gives

$$(R_{12}L_1)\lambda^2 + \left(R_1R_{12} + \frac{L_1}{C_2}\right)\lambda + \frac{R_1 + R_{12}}{C_2} = 0 \qquad (265)$$

The roots of this equation, λ_1 and λ_2, are found to be

$$\lambda_1, \lambda_2 = -\left(\frac{R_1}{2L_1} + \frac{1}{2R_{12}C_2}\right)$$
$$\pm \sqrt{\left(\frac{R_1}{2L_1} + \frac{1}{2R_{12}C_2}\right)^2 - \left(\frac{1}{L_1C_2} + \frac{R_1}{R_{12}L_1C_2}\right)} \qquad (266)$$

Since Eq. (265) has two roots, there will be two normal modes in the transient components of both i_1 and i_2. To these will be added the steady-state components. In circuit 2, however, there can be no steady direct current because of the condenser, so the transient component is the entire current. But in circuit 1 a current can flow through R_1 and R_{12} and the steady-state component of i_1 is E/R_{11}. We may now write

$$i_1 = K_{11}\epsilon^{\lambda_1 t} + K_{12}\epsilon^{\lambda_2 t} + \frac{E}{R_{11}} \tag{267}$$

$$i_2 = K_{21}\epsilon^{\lambda_1 t} + K_{22}\epsilon^{\lambda_2 t} \tag{268}$$

One pair of coefficients must be found from initial conditions, and it is necessary to know whether there is any current in the inductance and any charge on the condenser at the instant of closing the switch. Let us consider that case in which the network is initially at rest; we may then write that when

$$t = 0, \qquad \left. \begin{array}{l} i_1 = 0 \\ i_2 = 0 \end{array} \right\} \tag{269}$$

These relations are used to form simultaneous equations containing K_{11} and K_{12}; the first is found by substituting (269) in Eq. (267):

$$0 = K_{11} + K_{12} + \frac{E}{R_{11}} \tag{270}$$

In deriving the other equation, (269) is substituted in the voltage equation (262) to show that initially

$$pi_1 = \frac{E}{L_1} \tag{271}$$

Since, in general,

$$pi_1 = K_{11}\lambda_1 \epsilon^{\lambda_1 t} + K_{12}\lambda_2 \epsilon^{\lambda_2 t} \tag{272}$$

we can make time equal zero and equate (271) and (272):

$$\frac{E}{L_1} = K_{11}\lambda_1 + K_{12}\lambda_2 \tag{273}$$

Simultaneous solution of Eqs. (270) and (273) gives

$$\left. \begin{array}{l} K_{11} = E\, \dfrac{R_{11} + L_1\lambda_2}{R_{11}L_1(\lambda_1 - \lambda_2)} \\[3mm] K_{12} = -E\, \dfrac{R_{11} + L_1\lambda_1}{R_{11}L_1(\lambda_1 - \lambda_2)} \end{array} \right\} \tag{274}$$

These values, in Eq. (267), complete the solution for i_1.

Let us now find the coefficients of i_2, relating them to the coefficients of i_1 by means of the differential equations (262) and (263). Either of the differential equations will give the desired relation, and (262) is the easier one to use as we have already obtained expressions for its three time functions: i_1, i_2, and pi_1. Their values are taken from Eqs. (267), (268), and (272), respectively, and are substituted in (262) to give

$$L_1(K_{11}\lambda_1 \epsilon^{\lambda_1 t} + K_{12}\lambda_2 \epsilon^{\lambda_2 t}) + R_{11}\left(K_{11}\epsilon^{\lambda_1 t} + K_{12}\epsilon^{\lambda_2 t} + \frac{E}{R_{11}}\right)$$
$$- R_{12}(K_{21}\epsilon^{\lambda_1 t} + K_{22}\epsilon^{\lambda_2 t}) \equiv E \quad (275)$$

Grouping the coefficients of similar time functions gives

$$(K_{11}L_1\lambda_1 + K_{11}R_{11} - K_{21}R_{12})\epsilon^{\lambda_1 t}$$
$$+ (K_{12}L_1\lambda_2 + K_{12}R_{11} - K_{22}R_{12})\epsilon^{\lambda_2 t} + E \equiv E \quad (276)$$

and, since this is an identity that must be true for all values of time,

$$\left.\begin{array}{l} K_{11}L_1\lambda_1 + K_{11}R_{11} - K_{21}R_{12} = 0 \\ K_{12}L_1\lambda_2 + K_{12}R_{11} - K_{22}R_{12} = 0 \end{array}\right\} \quad (277)$$

Rearrangement of these equations gives explicit expressions for the coefficients of i_2:

$$\left.\begin{array}{l} K_{21} = K_{11}\dfrac{L_1\lambda_1 + R_{11}}{R_{12}} \\[2mm] K_{22} = K_{12}\dfrac{L_1\lambda_2 + R_{11}}{R_{12}} \end{array}\right\} \quad (278)$$

Numerical computation, in any specific problem, will now proceed directly from Eq. (278), for all quantities in the right-hand members are known.

The coefficients of i_2 may also be found directly from the initial conditions of the network, and, since several interesting facts appear in such a solution, it will be well to determine K_{21} and K_{22} by this means also. First, by substitution of the initial conditions of Eq. (269) in (268) we obtain

$$K_{21} + K_{22} = 0 \quad (279)$$

An expression for pi_2 is then found by differentiating (268):

$$pi_2 = K_{21}\lambda_1\epsilon^{\lambda_1 t} + K_{22}\lambda_2\epsilon^{\lambda_2 t} \quad (280)$$

The specific initial value of pi_2 may be found from the circuit equations; however, since neither Eq. (262) nor (263) contains pi_2, we differentiate Eq. (263). This gives

$$-R_{12}pi_1 + R_{12}pi_2 + \frac{1}{C_2}i_2 = 0$$

Then, since i_2 is zero when time is zero, it follows that when

$$t = 0, \qquad pi_2 = pi_1 = \frac{E}{L_1}$$

But the general expression, Eq. (280), tells us that when

$$t = 0, \qquad pi_2 = K_{21}\lambda_1 + K_{22}\lambda_2$$

and this may be equated to the specific value to give

$$K_{21}\lambda_1 + K_{22}\lambda_2 = \frac{E}{L_1} \qquad (281)$$

Simultaneous solution of Eq. (279) and (281) then gives

$$\left.\begin{array}{l} K_{21} = \dfrac{E}{L_1(\lambda_1 - \lambda_2)} \\[2ex] K_{22} = -K_{21} = -\dfrac{E}{L_1(\lambda_1 - \lambda_2)} \end{array}\right\} \qquad (282)$$

That these values are equivalent to those of Eqs. (278) may be shown by expansion and simplification of the formulas of (278).

10. Discussion of Current in Circuit 1. The form of this solution for current in the network of Fig. 32, as given in Eqs. (267) and (268), is very like the solution for current in the network of Fig. 30. But the similarity does not extend beyond the mathematical form, for the physical nature of current in the two networks is quite different. This is clearly shown by comparison of the curves of current in the two networks as illustrated in Figs. 31 and 33. The difference in the nature of the current, however, may become even more striking for, with certain combinations of parameters, current in the network of Fig. 32 will be oscillatory (see Fig. 34).

Before considering the oscillatory condition, let us discuss the surges of current that result when the values of λ are real. There are two chief reasons for such discussion and analysis: the first is to become familiar with the type of transient current to be expected under the given conditions, and the second is to check the correctness of the mathematical result. These considerations make it desirable to analyse carefully every solution of transient phenomena, for it is only through familiarity with the nature of the transient current that the engineer may distinguish between disturbances of importance and disturbances that are so small or so rapid as to be insignificant; and at the same time a qualitative check of the mathematics will help to avoid mistakes, faulty assumptions, and spurious mathematical results.

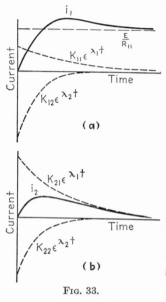

Fig. 33.

The current in circuit 1 is composed of two exponential terms and a steady-state term. These are expressed in Eq. (267), and the manner in which they appear is illustrated in Fig. 33a. The two exponential terms correspond to the two values of λ of Eq. (266), and if the positive sign in that equation is taken to correspond to λ_1 and the negative to λ_2, it is evident that λ_2 will be the numerically larger quantity. The normal mode containing λ_2 will therefore decay the more rapidly, as indicated in the figure.

It is not immediately apparent that K_{11} will always be positive and K_{12} always negative, but such is the case; it is indicated when any numerical values for the circuit parameters are substituted into Eq. (274), for no values can be found that will make the quantity $L_1\lambda_2$, which is negative, greater than R_{11}, which is positive—and in no other way can the fractions in Eqs. (274) be other than positive. Numerical example, however, is not proof (although often more helpful than rigorous proof would be), and to complete our study of the question we must determine the conditions that make

$$R_{11} + L_1\lambda_2 < 0$$

Substitution of λ_2 into this expression leads to

$$R_1 + R_{12} < 0$$

but this is physically impossible because it implies a negative resistance.

Since K_{11} is therefore always positive, it follows that K_{12} will always be negative with a magnitude equal to K_{11} and E/R_{11} together: this condition is necessary to make the initial current zero.

We now have enough information to sketch the curves of Fig. 33a. As steady-state component we draw a constant current of the proper magnitude. There will be two transient components, both exponential, the smaller one positive and slowly decaying, and the larger one negative and rapidly decaying. The total current will be the sum of these three components. It will start from zero. Its initial slope will be E/L_1. It will rise to a value greater than E/R_{11} and will then gradually descend toward the steady-state line that it approaches asymptotically. The curve of total current will always cross the line of the steady-state component, because for large values of time the positive normal mode will always be greater than the negative normal mode. Although the positive normal mode has the smaller coefficient it decays more slowly, and no matter how much smaller it may be at first it will eventually be the larger. To prove this it is only necessary to set the derivative of i_1, in Eq. (272), equal to zero, and since the resulting equation may be solved for a finite value of time it follows that the current curve will always have a maximum point.

11. Discussion of Current in Circuit 2.   The current in circuit 2 is a more familiar form than the current in circuit 1. As shown in Eq. (268), i_2 consists simply of two exponential terms. Since an initial condition of rest was assumed, it is necessary that current in circuit 2 be zero when time is zero; this makes $K_{22} = -K_{21}$, as in Eq. (282). The resulting surge of current and its two components are shown in Fig. 33b. In this, as in Fig. 33a, the fact that λ_1 is less than λ_2 results in a slower rate of decay for the positive exponential component. The current in circuit 2 is therefore always positive, as is indeed evident from the network. Because the coefficients are equal and opposite, the current equation may be rewritten:

$$i_2 = K_{21}(\epsilon^{\lambda_1 t} - \epsilon^{\lambda_2 t}) \qquad (283)$$

This is exactly the form of Eq. (148), which described the

current in a single circuit, and much of the discussion of that current applies equally to this. For instance, the component parts of i_2 are as in Fig. 17, and i_2 may take any of the shapes of Fig. 18.

It is interesting to note that the initial values of pi_1 and pi_2 are equal. At first, when the switch has just been closed, all the current of circuit 1 will also flow in circuit 2 because the condenser is initially uncharged and can offer no opposition to the current. Hence at the first instance $pi_2 = pi_1$. But as charge accumulates on the condenser a voltage will appear between its terminals; this same voltage will be across R_{12}, and much of i_1 will be diverted through the mutual resistance instead of flowing in circuit 2. Finally the condenser becomes fully charged, no more current flows in circuit 2, and the steady-state current of circuit 1 is all diverted through R_{12}.

12. Condition for Oscillatory Currents. It has been assumed in this discussion that the λ's are real; there is no doubt that they *may* be real, but we should investigate whether or not they *must* be real. From Eq. (266) they will be real if the quantity under the radical is positive, and therefore if

$$\left(\frac{R_1}{2L_1} + \frac{1}{2R_{12}C_2}\right)^2 > \frac{1}{L_1C_2} + \frac{R_1}{R_{12}L_1C_2} \qquad (284)$$

Now a small value of R_1 together with a large value of R_{12} will not satisfy this condition, for both terms of the left-hand member

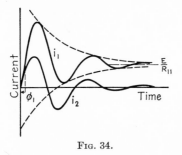

FIG. 34.

may become as small as desired, whereas the first term of the right-hand member remains constant. The left-hand member may therefore be the smaller, and when R_1 is so small and R_{12} so large that (284) is not satisfied, the values of λ will be conjugate complex. The current will then be oscillatory, as in Fig. 34.

13. Transformation of Equations into Sinusoidal Form. When the generalized angular velocities are complex, the equations that express the form of current may best be transformed into sinusoidal expressions. A similar transformation, from exponential to sinusoidal form, is made in Sec. 14 of Chap. IV, and the result obtained there may be used as a pattern for the present transformation. We found that a damped sinusoid could be substituted for the sum of two exponential terms when their exponents were conjugate-complex quantities, so we may now change the expression for the current in circuit 1 from

$$i_1 = K_{11}\epsilon^{\lambda_1 t} + K_{12}\epsilon^{\lambda_2 t} + \frac{E}{R_{11}} \qquad (267)$$

to

$$i_1 = A_1\epsilon^{-\alpha t} \sin(\omega t + \phi_1) + \frac{E}{R_{11}} \qquad (285)$$

The quantities α and ω are obtained from the values of λ, for by definition

$$\lambda_1 = -\alpha + j\omega \qquad \lambda_2 = -\alpha - j\omega \qquad (286)$$

Also it is shown in the previous chapter that A_1 and ϕ_1 are related to the coefficients K_{11} and K_{12} by

$$\left. \begin{aligned} A_1 &= 2\sqrt{K_{11}K_{12}} \\ \tan \phi_1 &= \frac{K_{11} + K_{12}}{j(K_{11} - K_{12})} \end{aligned} \right\} \qquad (287)$$

Numerical computations for current may be based on Eqs. (287); it is possible to compute numerical values for K_{11} and K_{12} and then to use the values so obtained in computing A_1 and ϕ_1. This is a regrettably indirect process, but it has one outstanding advantage: the solution for K_{11} and K_{12} is a straightforward process and will never lead—as the alternative method sometimes does—into a trigonometric cul-de-sac.

A simplification of Eqs. (287) is possible, but it is a method that applies only to the solutions of simple networks; it merely amounts to substituting expressions for K_{11} and K_{12} from Eqs. (274) in Eqs. (287) in order to eliminate the necessity of solving for numerical values of these coefficients. When this is done we find that

$$A_1 = 2\sqrt{K_{11}K_{12}} = \frac{2E}{R_{11}L_1(\lambda_1 - \lambda_2)} \sqrt{-(R_{11} + L_1\lambda_2)(R_{11} + L_1\lambda_1)}$$

$$= \frac{2jE\sqrt{R_{11}{}^2 - 2\alpha R_{11}L_1 + L_1{}^2(\alpha^2 + \omega^2)}}{R_{11}L_1[(-\alpha + j\omega) - (-\alpha - j\omega)]}$$

$$= E\frac{\sqrt{(\alpha L_1 - R_{11})^2 + (\omega L_1)^2}}{\omega L_1 R_{11}} \qquad (288.$$

and

$$\tan \phi_1 = \frac{K_{11} + K_{12}}{j(K_{11} - K_{12})} = \frac{(R_{11} + L_1\lambda_2) - (R_{11} + L_1\lambda_1)}{j[(R_{11} + L_1\lambda_2) + (R_{11} + L_1\lambda_1)]}$$

$$= \frac{L_1[(-\alpha - j\omega) - (-\alpha + j\omega)]}{j[2R_{11} + L_1(-\alpha + j\omega - \alpha - j\omega)]} = \frac{\omega L_1}{\alpha L_1 - R_{11}} \quad (289)$$

A_1 and ϕ_1 may now be computed from Eqs. (288) and (289), and the computation is very easy because of the fortuitous simplification of the algebra involved. In general, however, no such simplification is to be expected, and the form of (287) is then the final form.

The sinusoidal form of current in circuit 2 is most readily found from Eq. (283), although, if the network is not initially at rest, the more general form of Eq. (268) must be used. The sinusoidal form of Eq. (283) is

$$i_2 = A_2\epsilon^{-\alpha t} \sin \omega t \quad (290)$$

ϕ_2 disappears because the coefficients of the exponential terms are equal and opposite. A_2 may then be found:

$$A_2 = 2\sqrt{K_{21}K_{22}} = 2K_{21}\sqrt{-1} = 2jK_{21} \quad (291)$$

If it is desired to substitute for K_{21} from Eq. (282) we may write

$$A_2 = \frac{2jE}{L_1(\lambda_1 - \lambda_2)} = \frac{2jE}{L_1(-\alpha + j\omega + \alpha + j\omega)} = \frac{E}{\omega L_1} \quad (292)$$

and the current becomes

$$i_2 = \frac{E}{\omega L_1} \epsilon^{-\alpha t} \sin \omega t \quad (293)$$

The oscillatory form of currents in both circuits is illustrated in Fig. 34.

14. Direct Solution in Sinusoidal Form. Much algebra and arithmetic can often be saved, when the current in a network turns out to be oscillatory, by determining A and ϕ directly from initial conditions without any reference whatever to the exponential form of solution. This is the alternative method of solution which is mentioned in the previous section, and it has two hazards: the solution may become practically impossible because of unmanageable trigonometric expressions, and spurious results may appear in the mathematics in such a way that the true and the spurious can be separated only with difficulty. Nevertheless, it is generally the method of solution to be first attempted when the current is oscillatory, and if it appears impracticable the former method is then available.

Direct determination in the sinusoidal form has already become familiar to us, for we use that method in the examples of Secs. 15, 16, and 17 of the preceding chapter. Now, in the two-circuit network of Fig. 32, for which the general sinusoidal form of current is expressed by Eq. (285), it is not difficult to evaluate A_1 and ϕ_1 from initial conditions.

We will again specify that the network is initially at rest. Therefore when

$$t = 0, \qquad \begin{matrix} i_1 = 0 \\ i_2 = 0 \end{matrix} \Big\} \tag{294}$$

It has already been shown that in this circuit, and with the same initial conditions, when

$$t = 0, \qquad pi_1 = \frac{E}{L_1} \tag{271}$$

The form of current is

$$i_1 = A_1 \epsilon^{-\alpha t} \sin (\omega t + \phi_1) + \frac{E}{R_{11}} \tag{285}$$

and the derivative of current is

$$pi_1 = A_1[\omega \epsilon^{-\alpha t} \cos (\omega t + \phi_1) - \alpha \epsilon^{-\alpha t} \sin (\omega t + \phi_1)] \tag{295}$$

The zero value of initial current, from (294), shows that Eq. (285) will agree with known conditions at the initial instant only if

$$A_1 \sin \phi_1 + \frac{E}{R_{11}} = 0 \tag{296}$$

and Eq. (295) will agree with the known condition of (271) only if

$$\frac{E}{L_1} = A_1[\omega \cos \phi_1 - \alpha \sin \phi_1] \tag{297}$$

Equations (296) and (297) are now to be solved for A_1 and ϕ_1. From (296),

$$A_1 = -\frac{E}{R_{11} \sin \phi_1} \tag{298}$$

and when this is substituted in Eq. (297)

$$\frac{E}{L_1} = -\frac{E}{R_{11}}(\omega \cot \phi_1 - \alpha)$$

This may be simplified and transformed to

$$\omega \cot \phi_1 = \alpha - \frac{R_{11}}{L_1}$$

from which

$$\tan \phi_1 = \frac{\omega L_1}{\alpha L_1 - R_{11}} \tag{299}$$

Equation (299) is an adequate solution for ϕ_1. From it we obtain

$$\sin \phi_1 = \frac{\pm \omega L_1}{\sqrt{(\alpha L_1 - R_{11})^2 + (\omega L_1)^2}}$$

The uncertainty of sign in this expression corresponds to the uncertainty, in Eq. (299), of the quadrant in which ϕ_1 lies; it is possible for ϕ_1 to be in either the second or fourth quadrant. Either may be selected arbitrarily, for both lead to the same final answer. Let us use the negative sign for $\sin \phi_1$, thereby determining that ϕ_1 is in the fourth quadrant. Substitution of $\sin \phi_1$ into Eq. (298) then gives

$$A_1 = E \frac{\sqrt{(\alpha L_1 - R_{11})^2 + (\omega L_1)^2}}{\omega L_1 R_{11}} \tag{300}$$

A_1 and ϕ_1 have now been determined directly from the given initial conditions of the network, and it is interesting to compare the results in Eqs. (299) and (300) with the values obtained through transformation from the exponential form, these values being given in Eqs. (288) and (289).

When the current is oscillatory, Fig. 33a is no longer a correct picture of the current. Instead of being a single surge of current, i_1 is a sinusoidal oscillation that, as the oscillations decay, merges into the steady-state current. The form of i_1 is shown in Fig. 34; it is a damped sinusoid that is displaced upward from the axis so that the current oscillates about the value E/R_{11}, the steady-state value. The curve of current crosses the steady-state line periodically—each time the transient component becomes zero. That occurs when the quantity $(\omega t + \phi_1)$ is zero, π, 2π, 3π, and so on. ϕ_1 is a negative angle, for it was taken to be in the fourth quadrant.

The current wave-train is contained within an exponential envelope, as shown in the figure. Whether or not the current will cross the axis and become negative depends on the relative values of the parameters.

It is interesting to consider the manner in which the current in the circuit is able to adjust itself to satisfy the network's initial conditions. The *form* of the current is fixed by the network: that is, the natural frequency and the rate of decrement are established. But the *magnitude* of the whole wave-train and the *phase* of the wave-train are free to be fitted to initial conditions. This means, graphically, in Fig. 34, that the curve may adjust itself to initial conditions in two ways: the exponential envelope may be expanded or contracted, and the sinusoidal curve may be slid sideways within the envelope. If the only requisite were that the initial current be zero, either of these changes would suffice. But it is also essential that the curve have the correct slope at the origin, and this requires that both kinds of change be made in just the right proportions. It is to satisfy these two conditions that two equations must be solved simultaneously in finding values for the coefficients. In this particular network there are two normal modes and two undetermined coefficients in the solution for current; and by adjustment of the two coefficients (whether they are K_{11} and K_{12} or A_1 and ϕ_1) it is possible to satisfy two initial conditions. It seems on first thought that trouble would be encountered if a third initial condition were considered; if, for example, the second derivative of current were also specified. But this is not the case, for although it is always necessary to define as many initial conditions as there are normal modes, it is not consistent with the circuit-voltage equations or with the physical possibilities of the circuit to attempt to *arbitrarily* determine a greater number. A third initial condition would have to be consistent with the other two, and therefore would be automatically satisfied by the current curve when the first two conditions were met.

When current in circuit 1 is oscillatory, current in circuit 2 is oscillatory also. The general sinusoidal form of i_2, derived from Eq. (268) is

$$i_2 = A_2 \epsilon^{-\alpha t} \sin (\omega t + \phi_2) \qquad\qquad (301)$$

Since both circuits have the same values of λ, their currents have the same decrement and the same natural frequency. The values of A_2 and ϕ_2 are readily determined from initial conditions.

We have specified that the network is initially at rest, so the initial value of i_2 must be zero; hence it is necessary that ϕ_2 be zero. Equation (301) therefore becomes

$$i_2 = A_2\epsilon^{-\alpha t} \sin \omega t \qquad (302)$$

The initial value of the derivative of i_2 has been found to be E/L_1, as in Eq. (281). So we differentiate the current in Eq. (302) to get

$$pi_2 = A_2(\omega\epsilon^{-\alpha t} \cos \omega t - \alpha\epsilon^{-\alpha t} \sin \omega t) \qquad (303)$$

and when time is equal to zero we may write

$$A_2\omega = \frac{E}{L_1} \qquad (304)$$

This gives

$$A_2 = \frac{E}{\omega L_1} \qquad (305)$$

Finally, Eqs. (305) and (302) combine to give

$$i_2 = \frac{E}{\omega L_1} \epsilon^{-\alpha t} \sin \omega t \qquad (306)$$

This solution for i_2, which introduces the network's initial conditions directly into a sinusoidal form of current, arrives at an expression for current that is identical with the one obtained by transformation from the exponential form, as is shown by comparison of Eqs. (306) and (293).

15. A Limiting Case. If R_{12} in the circuit of Fig. 32 is made very great it will carry little current. The transient current in circuit 1 may not be greatly reduced, but most of it will flow to the condenser, and the mutual resistance will be less effective in shunting a part of the current. The steady-state current, however, will become very small. In the limiting case, R_{12} may be so greatly increased that the current through it is entirely negligible and all the current in circuit 1 will flow in circuit 2 also. In such a case, the two-circuit network has degenerated to a single circuit of L_1, R_1, and C_2 in

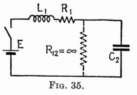

FIG. 35.

series with the source of voltage, and its behavior is merely that of a single circuit (see Fig. 35).

It is interesting to show that all equations for the two-circuit network reduce to the corresponding equations for the single circuit when $R_{12} = \infty$. In Eq. (266), for instance, let R_{12} be infinite; the three terms containing R_{12} in the denominator disappear and

$$\lambda_1, \lambda_2 = -\frac{R_1}{2L_1} \pm \sqrt{\left(\frac{R_1}{2L_1}\right)^2 - \frac{1}{L_1 C_2}} \tag{307}$$

These generalized natural angular velocities are identical with those found for the single circuit and presented in Eq. (133).

The values of the coefficients are similarly related. When K_{11} in Eq. (274) is slightly changed in form to

$$K_{11} = \frac{E}{L_1}\left(\frac{1}{\lambda_1 - \lambda_2} + \frac{L_1 \lambda_2}{(R_1 + R_{12})(\lambda_1 - \lambda_2)}\right)$$

It is evident that when $R_{12} = \infty$

$$K_{11} = \frac{E}{L_1}\frac{1}{\lambda_1 - \lambda_2} \tag{308}$$

Equation (308) is similar to Eq. (181).

A comparison of current in the single circuit, as in Eq. (134), with that in the two-circuit network, Eq. (267), shows that when the mutual resistance becomes infinite the forms of the currents are identical. We have shown that the K's and λ's are the same in the two cases; the steady-state current E/R_{11} becomes zero; therefore the two equations are in all ways equivalent.

Further comparisons can be made between the single-circuit current and i_2, and between the oscillatory forms. Such comparisons not only furnish a check on the correctness of the mathematics, but they also indicate the effects to be expected when the parameters of a network are changed.

16. Mutual Parameters. In the networks of Figs. 30 and 32 the only mutual parameter is resistance. No explicit definition of mutual resistance was needed, for there was no chance of misunderstanding. But when mutual inductance and mutual capacitance are considered it is necessary to define exactly what is meant by these terms.

Let us begin with a definition of mutual resistance, for we know what it is: **mutual resistance** is the ratio of voltage in one circuit to the current, in another circuit, that produces that voltage. To be specific, R_{12} is the ratio of a voltage in circuit 1, produced by a current in circuit 2, to the current in circuit 2. To write this in the form of an equation,

$$R_{12} = \frac{e_1}{i_2} \qquad (309)$$

where i_2 is current in circuit 2 and e_1 is a voltage in circuit 1 *produced by* i_2.

Under the terms of this definition, there is another mutual parameter distinct from R_{12}; it is R_{21}, and it is defined as

$$R_{21} = \frac{e_2}{i_1} \qquad (310)$$

where i_1 is current in circuit 1 and e_2 is a voltage in circuit 2 produced by i_1. The subscripts of mutual parameters are always written in this order: first, the number of the circuit in which a voltage appears; and second, the number of the circuit whose current produces that voltage. But it is obvious that in the networks of Figs. 30 and 32 there is no distinction between R_{21} and R_{12}; indeed, we may generalize and say that there is never any distinction and that the order of subscripts attached to a mutual resistance parameter is immaterial.

Mutual inductance is defined in a precisely similar manner. **Mutual inductance** is the ratio of voltage in one circuit to the rate-of-change of current, in another circuit, which produces that voltage. For example,

$$L_{12} = \frac{e_1}{pi_2} \qquad (311)$$

where pi_2 is the rate of change of current in circuit 2 which produces the voltage e_1 in circuit 1. Also,

$$L_{21} = \frac{e_2}{pi_1} \qquad (312)$$

where pi_1 is the rate of change of current in circuit 1 which produces the voltage e_2 in circuit 2.

When two circuits have a coil of wire in common, as in Fig. 36a, it is evident that $L_{21} = L_{12}$. This is less evident in Fig. 36b, in which the circuits have nothing in common but a magnetic field. And in Fig. 36c, where the number of turns in the coupled coils is unequal, there would seem to be reason to doubt that $L_{21} = L_{12}$. Nevertheless, it is still true. Although such proof is not within the scope of this book, it can be shown that it is always true.

As an example of the equality of the mutual inductances L_{21} and L_{12}, consider a transformer with a large turn-ratio. Let us suppose it to be an ordinary power transformer wound on an iron core, rated 2200 to 220 volts. It has, therefore, ten times as many turns in the primary winding as in the secondary, and if the number in the secondary is n the number in the primary is $10n$. If the secondary circuit is open and the primary current

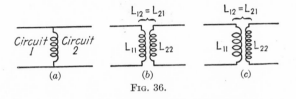

Fig. 36.

is allowed to change 1 amp. in 1 sec., there will be a change of flux that may be denoted by Φ during that second; this will induce a voltage of $n\Phi$ in the secondary winding and the mutual inductance is therefore $n\Phi$ divided by the rate of change of current, which is 1. If, on the other hand, the primary circuit is open and secondary current is allowed to change 1 amp. during 1 sec. there will be a change of flux that is only 0.1Φ. This is because the secondary winding has only one-tenth as many turns as the primary, and the change of ampere turns of magnetomotive force is proportionately less. The voltage induced in the open primary winding by this change of flux will average, during the second of time, $(0.1\Phi)(10n) = n\Phi$; again the mutual inductance is $n\Phi$ divided by 1, and we find that the mutual inductance is the same from secondary to primary as from primary to secondary.

In general, we may say of mutual inductance, as of mutual resistance, that the order of the subscripts is immaterial.

The definition of mutual capacitance is similar to the definitions of the other two mutual parameters. **Mutual capacitance** is the ratio of the integral-of-current in one circuit to the voltage that is produced in another circuit by that integral-of-current. Symbolically,

$$C_{12} = \frac{\int i_2 \, dt}{e_1} \tag{313}$$

where i_2 is the current in circuit 2 whose integral produces a voltage e_1 in circuit 1. Since we have selected a time scale such that current does not begin to flow until the reference time $t = 0$, we may use a *definite* integral of current and write

$$C_{12} = \frac{\frac{1}{p}i_2}{e_1} \tag{314}$$

C_{21} is similarly defined by

$$C_{21} = \frac{\frac{1}{p}i_1}{e_2} \tag{315}$$

and, as with the other parameters, $C_{21} = C_{12}$.

Sometimes it is preferred to give as the definition of mutual capacitance the equivalent formula

$$C_{12} = \frac{i_2}{pe_1} \tag{316}$$

which may be interpreted as the ratio of current to the rate of change of voltage that it produces.

But we will use the definition of Eq. (314), because we want an explicit expression for voltage to be used in the voltage equations of the networks. We want to know the effect that one circuit has on another through their mutual parameters, which is the voltage induced by one in the other. It is with this in mind that the definitions of mutual parameters have been arranged. They are quite analogous to the definitions of self-parameters in Eqs. (1), (2), and (47).

In summary, we may express the total effect that circuit h can have on circuit k as the voltage

$$R_{kh}i_h + L_{kh}pi_h + \frac{1}{C_{kh}p}i_h \tag{317}$$

The idea of mutual resistance has already been used in solution of the networks of Figs. 30 and 32, and mutual inductance will next be encountered in the network of Fig. 37.

17. Inductively Coupled Circuits.　In the first four chapters we consider a single circuit only.　Different combinations of parameters are so few that it is possible and highly desirable to consider them all.　In networks, the possible combinations are unlimited; to discuss all networks of even two circuits would be tedious, and what is more it would be unprofitable.　For it is not the need of the engineer to plod through a catalogue of specific solutions: his need is an understanding of the nature of transient phenomena.　His practice is replete with situations that give rise to transient currents and voltages, and he must judge their nature and importance.　He will find that most of the problems that arise can be solved by an examination that is hardly more than qualitative.　Others, much fewer, are amenable to a hasty approximation.　Hardly one problem in a hundred will demand exact analysis.　By all means, then, the essence of transient phenomena must be emphasized, and this may be done better by careful study of a few typical networks than by an encyclopedic treatment of all possible combinations of parameters.

In this chapter, therefore, we consider only a few two-circuit networks.　They are selected to illustrate the essential features of transient analysis, and they are also designed to emphasize those aspects that most commonly give trouble.　Two resistance-coupled networks have been discussed, and a transformer-coupled network will next be considered to illustrate inductive coupling.

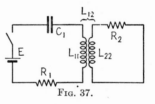

FIG. 37.

Figure 37 shows a network of two circuits coupled by the mutual inductance of a pair of coils with common magnetic field They may be the coils of a transformer, or they may be merely any two coils that are close enough together to have appreciable mutual inductance.　Their operation is defined by their voltage equations; in circuit 1, the applied voltage is equated to the sum of the voltages in circuit 1 that are due to current in circuit 1, plus the voltage in circuit 1 due to current in circuit 2:

$$R_1 i_1 + L_{11} p i_1 + \frac{1}{C_1 p} i_1 - L_{12} p i_2 = E \qquad (318)$$

Since a positive rate-of-change of current in circuit 2 may produce either a positive or negative voltage in circuit 1, depending on the direction of winding of the coils of the two circuits, the induced voltage term may be preceded by either a plus or a minus sign. The solution will be physically the same in either case, provided the voltage equation of circuit 2 is consistent with that of circuit 1, and either sign may be used. We will use the minus sign.

In circuit 2 the sum of the voltages due to current in circuit 2 and due to current in circuit 1 is equated to zero:

$$R_2 i_2 + L_{22} p i_2 - L_{12} p i_1 = 0 \tag{319}$$

In writing Eq. (318) for circuit 1, it is assumed that there is no initial charge on the condenser and that its voltage can be fully described by the term $(1/C_1 p)i_1$. Since the operator $1/p$ represents an integration with the definite limits zero and t, it follows that the above term for condenser voltage is, in reality, the *change* of condenser voltage after the initial instant. Its value is zero when t is zero. If the condenser is initially charged to a voltage e_0, an additional term must be used to express the condenser voltage: $(1/C_1 p)i_1 + e_0$. The voltage equations of the circuit must then be changed from the form of (318) to

$$R_1 i_1 + L_{11} p i_1 + \left(\frac{1}{C_1 p} i_1 + e_0 \right) - L_{12} p i_2 = E$$

When there is no initial charge on the condenser, e_0 disappears.

If it is desired to find the impedance of the two-circuit network of Fig. 37 as viewed from the battery, in order to determine the natural angular velocities of the network in the usual way, it is necessary to solve in some manner for the impedance of the coupled inductive elements that constitute a transformer. A simple method is to replace the transformer with its so-called "equivalent circuit"; this is a familiar strategy, and the "equivalent network" of the transformer of Fig. 37 appears in Fig. 38. When voltage equations for the two circuits of Fig. 38 are written, they give proof that the network is equivalent to the transformer, for they are identical with Eqs. (318) and (319). L_1 and L_2 may be interpreted as leakage inductances if the number of turns in the two coils of the transformer is the same, but not otherwise. L_{12} is in any case the mutual inductance.

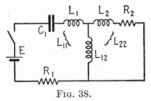

Fig. 38.

Solution for transient currents in the inductively coupled circuits proceeds according to the usual rules. Simultaneous solution of the differential Eqs. (318) and (319) is most easily accomplished by the artifice of writing the impedance of the network of Fig. 38 and equating it to zero. It was for that purpose that the "equivalent network" was introduced. The impedance is a parallel-series combination, giving

$$\frac{1}{C_1\lambda} + R_1 + L_1\lambda + \frac{L_{12}\lambda(L_2\lambda + R_2)}{L_{22}\lambda + R_2} = 0 \qquad (320)$$

Rearrangement[1] of (320) gives the cubic equation

$$\lambda^3(L_{11}L_{22} - L_{12}{}^2) + \lambda^2(R_1L_{22} + R_2L_{11}) + \lambda\left(\frac{L_{22}}{C_1} + R_1R_2\right) +$$
$$\frac{R_2}{C_1} = 0 \quad (321)$$

This same equation may be obtained from the differential equations (318) and (319), without use of an "equivalent network," if desired. Equate (318) to zero instead of E, replace p with λ, and solve simultaneously.

Since Eq. (321) is of the third degree, there will be three roots, λ_1, λ_2, and λ_3. To each of these roots will correspond a normal mode in the equations for transient current, so that

$$i_1 = K_{11}e^{\lambda_1 t} + K_{12}e^{\lambda_2 t} + K_{13}e^{\lambda_3 t} \qquad (323)$$
$$i_2 = K_{21}e^{\lambda_1 t} + K_{22}e^{\lambda_2 t} + K_{23}e^{\lambda_3 t} \qquad (324)$$

Since the condenser in circuit 1 blocks any steady flow of direct current, the transient current is also the total current.

It is possible for all three roots of Eq. (321) to be real, or one may be real and the other two a conjugate-complex pair. Under all conditions one of the roots must be real. This is a fortunate aid in solving for numerical values of the roots, for one real root may be evaluated by trial or by graphical methods. Since Eq. (321) has three roots it may be divided into three factors:

$$(\lambda - \lambda_1)(\lambda - \lambda_2)(\lambda - \lambda_3) = 0 \qquad (325)$$

---

[1] In reducing Eq. (320) to (321) the following transformation is used in order to eliminate L_1 and L_2, which are in this case mathematical quantities without physical reality:

$$L_1L_{22} + L_{12}L_2 = (L_{11} - L_{12})L_{22} + L_{12}(L_{22} - L_{12}) = L_{11}L_{22} - L_{12}{}^2 \quad (322)$$

If λ_1 is used to designate the real root whose numerical value is found by a process of "trial and error," the factor $(\lambda - \lambda_1)$ may be divided out of Eq. (321) by algebraic long division. This quantity, being a factor, will divide out evenly, leaving the equation reduced to quadratic form. Since Eq. (325) is just another way of writing Eq. (321), it is evident that the result of dividing Eq. (321) by $(\lambda - \lambda_1)$ is

$$(\lambda - \lambda_2)(\lambda - \lambda_3) = 0 \qquad (326)$$

This is a quadratic equation in λ that may easily be solved for λ_2 and λ_3 by formula.

The process of solution may therefore be somewhat as follows: introduce numerical values for the circuit parameters into Eq. (321); the result will be of the form

$$A\lambda^3 + B\lambda^2 + C\lambda + D = 0 \qquad (327)$$

where A, B, C, and D are numbers. One root, λ_1, can then be found. If the value of the left-hand side of Eq. (327) is plotted as a function of λ, the result is a cubic curve which will cross the axis of λ at least once; the value of λ where the curve crosses the axis is λ_1, and it may be found with as much accuracy as is desired by repeatedly substituting trial values of λ into Eq. (327), the choice of trial values being guided by plotting the previously computed points.

Equation (327) is next divided by the quantity $(\lambda - \lambda_1)$, in which λ_1 is a real numerical quantity. The result is an equation of the form

$$E\lambda^2 + F\lambda + G = 0 \qquad (328)$$

This is solved by formula for λ_2 and λ_3, which may be either real or complex. Equations (323) and (324) for the currents may then be written with numerical exponents, leaving the values of the K's to be determined from initial conditions.

There are other methods of solving cubic equations, which are treated in books on algebra and in mathematical handbooks. Any method of solution is, of course, quite satisfactory; the one outlined above is suggested only because it has proved to be among the easiest.

Since each of Eqs. (323) and (324), which express the currents of the network in exponential form, contains three undetermined coefficients, it is necessary to have three initial conditions for their evaluation. Let us consider a network initially at rest giving initial conditions: no initial charge on the condenser C_1, no initial current in circuit 1, and no initial current in circuit 2. The voltage equation (318) was written without any term corresponding to initial charge on the condenser: the other two conditions are expressed symbolically by

$$t = 0, \qquad \begin{aligned} i_1 &= 0 \\ i_2 &= 0 \end{aligned} \right\} \tag{329}$$

If the conditions of a problem are such that there is initial charge or initial current, the equations may readily be altered to correspond (as in Sec. 13 of Chap. I and Sec. 16 of Chap. IV).

In solving for K_{11}, K_{12}, and K_{13} it will be strategic to determine initial values for i_1, pi_1, and $p^2 i_1$. The initial value of i_1 is given by Eq. (329). The initial value of pi_1 is obtained by substituting Eqs. (329) into the circuit voltage equations (318) and (319), giving

$$t = 0, \qquad L_{11}pi_1 - L_{12}pi_2 = E \tag{330}$$

and

$$L_{22}pi_2 - L_{12}pi_1 = 0 \tag{331}$$

respectively. Simultaneous solution of Eqs. (330) and (331) leads to

$$t = 0, \qquad pi_1 = E\, \frac{L_{22}}{L_{11}L_{22} - L_{12}{}^2} \tag{332}$$

$$pi_2 = E\, \frac{L_{12}}{L_{11}L_{22} - L_{12}{}^2} \tag{333}$$

These equations will give numerical values for the initial derivatives.

An alternative method of finding the initial derivatives of current is sometimes preferred because it is more direct. It is based on the fact that at the initial instant, in an inductive network, there can be no voltage across any of the circuit elements except the inductances; since current has not begun to flow, the condensers and resistances produce no voltage drop. The effective network, then, consists entirely of inductances, and these can be combined in series and in parallel according to the rules that are customarily used to combine resistances. The same thought is expressed by saying that Kirchhoff's laws apply, in this case, to derivatives of current instead of to currents. Now by reference to the equivalent network of Fig. 38 we may determine the initial derivative of current in circuit 1: L_1, L_2, and L_{12} are the only inductive elements, and the applied voltage is initially consumed in producing an increase of current through L_1 in series with L_{12} and L_2 in parallel. The inductance of the parallel combination is

$$\frac{L_{12}L_2}{L_{12} + L_2} = \frac{L_{12}L_2}{L_{22}}$$

Since the voltage E is applied to this combination in series with L_1, it follows that initially

$$E = \left(L_1 + \frac{L_{12}L_2}{L_{22}}\right)pi_1$$

and that, when

$$t = 0, \qquad pi_1 = E\frac{L_{22}}{L_1L_{22} + L_{12}L_2} = E\frac{L_{22}}{L_{11}L_{22} - L_{12}^2}$$

This agrees with Eq. (332).

Since the derivative of current obeys Kirchhoff's laws, we may find how the derivative divides between the two parallel inductances L_{12} and L_2. That part of the derivative that appears in L_2 is the derivative of i_2, and it is found by considering that pi_1 divides in inverse proportion to the inductances L_{12} and L_2. When

$$t = 0, \qquad pi_2 = pi_1\frac{L_{12}}{L_{12} + L_2} = E\frac{L_{12}}{L_{11}L_{22} - L_{12}^2}$$

This agrees with Eq. (333).

Having determined the first derivatives of current by either of the alternative methods it is possible to determine the second derivatives. Equations (318) and (319) may be differentiated to obtain expressions containing the second derivatives, giving

$$R_1 pi_1 + L_{11}p^2i_1 + \frac{1}{C_1}i_1 - L_{12}p^2i_2 = 0 \qquad (334)$$

$$R_2 pi_2 + L_{22}p^2i_2 - L_{12}p^2i_1 = 0 \qquad (335)$$

When initial conditions are introduced from (329), Eqs. (334) and (335) reduce to

$$t = 0, \qquad R_1 pi_1 + L_{11}p^2i_1 - L_{12}p^2i_2 = 0 \qquad (336)$$

$$R_2 pi_2 + L_{22}p^2i_2 - L_{12}p^2i_1 = 0 \qquad (337)$$

Simultaneous solution for the second derivatives gives

$$t = 0, \qquad p^2i_1 = -\frac{R_2 L_{12}pi_2 + R_1 L_{22}pi_1}{L_{11}L_{22} - L_{12}{}^2} \qquad (338)$$

$$p^2i_2 = -\frac{R_1 L_{12}pi_1 + R_2 L_{11}pi_2}{L_{11}L_{22} - L_{12}{}^2} \qquad (339)$$

These may be considered as completed solutions for the second derivatives, for values of first derivatives can be obtained from Eqs. (332) and (333) and then be substituted in (338) and (339). We now have initial values for current and for its first and second derivatives in terms of network parameters.

Next, we derive expressions for the same quantities in terms of the unknown coefficients K_{11}, K_{12}, and K_{13}. In doing so we differentiate the expression for current in Eq. (323) once and twice:

$$i_1 = K_{11}\epsilon^{\lambda_1 t} + K_{12}\epsilon^{\lambda_2 t} + K_{13}\epsilon^{\lambda\ t} \qquad (323)$$

$$pi_1 = \lambda_1 K_{11}\epsilon^{\lambda_1 t} + \lambda_2 K_{12}\epsilon^{\lambda_2 t} + \lambda_3 K_{13}\epsilon^{\lambda_3 t} \qquad (340)$$

$$p^2i_1 = \lambda_1{}^2 K_{11}\epsilon^{\lambda_1 t} + \lambda_2{}^2 K_{12}\epsilon^{\lambda_2 t} + \lambda_3{}^2 K_{13}\epsilon^{\lambda_3 t} \qquad (341)$$

When, in these three equations,

$$t = 0, \qquad i_1 = K_{11} + K_{12} + K_{13} \qquad (342)$$

$$pi_1 = \lambda_1 K_{11} + \lambda_2 K_{12} + \lambda_3 K_{13} \qquad (343)$$

$$p^2i_1 = \lambda_1{}^2 K_{11} + \lambda_2{}^2 K_{12} + \lambda_3{}^2 K_{13} \qquad (344)$$

Numerical values may now be substituted for the left-hand members of these equations, for when $t = 0$, $i_1 = 0$ and pi_1 and p^2i_1 are given by Eqs. (332) and (338). Let us abbreviate by writing the initial value of pi_1, determined from Eq. (332), as M, and the initial value of p^2i_1, from Eq. (338), as N; then

$$\left. \begin{array}{l} K_{11} + K_{12} + K_{13} = 0 \\ \lambda_1 K_{11} + \lambda_2 K_{12} + \lambda_3 K_{13} = M \\ \lambda_1{}^2 K_{11} + \lambda_2{}^2 K_{12} + \lambda_3{}^2 K_{13} = N \end{array} \right\} \qquad (345)$$

All quantities are known in the three Eqs. (345) except the three K's, which may therefore be found by simultaneous solution. Use of determinants[1] simplifies the solution, and gives

---

[1] If the use of determinants is not familiar, it is possible to learn enough of their properties in a very short time to aid greatly in the solution of

$$K_{11} = \frac{\begin{vmatrix} 0 & 1 & 1 \\ M & \lambda_2 & \lambda_3 \\ N & \lambda_2{}^2 & \lambda_3{}^2 \end{vmatrix}}{\begin{vmatrix} 1 & 1 & 1 \\ \lambda_1 & \lambda_2 & \lambda_3 \\ \lambda_1{}^2 & \lambda_2{}^2 & \lambda_3{}^2 \end{vmatrix}}$$

$$= \frac{M\lambda_2{}^2 + N\lambda_3 - M\lambda_3{}^2 - N\lambda_2}{\lambda_2\lambda_3{}^2 + \lambda_1\lambda_2{}^2 + \lambda_3\lambda_1{}^2 - \lambda_3\lambda_2{}^2 - \lambda_1\lambda_3{}^2 - \lambda_2\lambda_1{}^2} \quad (346)$$

K_{12} and K_{13} are also found from Eqs. (345):

$$K_{12} = \frac{M\lambda_3{}^2 + N\lambda_1 - M\lambda_1{}^2 - N\lambda_3}{\lambda_2\lambda_3{}^2 + \lambda_1\lambda_2{}^2 + \lambda_3\lambda_1{}^2 - \lambda_3\lambda_2{}^2 - \lambda_1\lambda_3{}^2 - \lambda_2\lambda_1{}^2} \quad (347)$$

$$K_{13} = \frac{M\lambda_1{}^2 + N\lambda_2 - M\lambda_2{}^2 - N\lambda_1}{\lambda_2\lambda_3{}^2 + \lambda_1\lambda_2{}^2 + \lambda_3\lambda_1{}^2 - \lambda_3\lambda_2{}^2 - \lambda_1\lambda_3{}^2 - \lambda_2\lambda_1{}^2} \quad (348)$$

The denominators of the right-hand members of Eqs. (346), (347), and (348) are the same because they are expansions of the same determinant; this similarity is a considerable aid in numerical solution.

The solution for the current in circuit 1 of the network is now complete. It is too complicated to collect in a single equation, but the form of the current is

$$i_1 = K_{11}\epsilon^{\lambda_1 t} + K_{12}\epsilon^{\lambda_2 t} + K_{13}\epsilon^{\lambda_3 t} \quad (323)$$

Values for K_{11}, K_{12}, and K_{13} are found from Eqs. (346), (347), and (348). Values for λ_1, λ_2, and λ_3 are the roots of Eq. (321). To find the current in circuit 1 at any instant it is only necessary to substitute the corresponding value of t. The resulting current as a function of time is illustrated in Fig. 39a.

Since it is very difficult to make general statements that are clear and concise about the complicated behaviour of this network, let us rather consider a specific example.

18. An Example. The rectifier network of a certain public-address system contains coupled circuits similar to the network of Fig. 37. Find the current that flows when a battery voltage of

---

simultaneous equations. Any advanced algebra book may be used as reference, and the "Mechanical Engineers' Handbook" edited by Marks (McGraw-Hill Book Company, Inc., New York) contains the essential information in compact form.

100 volts is suddenly connected. Circuit parameters have the following values:

$L_{11} = 1.00$ henry. $R_1 = 750$ ohms.
$L_{22} = 1.00$ henry. $R_2 = 750$ ohms.
$L_{12} = 0.50$ henry. $C_1 = 10\mu f. = 10^{-5}$ farads.

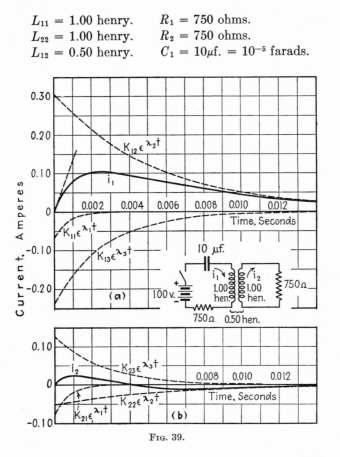

FIG. 39.

Solution: When the given values of parameters are substituted in Eq. (321) it becomes

$$0.75\lambda^3 + 1500\lambda^2 + 66.2 \times 10^4\lambda + 75 \times 10^6 = 0 \qquad (a)$$

By trial it is found that one root of Eq. (*a*) is -1433. This root is designated λ_1. Equation (*a*) is then divided by the algebraic factor $(\lambda + 1433)$, and the quotient is

$$0.75\lambda^2 + 425\lambda + 5.3 \times 10^4 = 0 \qquad (b)$$

The two remaining roots of Eq. (*a*) are now found by solution of Eq. (*b*):

$$\lambda_2, \lambda_3 = \frac{-425 \pm \sqrt{(425)^2 - 4(0.75)(5.3)10^4}}{2(0.75)} = -185 \text{ or } -381$$

Since the order in which these are numbered is immaterial, we may write

$$\left. \begin{aligned} \lambda_1 &= -1433 \\ \lambda_2 &= -185 \\ \lambda_3 &= -381 \end{aligned} \right\} \tag{c}$$

Numerical values for the initial derivatives of current are now obtained from Eqs. (332), (333), (338), and (339).

$$\left. \begin{aligned} pi_1 &= M = E \frac{1.00}{1.00 - 0.25} = 1.333E \\ pi_2 &= E \frac{0.50}{1.00 - 0.25} = 0.667E \\ p^2 i_1 &= N = -\frac{(750)(0.50)(0.667)E + (750)(1.00)(1.333)E}{1.00 - 0.25} \\ &= -1667E \\ p^2 i_2 &= -\frac{(750)(0.50)(1.333)E + (750)(1.00)(0.667)E}{1.00 - 0.25} \\ &= -1333E \end{aligned} \right\} \tag{d}$$

Solution of the simultaneous equations (345) is now needed to give the coefficients of the normal modes of i_1. Solution for K_{11} is given in Eq. (346), and, to substitute numerical values,

$$
\begin{array}{ll}
\lambda_2 \lambda_3^2 = -\ 26.8 \times 10^6 & \lambda_1 \lambda_3^2 = -208 \quad \times 10^6 \\
\lambda_1 \lambda_2^2 = -\ 49.0 \times 10^6 & \lambda_3 \lambda_2^2 = -\ 13.0 \times 10^6 \\
\lambda_3 \lambda_1^2 = -785 \quad \times 10^6 & \lambda_2 \lambda_1^2 = -381 \quad \times 10^6 \\
\hline
\qquad\quad -861 \quad \times 10^6 & \qquad\quad -602 \quad \times 10^6
\end{array}
$$

$$
\begin{array}{ll}
M\lambda_2^2 = \ 4.56 \times 10^4 E & M\lambda_3^2 = 19.35 \times 10^4 E \\
N\lambda_3 = 63.5 \quad \times 10^4 E & N\lambda_2 = 30.8 \quad \times 10^4 E \\
\hline
\qquad 68.1 \quad \times 10^4 E & \qquad 50.2 \quad \times 10^4 E
\end{array}
$$

$$K_{11} = \frac{[(68.1) - (50.2)] \times 10^4 E}{[(-861) - (-602)] \times 10^6} = \frac{17.9 \times 10^4 E}{-259 \times 10^6} =$$

$$-6.90 \times 10^{-4} E$$

Equations (347) and (348) show that K_{12} and K_{13} may be expressed as fractions whose denominators are, in each case, the value of -259×10^6, which is the denominator of K_{11}. Numerator for $K_{12} = M\lambda_3{}^2 + N\lambda_1 - M\lambda_1{}^2 - N\lambda_3$.

$$
\begin{array}{ll}
M\lambda_3{}^2 = 19.3 \times 10^4 E & M\lambda_1{}^2 = 274.5 \times 10^4 E \\
N\lambda_1 = 239 \times 10^4 E & N\lambda_3 = 63.5 \times 10^4 E \\
\hline
258 \times 10^4 E & 338 \times 10^4 E
\end{array}
$$

$$
K_{12} = \frac{[(258) - (338)] \times 10^4 E}{-259 \times 10^6} = 30.8 \times 10^{-4} E
$$

Numerator for $K_{13} = M\lambda_1{}^2 + N\lambda_2 - M\lambda_2{}^2 - N\lambda_1$

$$
\begin{array}{ll}
M\lambda_1{}^2 = 274.5 \times 10^4 E & M\lambda_2{}^2 = 4.56 \times 10^4 E \\
N\lambda_2 = 30.8 \times 10^4 E & N\lambda_1 = 239 \times 10^4 E \\
\hline
305.3 \times 10^4 E & 343.5 \times 10^4 E
\end{array}
$$

$$
K_{13} = \frac{[(305.3) - (343.5)] \times 10^4 E}{-259 \times 10^6} = -23.9 \times 10^{-4} E
$$

This completes the solution for i_1, and collection of terms in the form of Eq. (323) gives

$$
i_1 = (-6.9\epsilon^{-1433t} + 30.8\epsilon^{-185t} - 23.9\epsilon^{-381t})10^{-4} E \qquad (e)
$$

The voltage E is 100 volts. In Fig. 39a, i_1 and its three exponential components are plotted from Eq. (e).

As partial checks on the accuracy of the arithmetic of the solution, note that the sum of the three coefficients of the normal modes is zero [thereby satisfying Eq. (342)] and that the initial slope of i_1 is $1.33E$ [satisfying Eq. (d)].

Solution for i_2 is carried out in exactly the same manner. The generalized natural angular velocities are the same as in circuit 1. Initial values of pi_2 and $p^2 i_2$ have already been determined, and are given in Eqs. (333) and (339); let us designate these M' and N' respectively. A new group of equations is found by differentiating (324), the formal equation for i_2, and when $t = 0$ we obtain

$$
K_{21} + K_{22} + K_{23} = 0 \qquad (349)
$$
$$
\lambda_1 K_{21} + \lambda_2 K_{22} + \lambda_3 K_{23} = M' \qquad (350)
$$
$$
\lambda_1{}^2 K_{21} + \lambda_2{}^2 K_{22} + \lambda_3{}^2 K_{23} = N' \qquad (351)
$$

These three equations can now be solved simultaneously for K_{21}, K_{22}, and K_{23}; the resulting expressions for the coefficients will be identical with the right-hand members of Eqs. (346), (347), and (348) except that M' and N' will replace M and N.

To complete the example of the previous section it is desirable to compute i_2. The form of i_2 is given in Eq. (324), and when the coefficients are evaluated it is found that

$$i_2 = (-7.3\epsilon^{-1433t} - 5.1\epsilon^{-185t} + 12.4\epsilon^{-381t})10^{-4}E \qquad (f)$$

The exponential components and the total current are plotted in Fig. 39b.

It is interesting to notice that although the current in circuit 2 reverses its direction of flow when time, in this specific problem, is slightly over 0.004 sec., the current is not oscillatory. Current in this circuit reverses only once, whereas a truly oscillatory current reverses periodically. Moreover, i_2 in Eq. (f) is described as the sum of three real exponential terms, whereas oscillatory currents contain normal modes with complex exponents and complex coefficients. The reversal of current in Fig. 39b results from the rapid decay of the positive normal mode and the relatively slow decay of one of the negative normal modes. It is characteristic of the network; the direction of i_2 will always reverse at some time after the maximum of i_1 is passed.

19. Oscillatory Current. When two of the roots of the cubic equation (321) are found to be complex, as they will be if resistance in both circuits of the network is sufficiently low, the current will be oscillatory. It will not be simply sinusoidal, however, because there is one real normal mode in addition to the two complex normal modes, and the current can best be described as the sum of an exponential term and a sinusoidal term. The general form for the current is

$$i_1 = K_{11}\epsilon^{\lambda_1 t} + K_{12}\epsilon^{\lambda_2 t} + K_{13}\epsilon^{\lambda_3 t} \qquad (323)$$

and if λ_2 and λ_3 are conjugate-complex quantities such that

$$\left. \begin{aligned} \lambda_2 &= -\alpha + j\omega \\ \lambda_3 &= -\alpha - j\omega \end{aligned} \right\} \qquad (352)$$

the current may be written

$$i_1 = K_{11}\epsilon^{\lambda_1 t} + \epsilon^{-\alpha t}(K_{12}\epsilon^{j\omega t} + K_{13}\epsilon^{-j\omega t}) \qquad (353)$$

By combination of the exponential quantities, making use of the method employed to change Eq. (200) to (201) in Chap. IV, we get

$$i_1 = K_{11}\epsilon^{\lambda_1 t} + A_1 \epsilon^{-\alpha t} \sin (\omega t + \phi_1) \qquad (354)$$

wherein

$$A_1 = 2\sqrt{K_{12}K_{13}}$$

$$\phi_1 = \tan^{-1} \frac{K_{12} + K_{13}}{j(K_{12} - K_{13})}$$

Figure 40 illustrates the current that may flow in such a network. The exponential and sinusoidal components are indicated as well as the total current. At the initial instant, the components add to zero in order to satisfy the stipulated initial condition of rest.

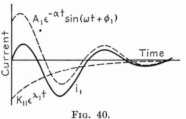

FIG. 40.

Numerical solution for current in Eq. (354) may proceed along either of two routes. It is possible to find K_{11}, K_{12}, and K_{13}, even though two of them are complex, by exactly the method employed when they are all real. A_1 and ϕ_1 may then be evaluated from K_{12} and K_{13}. On the other hand, it is possible to solve directly for K_{11}, A_1, and ϕ_1. Derivatives of current are found by differentiating Eq. (354):

$$i_1 = K_{11}\epsilon^{\lambda_1 t} + A_1 \epsilon^{-\alpha t} \sin (\omega t + \phi_1) \qquad (354)$$

$$pi_1 = K_{11}\lambda_1 \epsilon^{\lambda_1 t} +$$
$$A_1[\omega \epsilon^{-\alpha t} \cos (\omega t + \phi_1) - \alpha \epsilon^{-\alpha t} \sin (\omega t + \phi_1)] \qquad (355)$$

$$p^2 i_1 = K_{11}\lambda_1^2 \epsilon^{\lambda_1 t} +$$
$$A_1[(\alpha^2 - \omega^2)\epsilon^{-\alpha t} \sin (\omega t + \phi_1) - 2\alpha\omega\epsilon^{-\alpha t} \cos (\omega t + \phi_1)] \qquad (356)$$

Expressions for the initial values of current and its derivatives are obtained by setting t equal to zero in the above equations, and the resulting expressions are equated to the initial values of the derivatives and the current. The initial values of the derivatives were obtained in Eq. (332) and (338) and have been denoted by M and N, and the initial value of current is zero.

$$\left. \begin{array}{l} K_{11} + A_1 \sin \phi_1 = 0 \\ K_{11}\lambda_1 + A_1(\omega \cos \phi_1 - \alpha \sin \phi_1) = M \\ K_{11}\lambda_1^2 + A_1[(\alpha^2 - \omega^2) \sin \phi_1 - 2\alpha\omega \cos \phi_1] = N \end{array} \right\} \qquad (357)$$

Simultaneous solution of Eqs. (357) is now necessary to evaluate K_{11}, A_1, and ϕ_1. Although the resulting trigonometric expressions are quite intricate, the solution is possible, and, since it involves only real numbers, it is rather less laborious than the alternative method. But in the course of the trigonometric solution there may be introduced spurious roots which have no physical significance; the spurious roots can be distinguished from the true roots by checking the final results in Eqs. (357), though unnecessary confusion and trouble will sometimes result.

Choice between the methods of solution becomes, finally, a matter of judgment, with formal simplicity and generality somewhat favoring the exponential solution.

When the current in circuit 1 has a sinusoidal component, the current in circuit 2 will also be oscillatory. It will be

$$i_2 = K_{21}\epsilon^{\lambda_1 t} + A_2\epsilon^{-\alpha t} \sin{(\omega t + \phi_2)} \qquad (358)$$

with

$$A_2 = 2\sqrt{K_{22}K_{23}}$$

$$\phi_2 = \tan^{-1} \frac{K_{22} + K_{23}}{j(K_{22} - K_{23})}$$

Its appearance will be somewhat the same as i_1 (see Fig. 40, and also oscillogram 5 at end of this chapter), with the same values of λ_1, α, and ω, but different values of K_{22}, A_2, and ϕ_2.

20. A Case in Which Equal Roots Appear. In the example of Sec. 19 just preceding, the resistance in each circuit was 750 ohms. If each resistance had been reduced to 600 ohms, the current would have been oscillatory. There is, of course, a critical value of resistance that separates the oscillatory case from the non-oscillatory case, although there is no simple criterion to enable one to decide, without solving for the roots of the cubic equation, whether or not a given network will have an oscillatory transient current.

However, when one real root of the cubic equation has been found, and the factor containing it has been divided out of the cubic equation, leaving a quadratic equation of the form of (328), it is not difficult to know whether the two remaining roots will be real or complex. If the quantity under the radical in the solution of the quadratic equation is positive, the roots will be real; if negative, they will be complex. For instance, in the

numerical example of Sec. 19 the quadratic equation (b) has real
roots.   If circuit resistance had been lower, the roots of Eq. (b)
would have been complex, for the quantity under the radical
would have been negative.   But it is evident that there is a third
possibility: if the quantity under the radical had been zero the
two roots λ_2 and λ_3 would have been equal.

For this case of equal roots, the usual form of current equation
does not apply; the current cannot be expressed as the sum of
three exponential terms as in Eqs. (323) and (324).   But a
mathematical foundation for the treatment of this case is laid
in Chap. III.   The rule that concludes that chapter says,
"If the roots are all distinct the transient current will be

$$K_1 \epsilon^{\lambda_1 t} + K_2 \epsilon^{\lambda_2 t} + \cdots$$

If there are equal roots use expression (140)."   From expression
(140) we find that when two roots of the cubic equation are
equal, there will be a term in the current equation whose form is
$t \epsilon^{\lambda_m t}$, and instead of writing the current in circuit 1 as

$$i_1 = K_{11} \epsilon^{\lambda_1 t} + K_{12} \epsilon^{\lambda_2 t} + K_{13} \epsilon^{\lambda_3 t} \tag{323}$$

it becomes

$$i_1 = K_{11} \epsilon^{\lambda_1 t} + K_{12} \epsilon^{\lambda_m t} + K_{13} t \epsilon^{\lambda_m t} \tag{359}$$

Similarly,

$$i_2 = K_{21} \epsilon^{\lambda_1 t} + K_{22} \epsilon^{\lambda_m t} + K_{23} t \epsilon^{\lambda_m t} \tag{360}$$

As with the case of critical damping in a single circuit, discussed in Chap. IV, the practical importance of this case of equal
roots is due to the fact that it can be used as a good approximate
solution when two of the roots are so nearly equal that the error
is negligible.

21. Energy in the Coupled Circuits.   In the network of Fig. 37
there is a transfer of energy from one circuit to the other by
means of their common magnetic field.   The magnetic field is
supplied with energy from the battery as current increases in
circuit 1, and thereafter it is a pool of energy that may be drawn
upon by either circuit.

There are three magnetic fields in the network that must
be considered separately: there is the magnetic field that is
common to both circuits, and there are the two "leakage" fields,
each of which is associated with one circuit only.   In terms of

magnetic flux, lines that link only circuit 1 constitute the leakage field of circuit 1, lines that link only circuit 2 compose its leakage field, and lines that link both circuits are the lines of the mutual or common field.   These are shown in a highly diagrammatic manner in Fig. 41.

When current flows in circuit 1, owing to the action of the battery, it transfers magnetic energy to the leakage field of circuit 1 and to the common field.   But as the common field increases, it induces a voltage in circuit 2, and i_2 begins to flow, deriving its energy from the common field.   The energy carried away from the common magnetic field by i_2 is partly transferred to the leakage field of circuit 2, and part is lost as heat in the circuit resistance.

As the condenser in circuit 1 becomes partially charged, the current in circuit 1 reaches a maximum and begins to decrease. As it diminishes, it withdraws energy from the common magnetic field, as well as from its own leakage field.   Circuit 2 can no longer receive energy from the common field because of the rate at which that field is being reduced by circuit 1; in fact, the flow of power can be reversed, and some of the energy stored in the leakage field of circuit 2 may be returned to the common field and thence to circuit 1. Finally, all of the energy that has not been lost in the network resistance is delivered to the condenser, and current ceases to flow.

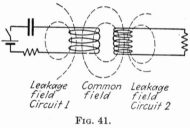

Leakage   Common   Leakage
field   field   field
Circuit 1   Circuit 2

FIG. 41.

When the common field begins to decrease, the shrinkage of flux lines induces voltage in both circuits; in circuit 1 it induces a voltage that aids the flow of current and thereby delivers power to the circuit, whereas in circuit 2 it induces a voltage that opposes the flow of current, and it is by this means that power is received from the leakage field that operates to maintain current.   When energy in the leakage field of circuit 2 is exhausted, i_2 becomes zero; but, since shrinkage of the common field is still inducing in circuit 2 a voltage that tends to drive current in a negative direction, there will be a reversal of current in circuit 2.   In a nonoscillatory network, this reverse current will continue as long as there is current in circuit 1, whereas if the current is oscillatory there will be further interchanges of energy between the two circuits.

The currents of Fig. 39 illustrate the behaviour of such a network. For the first 0.003 sec. the current in circuit 1 is increasing and energy is being carried from the battery to the leakage field of circuit 1 and to the common magnetic field. Energy withdrawn from the common field by i_2 is being taken to the resistance of circuit 2 and for the first 0.001 sec. it is also transferred to the leakage field of circuit 2. After the first 0.001 sec. the current in circuit 2 begins to decrease, and energy is withdrawn from its leakage field to become heat in the circuit resistance. From 0.003 to 0.004 sec. the common field is receiving energy from circuit 2 with the result that i_2 ceases to flow, and then after 0.004 sec., energy is again received by circuit 2 as its current flows in a negative direction. Both circuits receive energy from the common field after 0.004 sec.; in circuit 2 all energy received after that time is lost in heat, but in circuit 1 part of the energy is acquired by the condenser.

The total amount of electromagnetic energy in the network at any time is the sum of the energies in the three magnetic fields indicated in Fig. 41. Power delivered to the magnetic fields by circuit 1, at each instant, is the product of the current i_1 and the voltage induced in circuit 1. If the induced voltage in circuit 1 is designated by e_1, power delivered to the magnetic fields by that circuit is $e_1 i_1$, and, since energy is the time integral of power, it follows that total energy in the magnetic fields due to circuit 1 is $\int e_1 i_1 \, dt$. Induced voltage in circuit 1 is due to change of current in either circuit; just as in Eq. (318), two terms are needed to express the total induced voltage: $e_1 = L_{11} p i_1 - L_{12} p i_2$. Energy from circuit 1 is therefore

$$\int (L_{11} p i_1 - L_{12} p i_2) i_1 \, dt \qquad (361)$$

Similarly, the energy received by the combined magnetic fields from circuit 2 is $e_2 i_2$, and the total energy in the magnetic fields, received from both circuits, is

$$W = \int [(L_{11} p i_1 - L_{12} p i_2) i_1 + (L_{22} p i_2 - L_{12} p i_1) i_2] dt \qquad (362)$$

Remembering that p is here used to mean $\dfrac{d}{dt}$, we may write

$$W = \int L_{11} i_1 \, di_1 + \int L_{22} i_2 \, di_2 - \int L_{12} \left(i_1 \frac{di_2}{dt} + i_2 \frac{di_1}{dt} \right) dt$$

The terms in parentheses may be recognized as the derivative of a product, and the equation for energy becomes

$$W = \tfrac{1}{2}L_{11}i_1{}^2 + \tfrac{1}{2}L_{22}i_2{}^2 - L_{12}i_1i_2 \tag{363}$$

By expansion of the self-inductance terms, Eq. (363) may also be written

$$W = \tfrac{1}{2}L_1i_1{}^2 + \tfrac{1}{2}L_2i_2{}^2 + \tfrac{1}{2}L_{12}(i_1 - i_2)^2 \tag{364}$$

Having now obtained an expression for the total electromagnetic energy in the network, it is possible to determine the energy in each of the magnetic fields individually. Since each of the leakage fields is produced by a single current its energy may be expressed in terms of that current:

Energy in leakage field of circuit 1 $= \tfrac{1}{2}L_{f1}i_1{}^2$
Energy in leakage field of circuit 2 $= \tfrac{1}{2}L_{f2}i_2{}^2$

In these equations, L_{f1} and L_{f2} are inductances of the leakage fields of circuits 1 and 2 respectively. By subtraction from the total energy, expressed in Eq. (364), we obtain the energy stored in the common magnetic field as

$$\tfrac{1}{2}(L_1 - L_{f1})i_1{}^2 + \tfrac{1}{2}(L_2 - L_{f2})i_2{}^2 + \tfrac{1}{2}L_{12}(i_1 - i_2)^2 \tag{365}$$

If the common lines of flux have the same number of linkages with the turns of each circuit they will induce the same voltage in both windings, making $L_{12} = L_{11} - L_{f1}$. In this case, but in this case only, $L_1 = L_{f1}$ and $L_2 = L_{f2}$, and the energy in the common magnetic field is simply

$$\tfrac{1}{2}L_{12}(i_1 - i_2)^2 \tag{366}$$

Expression (366) is correct if a single coil is common to both circuits, as in Fig. 27b, or if two magnetically coupled coils (as in Fig. 39) have the same number of turns, similar dimensions, and are mutually symmetrical. In the network of Fig. 41, for example, expression (366) would not be valid because of inequality in the dimensions and numbers of turns of the coils. In the special case for which expression (366) is adequate we may identify the three terms of Eq. (364) as energy in leakage field of circuit 1, energy in leakage field of circuit 2, and energy in the common field.

22. Coupled Resonant Circuits. A network that is often encountered in radio communication consists of two circuits, each containing capacitance and inductance, inductively coupled.

It is illustrated in Fig. 42. Since the transient response of each part of a communication system will in some degree affect the fidelity of the system, it is necessary for the engineer to know at least the form and magnitude of transient disturbances.

An exact and complete solution for transient current in the circuit of Fig. 42 is entirely possible. The procedure is similar to that which is discussed in detail in Secs. 17 to 21 for a network which differs only in the absence of a condenser in circuit 2. When each circuit contains both inductance and capacitance, the impedance equation [corresponding to Eq. (321)] is of the fourth degree. This quartic equation does not necessarily have any real roots; if there are no real roots a formal solution for a quartic equation is needed since it is practically impossible to determine complex roots by trial. Two of the four roots of the

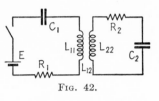

FIG. 42.

equation may be real; the real roots may be found by trial, and when the factors containing them are divided out of the equation, it will be reduced to a quadratic whose complex roots are the other two roots of the quartic. Finally, all four roots may be real; in this case, also, it is well to find two roots by trial and then to reduce the quartic equation to a quadratic from which the other two roots are found. Formal solution of a cubic equation is possible, but it is not usually as convenient for a numerical solution as the trial-and-error determination of the real root of the equation.[1]

When the four values of λ are determined, it remains to solve for the four coefficients which appear in the formal equations for each current. If the four values of λ are real, we may write

$$i_1 = K_{11}\epsilon^{\lambda_1 t} + K_{12}\epsilon^{\lambda_2 t} + K_{13}\epsilon^{\lambda_3 t} + K_{14}\epsilon^{\lambda_4 t} \qquad (367)$$

There is, of course, no steady-state component of current in the circuit of Fig. 42. If only two of the roots are real, the other two will be conjugate complex and can be combined in a sinusoidal term:

$$i_1 = A_{11}\epsilon^{-\alpha_1 t} \sin (\omega_1 t + \phi_1) + K_{13}\epsilon^{\lambda_3 t} + K_{14}\epsilon^{\lambda_4 t} \qquad (368)$$

[1] Regarding solution of algebraic equations, see I. S. Sokolnikoff and E. S. Sokolnikoff, "Higher Mathematics for Engineers and Physicists," McGraw-Hill Book Company, Inc., New York, 1941; Doherty and Keller, "Mathematics of Modern Engineering," John Wiley & Sons, Inc., New York, 1936.

If all four roots are complex, they will be in conjugate pairs that may be combined in two sinusoidal terms:

$$i_1 = A_{11}\epsilon^{-\alpha_1 t} \sin (\omega_1 t + \phi_1) + A_{13}\epsilon^{-\alpha_3 t} \sin (\omega_3 t + \phi_3) \quad (369)$$

Similar expressions may be written for i_2 with appropriate change of subscript.

In any one of these equations there are four constants that must be determined from initial conditions; in (367) they are K's, in (369) they are A's and ϕ's. Four simultaneous equations must be used, and the initial values of current and of its first three derivatives are satisfactory for this purpose. The solution is then complete.

The labor involved in such a solution is considerable. It is not prohibitive if complete information is needed, but usually it is possible to make simplifying approximations that lead to results with a degree of accuracy that is adequate for most purposes.

Chapter VII is devoted to a more complete discussion of coupled resonant circuits.

23. The Order of the Equation. It has been seen that the differential equations of a single circuit were of either first or second order and that the second-order equations appeared when inductance and capacitance were both present in the circuit. When there were two coupled circuits constituting a network it was necessary to solve two simultaneous differential equations, each of which might be of second order; these combined to give a single differential equation of any order up to fourth. In the course of each solution it became necessary to find roots of an algebraic equation of degree equal to the order of the differential equation. The solution of algebraic equations of high degree is the most difficult problem in the computation of transient currents in networks with lumped parameters, and the possibility of obtaining a solution for the network is largely dependent on the possibility of solving the algebraic equation. It is desirable, therefore, to know the degree of equation that will appear in the solution of any given network.

The rule for finding the order of the differential equation, or the degree of the algebraic equation, is quite simple: *the order of the differential equation is equal to the number of energy storage possibilities in the network.* Each inductance and each capacitance in a network will store energy, but if two coils or two condensers are in series their inductances and capacitances may be combined. So each circuit may have two parameters that store energy, or one, or none. The differential equation of a network of n circuits will not be of greater order than $2n$, and the order will be 1 less than $2n$ for each circuit that is without inductance and for each circuit that is without capacitance.

If resistance of a network is neglected, the degree of the algebraic equation that must be solved is divided by two, for alternate terms of the equation will disappear and the solution may be for λ^2 instead of λ. By this expedient it is sometimes possible to obtain an approximate solution for a network of several coupled circuits. An illustration of this method appears in Chap. VII.

Problems

1. Connect two circuits as in Fig. 30. Each circuit contains a coil with inductance and resistance, and they are coupled by mutual resistance. Record on an oscillograph the current in circuit 1 and the current in circuit 2 during the transient period after closing the switch. Current through the common resistance need not be recorded, as it is the difference between i_1 and i_2. Use inductance coils without iron cores and be sure there is no mutual inductance between the coils in the two circuits. The coupling resistance should be noninductive. Measure the network parameters.

Transfer the experimentally determined curves to a sheet of cross-section paper, and on the same sheet plot curves of current computed from the network parameters. Compare the computed and experimental results and discuss any differences that may appear.

If it is not convenient to record the currents, oscillogram 4 may be used. The lines on it, from top to bottom (at the right-hand edge) are:

a. A 60-cycle timing wave, with its zero line.

b. The transient current in circuit 1.

c. A calibration line for the oscillograph element in circuit 1; the calibrating current is 2.06 amp.

d. A calibration line for the oscillograph element in circuit 2; the calibrating current is also 2.06 amp.

e. The transient current in circuit 2.

f. The zero line for the oscillograph element in circuit 1.

g. The zero line for the oscillograph element in circuit 2.

Network parameters are as follows:

$$\begin{aligned}
E &= 65.0 \text{ volts.} & R_{11} &= 36.2 \text{ ohms.} \\
L_1 &= 0.326 \text{ henry.} & R_{22} &= 58.3 \text{ ohms.} \\
L_2 &= 1.36 \text{ henrys.} & R_{12} &= 30.5 \text{ ohms.}
\end{aligned}$$

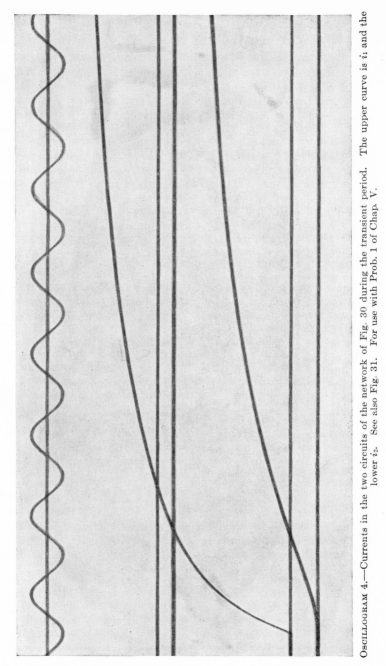

OSCILLOGRAM 4.—Currents in the two circuits of the network of Fig. 30 during the transient period. The upper curve is i_1 and the lower i_2. See also Fig. 31. For use with Prob. 1 of Chap. V.

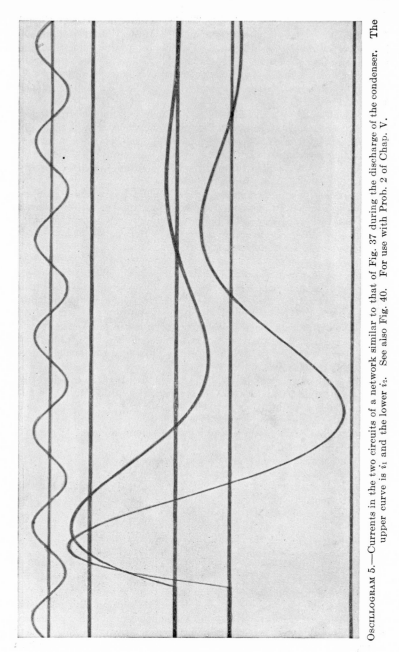

OSCILLOGRAM 5.—Currents in the two circuits of a network similar to that of Fig. 37 during the discharge of the condenser. The upper curve is i_1 and the lower i_2. See also Fig. 40. For use with Prob. 2 of Chap. V.

2. Connect two circuits as in Fig. 37, but without a battery. Circuit 1 contains a switch, a condenser, and a coil, with the resistance of the coil but no extra resistance. Circuit 2 is a coil only, with inductance and resistance. The circuits are coupled inductively. After charging the condenser in circuit 1 to a known voltage, close the switch and allow the condenser to discharge. Record on an oscillograph the currents in circuits 1 and 2.

The inductance coils should not have iron cores, and their resistances should be low enough to permit the current to be oscillatory. A single coil with a tap may be used instead of two separate coils, provided no part of the winding is common to both circuits; in such a case circuit 2 is merely a number of short-circuited turns in the coil of circuit 1, and the problem demonstrates the effect of short-circuited turns.

Measure the network parameters, including mutual inductance. Mutual inductance is found by measuring the inductance of the coils of circuits 1 and 2 in series, with the coils in the proper relative position. Inductance measured in this way is either $L_{11} + L_{22} + 2L_{12}$ or $L_{11} + L_{22} - 2L_{12}$, depending on the method of series connection. It is best to measure both of these combinations by reversing the connection to one coil; the difference between the resulting measured inductances is then *four times* the mutual inductance. If it is not possible to reverse the connection to one of the coils, subtract the inductances of each coil alone (L_{11} and L_{22}) from the inductance of the coils in series, and divide by 2.

Plot the experimentally determined curves of current on cross-section paper, and on the same sheets plot curves of current computed from the network parameters. Compare the computed and experimental results and discuss any differences that may appear.

If it is not convenient to make photographic records of the transient currents, oscillogram 5 may be used. It is a record of currents in such a network. The lines on it, from top to bottom, are:

a. A 60-cycle timing wave, with its zero line.

b. A calibration line for the oscillograph element in circuit 1; the calibrating current is 0.87 amp.

c. The transient current in circuit 1, and its zero line.

d. The transient current in circuit 2, and its zero line.

e. A calibration line for the oscillograph element in circuit 2; the calibrating current is −1.48 amp.

Network parameters are as follows:

$$L_{11} = 1.014 \ \text{henrys.} \qquad C_1 = 103.1 \ \mu\text{f.}$$
$$L_{12} = 0.166 \ \text{henry.} \qquad R_1 = 22.34 \ \text{ohms.}$$
$$L_{22} = 0.0568 \ \text{henry.} \qquad R_2 = 5.03 \ \text{ohms.}$$

Initial condenser voltage = 123.2 volts.

3. A specially designed transformer is used to give an extremely large surge of current, of short duration, for purposes of magnetizing permanent magnets, etc. Direct current is passed through a primary winding of many turns, and surges of current are developed in a secondary loop of **one turn**

on both closing and opening the primary circuit.[1] Consider the following example of its operation:

Primary voltage $=$ 100 volts (dc).
Primary resistance $=$ 20 ohms.
Primary current $=$ 5 amp.
Primary turns $=$ 2000
Secondary turns $=$ 1

The peak of the current surge:

On closing the circuit $=$ 5000 amp.
On opening the circuit $=$ 10,000 amp.

a. Explain the difference between the numerical values of secondary current on closing and opening the circuit.

b. Plot curves of current in both windings when the primary circuit is closed and when it is opened.

c. Why is it necessary to have an extremely quick-opening switch in the primary circuit?

d. What is the resistance of the secondary circuit?

e. How is performance of the transformer affected by the size of its core? Is an iron core needed?

4. In impulse-voltage testing it is frequently necessary to take into account the capacitance of the test specimen. Using the data of Prob. 3 of Chap. 4, plot voltage across the test specimen as a function of time, the capacitance of the test specimen being 500 $\mu\mu$f (5×10^{-10} farad). Use both values given for R_1.

5. Selective operation of circuit breakers can sometimes be controlled by design of shunts on trip coils. The circuit shown here represents such an arrangement, with R and L as the resistance and inductance of the main circuit, R_c and L_c the parameters of the trip coil, and R_s and L_s the parameters of the shunt.[2] Remembering that R is very much greater than R_c or R_s and that L is very much greater than L_c or L_s, find a good approximation for the current through the trip coil when the whole system is suddenly energized. How can the time of operation of the trip coil be controlled by adjusting the shunt?

Prob. 5.   Prob. 6.

6. The circuit shown in the diagram is used in some large electrical machines to produce end play of the shaft, for the purpose of equalizing wear on the commutator. The inductance is a magnet, energized by the

[1] HENDRICKS and MAUNDER, The Current Impulse Transformer, *Gen. Elec. Rev.*, **33**, 241, 1930.

[2] HENSHAW, M. D., Characteristics of the High-speed Circuit Breakers for the Lackawanna Suburban Electrification, *Gen. Elec. Rev.*, **35**, 154, 1932.

contactor S which is automatically closed by motion of the shaft.   The condenser is used to prevent undue arcing at the contactor, and the condenser is shunted with resistance r to prevent dangerous voltage across the condenser.   With parameters as given below, what value of shunting resistance will be just sufficient to keep the condenser voltage from exceeding 400 volts when the contactor opens?

$$E_{DC} = 300 \text{ volts.}$$
$$L \quad = 380 \text{ henrys.}$$
$$R \quad = 850 \text{ ohms.}$$
$$C \quad = \quad 1 \ \mu\text{f.}$$

7. In the circuit of Prob. 6, what value of shunting resistance r is just enough to prevent oscillation of current in the circuit?   Plot a curve of maximum condenser voltage as a function of shunting resistance up to the value of resistance at which current oscillates.

8. The network shown in the diagram is equivalent to the filter and keying circuit of a radiotelegraph transmitter.[1]

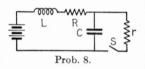

Prob. 8.

Undesirable fluctuations of voltage are produced by the action of the filter circuit.   Plot voltage across r as a function of time, after closing the switch S; plot voltage after opening it.   The   parameters   are $L = 1.5$ henrys, $R = 96$ ohms, $C = 3 \ \mu\text{f}$, $r = 1920$ ohms.

9. (*a*) Find current in the resistance of the network shown in the diagram after the switch S is closed at $t = 0$.   The circuit is initially at rest (no stored energy).   (*b*) Find current in the condenser.   (*c*) Formulate conditions for oscillation of current.

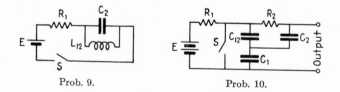

Prob. 9.   Prob. 10.

10. A cathode-ray-tube sweep circuit designed to make output voltage closely proportional to time is shown in the diagram. $R_1 = 1000$ ohms, $R_2 = 3000$ ohms; $C_{12} = 1 \ \mu\text{f}$, $C_1 = 1 \ \mu\text{f}$, $C_2 = 0.2 \ \mu\text{f}$.   Switch S is closed until $t = 0$ and is then opened.   At $t = 0$, C_2 is charged to voltage $0.5E$ (this is charge remaining from the previous cycle of operation).   Compute and plot output voltage as a function of time.   How long is the voltage-time relation approximately linear?

[1] LEE, R., Radiotelegraph Keying Transients, *Proc. I.R.E.*, **22**, 213, 1934.

CHAPTER VI

RESPONSE TO ALTERNATING VOLTAGE

1. The Need for Transient Current. When alternating voltage is suddenly applied to a circuit, the steady flow of alternating current is preceded by a period of adjustment during which transient current flows. The form and amplitude of the steady-state current will depend on the form and amplitude of the applied voltage, as is well known. The amplitude of the transient component will be governed by the circuit parameters, by the amplitude of the applied voltage, and also by the instant of the alternating-voltage cycle at which voltage is applied to the circuit. But the *form* of the transient component of current will depend only on the nature of the circuit.

In a circuit of inductance and resistance, the transient current will be an exponential surge of the form $K\epsilon^{-\frac{R}{L}t}$, regardless of the form of the applied voltage. In a circuit containing inductance, resistance, and capacitance, the transient current will be a single surge or a damped sinusoidal oscillation depending on the circuit parameters and not on the voltage. The total current in a circuit will be the sum of the transient component and the steady-state component and so may appear quite unfamiliar, but analysis will always show its two simple parts.

The steady-state current is a partial solution that satisfies the differential voltage equation of the circuit; the transient current exists to satisfy initial conditions. It is true with alternating voltage, as with direct, that the steady-state current is a solution of the differential equation of the circuit (although not the complete solution) and that we may consider the entire applied voltage to be consumed in circulating the steady-state current through the network. But, since the steady-state current will not, usually, agree with a circuit's initial conditions of current and charge, it is necessary to superimpose upon the steady-state current another current that can flow in such amount that initial conditions of the system are satisfied. To avoid disturbance

185

of the voltage equation, this additional current must be able to flow without any external voltage; that is, the sum of the voltages that it produces in the parameters of the circuit must be zero. It is the transient component of current, and to find its form we "write the differential equation of the circuit, with zero substituted for the applied voltage, and solve." To find the amount of the transient component we determine the current necessary to bridge the gap between known initial conditions in the network and those conditions that would be found when $t = 0$ if the steady-state current existed alone.

2. An Inductive Circuit. A simple example will best illustrate the method. Figure 43 shows a sinusoidal voltage wave e, which is suddenly applied to a circuit consisting of inductance and

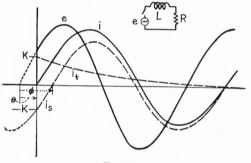

Fig. 43.

resistance. Voltage is applied by closing a switch in the circuit, and the moment of closing the switch is important in determining the transient response; the switch is closed when $t = 0$, so if the voltage is written

$$e = E \sin (\Omega t + \theta) \tag{370}$$

it follows that the instantaneous value of voltage when the switch closes is $e_0 = E \sin \theta$, and that θ is a measure of the time interval between the instant of zero voltage and the instant of closing the switch. The angle θ is shown in Fig. 43, an example in which its value is about 35 deg.: that is, the applied voltage wave has passed through 35/360ths of a cycle before the switch is closed, and, if the voltage has a frequency of 60 cycles per sec., the angle θ represents $\left(\frac{35}{360}\right)\left(\frac{1}{60}\right)$ sec. or 0.0016 sec.

A dash curve in the figure marked i_s indicates the steady-state component of current. This is the current that would have flowed at this time if the switch had been closed a very long time before $t = 0$. Like the applied voltage, it is sinusoidal, and our knowledge of steady-state theory tells us that it will be related to the voltage in magnitude by the impedance of the circuit and in angle by the power-factor angle of the circuit. From the voltage, which is given in Eq. (370), we know that the steady-state component of current is

$$i_s = \frac{E \sin (\Omega t + \theta - \phi)}{\sqrt{R^2 + (\Omega L)^2}} \tag{371}$$

The power-factor angle is denoted by ϕ, and is

$$\phi = \tan^{-1} \frac{\Omega L}{R} \tag{372}$$

If the frequency of the applied voltage is F, the angular velocity of the applied voltage is

$$\Omega = 2\pi F$$

so that ΩL is the reactance of the circuit to current of the generator frequency. Hence, the denominator of Eq. (371) is the impedance of the circuit.

The voltage equation for the circuit of Fig. 43 is

$$Ri + Lpi = E \sin (\Omega t + \theta) \tag{373}$$

When it is stated that Eq. (371) gives the steady-state current in the circuit it is implied that Eq. (371) is a solution of the voltage equation (373). We wrote it from previous experience; let us prove that it is correct. If Eq. (371) gives i, then its derivative

$$pi = \frac{E}{\sqrt{R^2 + (\Omega L)^2}} \Omega \cos (\Omega t + \theta - \phi) \tag{374}$$

and substitution in Eq. (373) gives

$$R \frac{E}{\sqrt{R^2 + (\Omega L)^2}} \sin (\Omega t + \theta - \phi)$$
$$+ L \frac{E}{\sqrt{R^2 + (\Omega L)^2}} \Omega \cos (\Omega t + \theta - \phi) = E \sin (\Omega t + \theta) \tag{375}$$

Divide out E. Expand the sine and cosine terms of the left-hand member by considering them as functions of the difference of the two angles $(\Omega t + \theta)$ and ϕ.   Then, noting from Eq. (372) that

$$\left. \begin{aligned} \sin \phi &= \frac{\Omega L}{\sqrt{R^2 + (\Omega L)^2}} \\[2ex] \cos \phi &= \frac{R}{\sqrt{R^2 + (\Omega L)^2}} \end{aligned} \right\} \tag{376}$$

and

we find that Eq. (375) is reduced to an identity.   The correctness of Eq. (371) as an expression for steady-state current is thereby proved.

Since, in the circuit of Fig. 43, it is not possible to have current until the switch is closed, it follows that when $t = 0$, $i = 0$.   This condition is not satisfied by the steady-state current alone, for if $t = 0$ in Eq. (371) we find that the initial value of the steady-state component is

$$\frac{E \sin (\theta - \phi)}{\sqrt{R^2 + (\Omega L)^2}} \tag{377}$$

To satisfy the initial condition, therefore, another current must simultaneously exist in the circuit, and its initial value must be equal and opposite, or

$$-\frac{E \sin (\theta - \phi)}{\sqrt{R^2 + (\Omega L)^2}} \tag{378}$$

Moreover, the additional current must be of such a form that, when substituted in Eq. (373), it will add nothing to the left-hand member, for if it did add anything it would disturb the equality of the two members.   It must be of such a form, then, that for it alone

$$Ri + Lpi = 0 \tag{379}$$

Since the current which satisfies Eq. (379) is of exponential form, with exponent $-(R/L)t$, we know the transient component of current must be

$$-\frac{E \sin (\theta - \phi)}{\sqrt{R^2 + (\Omega L)^2}} \epsilon^{-\frac{R}{L}t} \tag{380}$$

It is indicated in Fig. 43 by the dash line i_t; its initial value is K, whereas the initial value of the steady-state component is

$-K$. The sum of the two components is shown as the solid curve i, whose equation is the complete solution of Eq. (373):

$$i = E \frac{\sin (\Omega t + \theta - \phi) - \sin (\theta - \phi)\epsilon^{-\frac{R}{L}t}}{\sqrt{R^2 + (\Omega L)^2}} \tag{381}$$

This solution, although presented slightly differently, is exactly similar to all solutions of previous chapters. The same four rules of Sec. 10, Chap. I, have been implicitly followed. First, the form of the transient component was determined as the solution of Eq. (379). Second, the steady-state current was found from steady-state theory and was checked by substitution in the differential equation; it is given in Eq. (371). Third, transient component and steady-state component were added to give the total current:

$$i = K\epsilon^{-\frac{R}{L}t} + \frac{E \sin (\Omega t + \theta - \phi)}{\sqrt{R^2 + (\Omega L)^2}} \tag{382}$$

Fourth, K is unknown in this expression, but by substituting the initial condition that when $t = 0$, $i = 0$, we obtain

$$0 = K + \frac{E \sin (\theta - \phi)}{\sqrt{R^2 + (\Omega L)^2}} \tag{383}$$

which leads to expression (378) for K and thereby completes the solution.

3. Effect of Various Initial Times. When the circuit and the applied voltage are known, the steady-state component of current is defined. But the transient component cannot be determined until the instant of closing the switch is known. Figure 44 illustrates various possibilities: if the voltage e is applied to a circuit of inductance and resistance, the steady-state component of current may be shown by the curve i_s. The current curve will pass through zero at a later time than the voltage curve, and the angle of lag is indicated by ϕ.

Closing of the switch at time t_1, in Fig. 44, corresponds to the condition that was illustrated in Fig. 43, and the initial value of the transient current is shown to be equal and opposite to the instantaneous steady-state current at that time. If the switch had not closed until a later time t_2, the transient response would have been smaller, for the value of steady-state current is smaller. At t_3 the direction of flow of the transient current would be reversed. At t_4 the transient current will attain its greatest value, for that time corresponds to a maximum value of the steady-state component of current.

It might seem that there would be no transient current if the switch were closed when the instantaneous voltage was zero, but such is not the case, as is shown at t_5. The transient current at the instant of closing the switch has very nearly its maximum value in a circuit whose reactance is high compared to its resistance. There is an instant, however, at which the switch may be closed without producing any transient component of current:

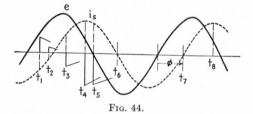

Fig. 44.

it is the instant at which the steady-state component is zero, and it is illustrated at t_6 and also at t_7.

No transient current results when the switch is closed at such a time that θ equals ϕ, thereby making the coefficient of the transient term zero. The coefficient, which is given in Eq. (378), becomes zero when $\theta = \phi$. It will be seen in Fig. 44 that, since ϕ is the angular displacement of zero current from zero voltage, and since θ is the angular displacement of switch operation from zero voltage, if $\theta = \phi$ the switch is closed when the steady-state component of current is zero. This is the only time at which the steady-state current alone can satisfy the circuit's initial condition of zero current.

From the point of view of instantaneous relations of voltage and current, the phenomenon may also be explained. Let voltage be applied to the circuit at t_7 in Fig. 44; current will at once begin to increase with a rate of change equal to e/L. Current will continue to increase, but at a diminishing rate, as the value of voltage decreases. At t_8 voltage is all consumed in the circuit's resistance and current can increase no more; and as voltage grows still less, and then reverses sign, the current begins to diminish. The resulting curve of current is sinusoidal, identical in every way with the sinusoidal curve of steady-state current; each instantaneous value of the current that flows is equal to the corresponding value of the steady-state current that would be produced by such a voltage. So the total current during the transient period is merely the steady-state current, and there is no exponential transient current.

From the point of view of energy another interpretation appears. A transient component of current may be avoided if the energy distribution in the circuit at the instant of closing the switch is exactly the energy distribution that would appear at that point of the voltage wave if steady-state current were flowing. In the circuit of inductance and resistance, energy can be contained in the inductance only. Whenever current in the circuit is zero, there is no energy in the inductance. So if the switch is closed, with no energy stored in the inductance, at that point of the voltage wave that corresponds to zero steady-state current, there will be no transient component. In other words, the distribution of energy in the circuit when the switch is closed at t_7 is just what it would have been at the same instant if steady-state current had been flowing, and the circuit cannot distinguish in its future action between the two possibilities. All transient behaviour of networks can be interpreted as phenomena necessary to distribute energy throughout the circuits until steady-state distribution is reached, and it is evident that if the initial condition agrees with the steady-state condition there is no need for redistribution by transient current, and there will be no transient current.

The other instant of closing the switch that should be distinguished is the time that gives maximum transient current. From Eq. (378), it occurs when $\sin (\theta - \phi) = \pm 1$, the maximum value of the sine function. This requires that $\theta - \phi = \pi/2$, or some odd multiple thereof. The instant of closing the switch, therefore, that gives maximum transient component of current is that for which

$$\theta = \phi + \frac{\pi}{2} \quad \text{or} \quad \phi + \frac{3\pi}{2} \tag{384}$$

Such instants are illustrated as t_4 and t_8.

When the switch is closed at such an instant that there is no transient component of current, the appearance of the resulting wave of current is shown in Fig. 45a; it is merely a sinusoidal wave, symmetrical about the time axis.   But, when the switch is closed at any other instant, the current appears as an offset wave, as in Fig. 45b.   The offset is due to the addition of an exponential component; it is just great enough to make the total current begin at the origin, and as it dies away the current

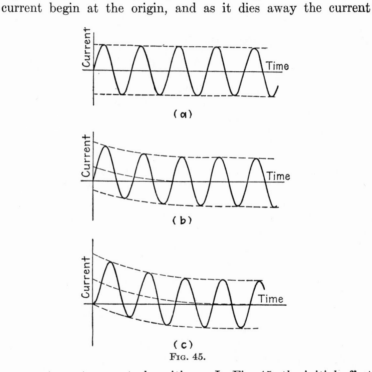

Fig. 45.

wave returns to a central position.   In Fig. 45c the initial offset is complete and the transient component has its maximum possible value.   In Fig. 45a there was no initial offset.   Any intermediate condition may appear if current begins to flow at an intermediate point on the voltage wave, and the offset may of course be either up or down.

If the circuit to which alternating voltage is applied consists purely of inductance, with resistance so small as to be negligible, the greatest transient component of current appears when the switch is closed at the instant of zero voltage.   If resistance in the circuit of Fig. 44 were negligible, the steady-state current wave would be lagging just a quarter-cycle behind the voltage wave, and it is evident that maximum steady-state current would correspond to zero voltage. If the switch were closed at that instant, the transient current would also be maximum, whereas closing the switch when the voltage wave was at its maximum, either positive or negative, would produce no transient current at all.

If resistance were truly zero, however, and the sinusoidal wave of current were initially offset, it would remain offset for all time. The transient component can disappear only because of energy loss in resistance, and if there were no resistance the transient component of current would continue undiminished. The essential fact that must be remembered when the steady-state current is alternating is that the root-mean-square value of a symmetrical sine wave is less than the root-mean-square value of the same sine wave when it is offset from the axis. In Fig. 45b, therefore, the resistance loss is greater during the first few cycles of current than it is after the transient component has disappeared, and this is the basic reason for the disappearance of the transient component. The alternating-current generator can supply only enough energy to maintain the steady-state current, and, when the initial excess of energy (which was received during the first quarter-cycle) is consumed, the transient component of current has died away.

4. A Capacitive Circuit. When alternating voltage is suddenly applied to a circuit of resistance and capacitance, there will be a somewhat similar transient component of current. The initial condition of current, however, is different, the initial current being limited only by the circuit resistance. In the circuit of Fig. 46, therefore, the initial condition is that when

$$t = 0, \qquad i = \frac{e}{R} \tag{385}$$

Since, in general, this value does not agree with the value of the steady-state current in the circuit when $t = 0$, there will be a transient component of current.

The voltage equation of the circuit of Fig. 46 is

$$Ri + \frac{1}{Cp}i = e \tag{386}$$

Let us, as before, apply a sinusoidal voltage such that

$$e = E \sin (\Omega t + \theta) \tag{387}$$

The steady-state current will be, by inspection,

$$i_s = \frac{E \sin (\Omega t + \theta + \phi)}{\sqrt{R^2 + (1/\Omega C)^2}} \tag{388}$$

wherein

$$\phi = \tan^{-1} \frac{1}{\Omega C R}$$

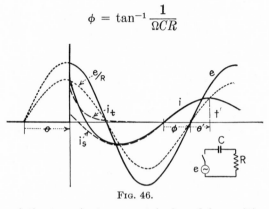

Fig. 46.

The form of the transient current is found by writing zero for e in Eq. (386), the solution for which may be taken from Eq. (53):

$$i_t = K \epsilon^{-\frac{1}{RC}t} \tag{389}$$

The total current is therefore

$$i = K \epsilon^{-\frac{1}{RC}t} + \frac{E \sin (\Omega t + \theta + \phi)}{\sqrt{R^2 + (1/\Omega C)^2}} \tag{390}$$

Now K may be evaluated by substitution of Eq. (385), giving

$$\frac{e}{R} = K + \frac{E \sin (\theta + \phi)}{\sqrt{R^2 + (1/\Omega C)^2}} \tag{391}$$

Since initially

$$\frac{e}{R} = \frac{E \sin \theta}{R}$$

it follows that

$$K = \frac{E \sin \theta}{R} - \frac{E \sin (\theta + \phi)}{\sqrt{R^2 + (1/\Omega C)^2}} \tag{392}$$

or finally[1]

$$K = -\frac{E}{R} \cos (\theta + \phi) \sin \phi \qquad (393)$$

When this value of K is substituted in Eq. (390), the expression for current is complete.

Although the current that flows in a capacitive circuit is composed of an exponential component and a sinusoidal component, just as is the current in an inductive circuit with alternating voltage applied [compare Eqs. (390) and (382)], the appearance of the plotted curve of current is somewhat different. It is not very desirable to look upon the transient component of current in the capacitive circuit as an offset of the steady-state current wave, for its duration is in general very short compared to the frequency of the steady-state current, and it appears rather as a distortion of the first cycle than as a shift of the entire wave-train. Figure 46 illustrates this effect. It is inherent in the circuit that the transient component of current will diminish very rapidly to an insignificant value.

There is an instant in each half-cycle of applied voltage at which the switch may be closed with no resulting transient component. The basic criteria for determining the instant of closing that gives no transient component of current are the same as for the inductive circuit: in terms of current, there is no transient component if the steady-state component alone is able to satisfy the condition that initial current is equal to e/R; in terms of energy, there is no transient component if the switch is closed

---

[1] The trigonometric transformation to obtain Eq. (393) from (392) may be accomplished as follows:

$$K = \frac{E}{R}\left(\sin \theta - \frac{\sin (\theta + \phi)}{\sqrt{1 + (1/\Omega CR)^2}} \right)$$

Since $(1/\Omega CR)^2 = \tan^2 \phi$

$$K = \frac{E}{R}\left(\sin \theta - \frac{\sin (\theta + \phi)}{\sec \phi} \right) =$$

$$\frac{E}{R}(\sin \theta - \sin \theta \cos^2 \phi - \cos \theta \sin \phi \cos \phi)$$

$$= \frac{E}{R}(\sin \theta (1 - \cos^2 \phi) - \cos \theta \sin \phi \cos \phi)$$

$$= \frac{E}{R} \sin \phi (\sin \theta \sin \phi - \cos \theta \cos \phi) = -\frac{E}{R} \sin \phi \cos (\theta + \phi)$$

at a point on the voltage wave that, in the steady state, would correspond to zero energy in the condenser.

Let us first consider the current criterion. In Fig. 46, a dotted curve is drawn, everywhere proportional to the applied voltage e and of such amplitude that it is a curve of e/R. Whatever the instant of closing the switch, the initial point of the total current i must lie on this dotted curve. The initial difference between this e/R curve and the steady-state i_s curve is the initial value of the transient component, as illustrated in the figure. Consequently, if the e/R curve and the i_s curve coincide at the initial instant, there is no transient component. Such would have been the case, for instance, if operation of the switch had been delayed until the time marked t'. The relation here discussed is expressed symbolically in Eq. (392), the first term of the right-hand member being the value of e/R when $t = 0$, and the second term being the initial value of the steady-state component of current. If they are equal, K disappears.

But Eq. (392) does not show on inspection that the instant of closing the switch that corresponds to no transient component of current is also the instant of maximum steady-state component. This is brought out by Eq. (393). We have assumed that there is no charge on the condenser before the switch is closed, and that the condenser can therefore have no initial energy. In each half-cycle of steady-state operation there is an instant at which the condenser has no energy; it is when the charge is zero or, with a sinusoidal wave, when the current is maximum. If the switch is closed at this instant, all conditions in the circuit are exactly what they would have been if the steady state had existed, and future action of the circuit therefore cannot be other than steady-state performance. The power-factor angle ϕ is indicated in Fig. 46, and, if the angle between zero voltage and the instant of closing the switch is θ', such that $\phi + \theta' = \pi/2$, and the switch is closed at the instant of maximum steady-state current, it follows that there will be no transient component of current. This is seen analytically from Eq. (393), for, if $\phi + \theta = \pi/2$, the cosine factor is zero, and K is zero.

But in general a transient component exists, and it may be of any magnitude. Low resistance in the circuit, compared to the reactance, allows a large transient component of current. Closing the switch when voltage is near its maximum will produce

an extremely high initial rush of current in such a circuit.   This
condition is illustrated in Fig. 47; low resistance gives a large
value of e/R, as shown, compared to the steady-state current
whose magnitude is limited by impedance of the circuit.   Since
resistance is small compared to reactance, the initial current is
large compared to the steady-state current, and for the same
reason the steady-state current leads the voltage by nearly 90 deg.
The switch is closed in the illustration when the steady-state
component of current is zero, so the instantaneous current is
equal to e/R, or practically E/R.   Because of low resistance in

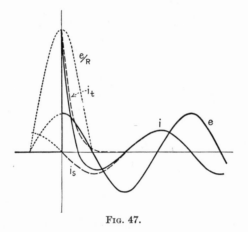

FIG. 47.

the circuit, the transient component dies out very rapidly;
analytically, the exponent in Eq. (389) is large.   If resistance
of the circuit is reduced still further, the transient surge will be
larger, but of shorter duration, until in the limiting case resistance
is zero and the initial pulse of current is infinite in amplitude but
zero in duration.

Practically, of course, such a condition cannot be obtained.
It is impossible to have zero resistance.   But also it is impossible
to have zero inductance.   It is often possible, if resistance is
not too small, to neglect the effect of inductance, but inductance
must always exist in at least the amount represented by the one
turn of the closed circuit, and its most apparent effect will be
to prevent the discontinuity of current which has been indicated
at the initial instant in Figs. 46 and 47.   The initial peak in
Fig. 47 will be rounded and reduced in height.   Nevertheless,

for practical purposes it is often easiest and best to neglect a small value of inductance.

5. The Circuit with Inductance, Capacitance, and Resistance. When inductance, capacitance, and resistance are all present in considerable amounts in a circuit, as in Fig. 48e, the voltage equation is

$$Ri + Lpi + \frac{1}{Cp}i = e \tag{394}$$

and if the applied voltage is sinusoidal it may be represented as before by

$$e = E \sin (\Omega t + \theta) \tag{395}$$

The transient component of current may be a single surge containing two exponential components, or it may be oscillatory in the form of a damped sinusoid; the form of the transient component is found by solution of Eq. (394) with zero substituted for e. This solution, in Chap. III, gave Eq. (123) as the transient component of current:

$$i_t = K_1\epsilon^{\lambda_1 t} + K_2\epsilon^{\lambda_2 t} \tag{396}$$

with

$$\lambda_1, \lambda_2 = -\frac{R}{2L} \pm \sqrt{\frac{R^2}{4L^2} - \frac{1}{LC}} \tag{397}$$

If λ_1 and λ_2 are complex, it is more convenient to write

$$i_t = A\epsilon^{-\alpha t} \sin (\omega t + \psi) \tag{398}$$

where

$$\alpha = \frac{R}{2L} \qquad \omega = \sqrt{\frac{1}{LC} - \frac{R^2}{4L^2}} \tag{399}$$

A and ψ are to be determined from initial conditions.

The steady-state component of current is, by inspection,

$$i_s = \frac{E \sin (\Omega t + \theta - \phi)}{\sqrt{R^2 + \left(\Omega L - \frac{1}{\Omega C}\right)^2}} \tag{400}$$

with

$$\phi = \tan^{-1} \frac{\Omega L - \frac{1}{\Omega C}}{R} \tag{401}$$

The remaining steps of the solution will be simplified by introducing a new symbol, Z, defined as

$$Z = \sqrt{R^2 + \left(\Omega L - \frac{1}{\Omega C}\right)^2} \qquad (402)$$

This quantity is the magnitude of the circuit's impedance.[1]

The unknown constants in the transient component must be evaluated; either the exponential form of Eq. (396) or the sinusoidal form of Eq. (398) may be used. The sinusoidal form is more interesting for several reasons, so let us write total current as

$$i = A\epsilon^{-\alpha t} \sin (\omega t + \psi) + \frac{E}{Z} \sin (\Omega t + \theta - \phi) \qquad (403)$$

It helps avoid confusion to notice that Ω is related to the frequency of the applied voltage, whereas ω is related to the natural frequency of the oscillatory circuit, and they are quite unrelated to each other. The time of closing the switch is indicated by θ, and ϕ is the power-factor angle of the circuit. A and ψ remain to be evaluated.

Since there are two unknown constants, it is necessary to know two initial conditions, and we may use the same two that were determined in Chap. IV. With the necessary modification that initial applied voltage is $E \sin \theta$ when the applied voltage is alternating, we have, when

$$t = 0, \qquad i = 0 \qquad (404)$$

and

$$pi = \frac{E \sin \theta}{L} \qquad (405)$$

Substitution of Eq. (404) in (403) gives

$$0 = A \sin \psi + \frac{E}{Z} \sin (\theta - \phi) \qquad (406)$$

---

[1] Z is a real number, for, in the absence of a conventional representation of sinusoidal quantities by rotating vectors, it is meaningless to express current or voltage as a complex quantity. No such convention has been introduced in the present discussion, and a complex value for current, voltage, charge, or other physical entity would be merely an indication of error.

To make use of the other initial condition it is necessary to differentiate the expression for current, obtaining

$$pi = -\alpha A \epsilon^{-\alpha t} \sin (\omega t + \psi) + \omega A \epsilon^{-\alpha t} \cos (\omega t + \psi)$$
$$+ \Omega \frac{E}{Z} \cos (\Omega t + \theta - \phi) \quad (407)$$

Substituting Eq. (405) in (407),

$$\frac{E \sin \theta}{L} = -\alpha A \sin \psi + \omega A \cos \psi + \Omega \frac{E}{Z} \cos (\theta - \phi) \quad (408)$$

Simultaneous solution of Eqs. (406) and (408) will evaluate A and ψ. The result[1] is

$$\cot \psi = \frac{\Omega L \cos (\theta - \phi) - Z \sin \theta}{\omega L \sin (\theta - \phi)} + \frac{\alpha}{\omega} \quad (409)$$

and

$$A = -\frac{E}{Z} \frac{\sin (\theta - \phi)}{\sin \psi} \quad (410)$$

This solution does not result in an explicit expression for current in terms of circuit parameters and applied voltage but is convenient for numerical evaluation. When values for ψ and A are found from Eqs. (409) and (410) they may be substituted in the formal Eq. (403).

6. Resulting Waves of Current. The current in the circuit is shown by Eq. (403) to consist of a damped sinusoidal component added to an undamped sinusoidal component. The two components will in general be of different frequencies, and the appearance of the resulting wave of total current may vary widely. In Fig. 48 some of the possible forms of current are illustrated. If the natural frequency is high and the applied frequency relatively low, the result may appear as in Fig. 48a, with a high-frequency transient component superimposed upon a

---

[1] The solution may be as follows: from Eq. (406)

$$A = -\frac{E}{Z} \frac{\sin (\theta - \phi)}{\sin \psi} \quad (410)$$

(410) in (408) gives

$$\frac{E \sin \theta}{L} = \frac{E}{Z}[\alpha \sin (\theta - \phi) - \omega \cot \psi \sin (\theta - \phi) + \Omega \cos (\theta - \phi)]$$
$$\cot \psi = \frac{\Omega \cos (\theta - \phi)}{\omega \sin (\theta - \phi)} + \frac{\alpha}{\omega} - \frac{Z \sin \theta}{\omega L \sin (\theta - \phi)}$$

low-frequency steady-state current.   If, on the other hand, the
frequency of the applied voltage is several times the natural
frequency of the circuit the result will be as in Fig. 48*b*.

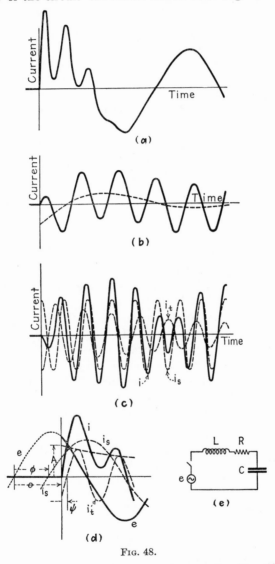

Fig. 48.

Figure 48*d* shows part of a current wave for identifying the
symbols of Sec. 5.   Dash lines show the components of current.

The curve marked e is the wave of applied voltage. The steady-state current is displaced from the voltage wave by the angle ϕ. The zero point of the voltage wave is displaced from the origin by the angle θ. The current wave is therefore displaced from the origin by an angle $(\theta - \phi)$, as in Eq. (400). The zero point of the transient component is displaced from the origin by the angle ψ, and the transient wave is contained within an envelope whose initial height is A. The envelope, of exponential form, determines the rate of attenuation of the transient component, the natural decrement α being $R/2L$.

The applied frequency in Fig. 48a is low compared to the natural frequency of the circuit; in the steady state the circuit is therefore predominantly capacitive. At the steady-state frequency the capacitive reactance of the condenser is much greater than the inductive reactance of the coil. (It will be recalled that at the circuit's natural frequency the two reactances are equal.) Because the circuit is predominantly capacitive, we may compare its action with the action of a circuit that is purely capacitive, as in Fig. 47. The first surge of current in Fig. 48a is not instantaneous, as in Fig. 47, nor is it so high, but it exists. It is followed, however, by further crests, both positive and negative, which do not exist in the non-oscillatory case of Fig. 47. But the two cases are closely related; if a small amount of inductance were introduced into the circuit of Fig. 47, Fig. 48a would result. One important characteristic they have in common: the transient component in each is largest when voltage is applied near the crest of the voltage wave.

Figure 48b shows the current when the circuit is predominantly inductive in the steady state. The natural frequency is much lower than the applied frequency. Since the circuit is, on the whole, inductive, it may be compared with the purely inductive circuit of Fig. 45b. In each case a transient component is added to a sinusoidal steady-state component; in one case, however, the transient component is an exponential curve, while in the other it is a damped sine wave.

If the frequency of the applied voltage is nearly equal to the natural frequency of the circuit, the wave of current appears quite different, as illustrated in Fig. 48c. In Figs. 48a and 48b it is plain that the total current is the sum of sinusoidal components, but in Fig. 48c the curve of total current has no appearance of being composed of two waves of different frequency. In fact, it appears to be a wave of a single frequency that is modulated in a somewhat sinusoidal manner. But the component parts are shown in Fig. 48c, and, when they are added at each point of time, the result is the modulated curve of total current.

To show that the modulated form of curve is in agreement with the mathematical derivation, we may alter Eq. (403). For simplicity let us consider a special case; let us assume, first, that resistance is negligibly small, and, second, that the switch in the circuit is closed when the instantaneous voltage is zero, making $\theta = 0$. In this special case, $\alpha = 0$ and $\phi = \pi/2$, making $\psi = \pi/2$ and $A = E/Z$. Substitution of these values in Eq. (403) gives

$$i = \frac{E}{Z}(\cos \omega t - \cos \Omega t) \tag{411}$$

This equation can never be exactly true, for energy loss in resistance cannot be entirely avoided. But it is theoretically interesting because a simple trigonometric change gives

$$i = \frac{2E}{Z} \sin \left(\frac{\omega + \Omega}{2} t\right) \sin \left(\frac{\omega - \Omega}{2} t\right) \tag{412}$$

Interpreting Eq. (412), we see that it represents a sine wave of high frequency multiplied by a sine wave of low frequency; it therefore is an analytical statement of the modulated form that we observed in the curve of Fig. 48c. In the ideal case of Eq. (412), the frequency of current in the circuit is the average of the applied frequency and the natural frequency, and it is modulated by a frequency that is half the difference of the applied and natural frequencies. This frequency relationship remains practically true even though there is resistance in the circuit, and it may be observed in Fig. 48c. But the amount of modulation is greatly affected by resistance, and it can be seen in the figure that the variations of amplitude become less and less extreme as the total current merges into the steady-state current. See also oscillogram 6 at the end of this chapter.

When voltage is first applied to the circuit, there is no energy in either the inductance or the capacitance, but the circuit immediately begins to gain energy from the source of voltage. At first the wave of total current is in phase with the applied voltage, and the circuit is receiving energy from the generator. During the first two and a half cycles, in Fig. 48c, the amplitude of the total current wave is increasing; this increase indicates a gain of energy in the circuit. But the total current does not have the same frequency as the applied voltage, and, although the current was initially in phase with the voltage, it gradually lags until after about two and a half cycles the current and voltage are in quadrature and the circuit has ceased to gain energy. At this instant, the amplitude of the total current attains a maximum; the transient component, the steady-state component, and the total current are all in phase with each other, and, neglecting resistance, they are all in quadrature with the voltage.

The wave of total current continues to be retarded relative to the applied voltage, and when it lags behind the voltage more than a quarter of a cycle it begins returning energy to the generator at the expense of stored energy of the circuit. The amplitude of current in the circuit becomes smaller for several cycles and approaches a minimum. Then, again, current becomes partially in phase with the voltage, and again the circuit receives energy as the amplitude of current rises toward a second maximum. The phase relation of current and voltage may be read from Fig. 48c by remembering that the steady-state component of current is practically in quadrature with the applied voltage: when total current leads the steady-state component (as it does while its amplitude is increasing) it is receiving energy from the generator; when total current lags behind the steady-state component (as it does while its amplitude is decreasing) it is returning energy to the generator.

Figures 48a and 48b can be described as modulated waves, their appearance to the contrary notwithstanding, and we have already seen that Fig. 48c can be described as superimposed waves. When the applied frequency is nearly equal to the natural frequency, the modulated form is the more obvious, whereas an impression of superimposed waves results if the applied frequency and natural frequency are widely different. But intermediate cases also exist, in which there is no clear distinction. When the applied frequency is $1\frac{1}{2}$ times to $2\frac{1}{2}$ times the natural frequency, or vice versa, the resulting wave of total current is not easily recognizable, but may be analysed into either form.

7. Conditions to Preclude the Transient Component. It is possible to apply alternating voltage to a circuit of resistance and inductance without causing a transient component of current; we found that this could be done by closing the switch at an instant corresponding to zero steady-state current in the inductance. When alternating voltage is applied to a circuit of resistance and capacitance, it is possible to prevent a transient component of current by closing the switch at an instant that would correspond, in the steady state, to zero charge on the condenser. In each case the initial condition in the circuit corresponds exactly to that which would have existed if the steady state had already been established. There is no need for a transient current, and the first instant is indistinguishable from a similar instant in each cycle thereafter.

But when a circuit, initially without stored energy, contains both inductance and capacitance, it is not possible to apply sinusoidal voltage without producing a transient current. The initial condition of zero current in the inductance and zero charge on the condenser does not correspond to any point of the steady-state cycle. Either initial condition may be matched, but not both, for when the steady-state current is zero the charge is maximum, and vice versa.

It appears superficially from Eq. (410), which expresses the coefficient of the transient term, that A would become zero when $\theta = \phi$. If this were true a condition would be determined that would produce no transient current. But it is not true, for when $\theta - \phi$ equals zero in the numerator of Eq. (410), ψ in the denominator is also zero [as may be seen from Eq. (409)] and A is indeterminate. Equation (408) will evaluate A in such a case; if $\psi = 0$ and $\theta - \phi = 0$, Eq. (408) is reduced to

$$\frac{E \sin \theta}{L} = \omega A + \frac{\Omega E}{Z}$$

from which

$$A = E\left(\frac{\sin \theta}{\omega L} - \frac{\Omega}{\omega Z}\right)$$

So neither this condition nor any other will eliminate a transient component.

If the circuit is not initially without stored energy, it is possible under special circumstances to apply voltage without producing a transient current.   If, for example, there is initial charge on the condenser, it will be possible to select a steady-state current that would produce that exact amount of charge at the instant of zero current.   If the corresponding voltage is then applied at the right instant, there will be no transient current.   It is possible to find one certain sinusoidal voltage that will produce no transient component for each initial condition (other than rest), but both angle and amplitude of applied voltage must be correctly chosen.

8. Non-sinusoidal Alternating Voltage.   When the voltage applied to a circuit is alternating in a periodic manner, but is

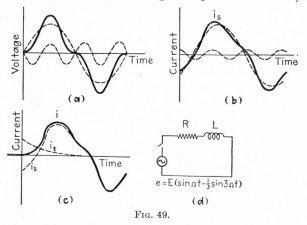

Fig. 49.

of a form that is not simply sinusoidal, the total current may be found most readily by analysing the voltage into sinusoidal components.   If the voltage is expressed as a Fourier series, and the current response to each term of the series is found separately, the total current is merely the sum of the individual components.   But it is not necessary to determine transient components for each of the terms of the Fourier series of voltage; it is only the steady-state current that must be found by Fourier analysis.   The transient component of current has a form independent of the applied voltage, as has been pointed out, and when Fourier analysis has given the steady-state current it only remains to evaluate the coefficients of the transient component.

The method is best explained through an example, and for simplicity the example will be made partly numerical.   The voltage of Fig. 49a is applied to a circuit of resistance and inductance.   The voltage, when analysed, is found to contain a large third-harmonic component, and an equation for voltage is written as

$$e = E(\sin \Omega t - \tfrac{1}{3} \sin 3\Omega t) \tag{413}$$

The steady-state component of current is found by dividing each component of voltage by its proper impedance and introducing the proper angle of lag for the current:

$$i_s = E\left[\frac{\sin\left(\Omega t - \tan^{-1}\dfrac{\Omega L}{R}\right)}{\sqrt{R^2 + (\Omega L)^2}} - \frac{\sin\left(3\Omega t - \tan^{-1}\dfrac{3\Omega L}{R}\right)}{3\sqrt{R^2 + (3\Omega L)^2}}\right] \tag{414}$$

Numerical values are now introduced: $R = 1$; frequency is 60 cycles per sec., so $\Omega = 377$; let $L = \tfrac{1}{377}$, making $\Omega L = 1$.   The steady-state current is hence

$$i_s = E\left[\frac{\sin\left(\Omega t - \tan^{-1}1\right)}{\sqrt{2}} - \frac{\sin\left(3\Omega t - \tan^{-1}3\right)}{3\sqrt{10}}\right] \tag{415}$$

as shown in Fig. 49*b*.   Total current, which includes the transient component, is

$$i = K\epsilon^{-\frac{R}{L}t} + i_s \tag{416}$$

Since the switch in the circuit (see Fig. 49*d*) is not closed until zero time, there can be no previous current in the circuit, and when

$$t = 0, \qquad i = 0 \tag{417}$$

This supplies an initial condition that can be used in Eq. (416) to evaluate K.   When Eq. (415) is substituted in (416) for i_s, and when zero is substituted for t and i according to Eq. (417), the result is

$$0 = K + E\left[\frac{\sin\left(-\tan^{-1}1\right)}{\sqrt{2}} - \frac{\sin\left(-\tan^{-1}3\right)}{3\sqrt{10}}\right]$$

But when the tangent of an angle is 1, the sine of that angle is $1/\sqrt{2}$, and when the tangent is 3 the sine is $3/\sqrt{10}$.   So

$$K = E(\tfrac{1}{2} - \tfrac{1}{10}) = \tfrac{2}{5}E \tag{418}$$

The total current therefore is

$$i = \tfrac{2}{5}E\epsilon^{-377t} + i_s \tag{419}$$

with i_s given by Eq. (415).   The curves of total current and its transient and steady-state components are plotted in Fig. 49*c*.

It is interesting to note that the slow increase of current after the switch is closed corresponds to the peculiar shape of the applied voltage.

9. Non-periodic Applied Voltage.   When the applied voltage is neither a constant unidirectional voltage nor a periodically varying voltage, a difficulty is encountered in the course of solution: there is no steady state of either voltage or current.   In Sec. 6 of Chap. III we saw that the portion of the current that we call the steady-state component is described by the particular integral of the differential equation.   Only a voltage that can be expressed by a Fourier series, however, will produce a steady-

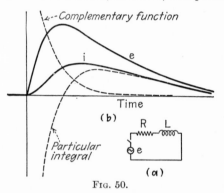

Fig. 50.

state current, and the discussion of Chap. III was limited to such periodic voltages.

The ordinary concept of steady-state current has no meaning when voltage has the form shown in Fig. 50, for example.   There is one voltage impulse, and one corresponding surge of current; and, although the current is composed of a particular integral and a complementary function, it cannot be said to have a transient component and a steady-state component.   The entire current is essentially transient.

When it is not possible to evaluate the particular integral by means of the steady-state current, some other approach must be found.   Sometimes it is convenient to evaluate the particular integral directly by integration; this is most helpful when the voltage is a simple function of time.   The voltage curve in Fig. 50 is a good illustration, for it has the simple analytical form

$$e = E(t\epsilon^{-\Delta t}) \tag{420}$$

E and Λ are constant coefficients which were selected in an entirely arbitrary manner to describe the voltage; they are analogous to E and Ω in the expressions for alternating voltage which appear in the early sections of this chapter.

Let us solve for current when this voltage impulse is applied to the circuit shown in Fig. 50a. The circuit consists of inductance and resistance, and its differential equation is of the first order:

$$Lpi + Ri = e \tag{421}$$

The solution of this differential equation consists of two parts: the complementary function, and the particular integral.

First, the complementary function of this equation is

$$K\epsilon^{-\frac{R}{L}t} \tag{422}$$

This is familiar, as it has been used in many of the foregoing solutions, but for formal proof we may refer to Eq. (89) Chap. III.

Second, the particular integral is needed. Equation (89) gives the particular integral for a first-order differential equation, such as Eq. (421), and when its coefficients are altered from the general form of Eq. (84) to the specific values of Eq. (421) we have, as the particular integral of Eq. (421),

$$\frac{1}{L}\epsilon^{\lambda t}\int \epsilon^{-\lambda t}f(t)dt \tag{423}$$

where

$$\lambda = -\frac{R}{L} \quad \text{and} \quad f(t) = e = E(t\epsilon^{-\Lambda t})$$

It may be said in general that the particular integral can be evaluated if the voltage is known as a function of time, although the actual performance of the integration will sometimes be difficult. In the case under consideration, the voltage is known from Eq. (420), and it replaces $f(t)$ in (423) to give

$$\frac{1}{L}\epsilon^{\lambda t}\int \epsilon^{-\lambda t}Et\epsilon^{-\Lambda t}dt$$

The result of integration in the particular integral is

$$\frac{E}{L\left(\frac{R}{L}-\Lambda\right)^2}\epsilon^{-\Lambda t}\left[\left(\frac{R}{L}-\Lambda\right)t-1\right] \tag{424}$$

Third, the complementary function is added to this particular integral to give the total current:

$$i = K\epsilon^{-\frac{R}{L}t} + \frac{E}{L\left(\frac{R}{L} - \Lambda\right)^2}\epsilon^{-\Lambda t}\left[\left(\frac{R}{L} - \Lambda\right)t - 1\right] \quad (425)$$

Fourth, the coefficient K must be evaluated from an initial condition. Because of the switch in the circuit, and the inductance, the initial current is zero. At zero time, therefore, Eq. (425) becomes

$$0 = K - \frac{E}{L\left(\frac{R}{L} - \Lambda\right)^2}$$

and

$$K = \frac{E}{L\left(\frac{R}{L} - \Lambda\right)^2}$$

The complete expression for current is now obtained by substituting this value for K in Eq. (425):

$$i = \frac{E}{L\left(\frac{R}{L} - \Lambda\right)^2}\left\{\epsilon^{-\frac{R}{L}t} + \epsilon^{-\Lambda t}\left[\left(\frac{R}{L} - \Lambda\right)t - 1\right]\right\} \quad (426)$$

This current is plotted in Fig. 50*b* for a specific combination of parameters, and a value of Λ that is half as great as R/L. When Λ is greater than R/L, the particular integral will be negative for all values of time, but the total current will be of the same general shape.

It is interesting to see that the four rules of Chap. I are of such wide application. But they are merely a statement of the classical solution of transients problems. A totally different attack makes use of Laplace transformation, which analyzes the voltage into components (as the Fourier series analyzes a periodic voltage into harmonics) and then finds the current that is due to each. This concept is mentioned in the next section in discussing current produced by a square wave of voltage.

10. Superposition of Transient Currents. When voltage is suddenly applied to a circuit, and then remains constant until it suddenly changes to a new value and is again constant thereafter, a transient response may be found for each of the sudden changes of voltage. The procedure may be extended to include any number of sudden changes of voltage. Let us consider an example.

Voltage of 10 volts is suddenly applied to a transformer. It remains constant for 1 sec., and is then reversed in polarity.

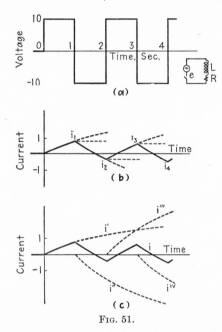

Fig. 51.

At the end of another second, it is again reversed, and so on, as in Fig. 51a. The inductance of the transformer is 10 henrys, and its resistance is 5 ohms, the circuit being as shown in the figure.

During the first second, the current is

$$i = \frac{E}{R}(1 - \epsilon^{-\frac{R}{L}t}) \tag{19}$$

$$= 2(1 - \epsilon^{-0.5t}) \tag{427}$$

At the end of the first second, when $t = 1$,

$$i_1 = 2(1 - \epsilon^{-0.5}) = 0.786 \tag{428}$$

At this instant there is a sudden change of voltage, and Eq. (427)

is no longer valid for current.   There are two methods of attack that may be employed, and either of them will give current during the succeeding intervals of time.   We will try both methods.

First, it is possible to consider that the period of time from $t = 1$ to $t = 2$ is entirely independent of the period of time from $t = 0$ to $t = 1$ and to solve for current during the second period on that basis.   Of course, the initial current at the beginning of the second period is identical with the current at the end of the first period, as found in Eq. (428), but this is the only effect of the first period on the second.   The transient component of current during the second period is

$$K\epsilon^{\lambda(t-1)} \tag{429}$$

in which λ is $-\dfrac{R}{L}$.   Owing to the fact that the voltage disturbance which produces this transient current occurs when $t = 1$, and not when $t = 0$, it is necessary to subtract 1 from all values of time.   The transient current is unchanged in shape, but is delayed 1 sec.   Mathematically, this accomplishes a shift of the time axis.   So, in Eq. (429), $(t - 1)$ appears instead of t.

The steady-state component during the second period of time is that value which would be reached if -10 volts were applied to the circuit for an indefinitely long time.   It is therefore -2 amp.   The total current is

$$i = K\epsilon^{-0.5(t-1)} - 2 \tag{430}$$

Knowing that when $t = 1$, $i = 0.786$, we evaluate K in Eq. (430), and obtain a complete expression for current during the second period:

$$i = 2.786\epsilon^{-0.5(t-1)} - 2 \tag{431}$$

This expression is plotted in Fig. 51b, beginning with i_1 and ending with i_2.   The value of i_2 is found from Eq. (431) to be

$$i_2 = -0.309 \tag{432}$$

It is evident that this method may be continued indefinitely. The initial current for the third period is i_2, the equation for current during the third period is

$$i = -2.309\epsilon^{-0.5(t-2)} + 2 \tag{433}$$

and the final current at the end of the period is

$$i_3 = 0.598 \qquad (434)$$

This method may be continued as long as desired, and if the applied voltage retains its cyclic form, a steady-state current will eventually be reached.

The alternative method of solution is that of superposition. The curve of current that is produced by the application of 10 volts at $t = 0$ is found. This current, which is described by Eq. (427), flows indefinitely thereafter. But when $t = 1$ another voltage is applied to the circuit. This new voltage is -20 volts, and since the original voltage is still acting, the total voltage in the circuit after $t = 1$ is -10 volts. During the period of time from $t = 1$ to $t = 2$ both voltages are in the circuit; each is producing a transient current, and the total current is the sum of the two. In Fig. 51c the current due to application of 10 volts at $t = 0$ is marked i'. The current due to application of -20 volts at $t = 1$ is marked i''. The total current during the second period is the sum and is shown as a solid line in the figure. At the end of the second period, when $t = 2$, another voltage is introduced into the circuit: its value is $+20$ volts, so that the total voltage in the circuit is again $+10$, and the current during the third period is the sum of three components. This method, also, may be carried on indefinitely.

During the first period of time, the total current is that produced by the initial voltage. Let us call it i'.

$$i = i' = 2(1 - \epsilon^{-0.5t}) \qquad (435)$$

At the beginning of the second period, a voltage of -20 volts is suddenly injected into the circuit. The response to it is found as if it were the only voltage present and the circuit were at rest (without energy) when it was introduced. This response may be called i'', and is

$$i'' = \frac{E}{R}(1 - \epsilon^{\lambda(t-1)}) \qquad (436)$$

This is the usual form of current in a circuit of inductance and resistance, initially at rest, when voltage is suddenly applied. Since voltage is applied when $t = 1$ the current is a function of $(t - 1)$ instead of t. The value of E is -20, that being the amount of the change of voltage that produces i''. The two components of current are added to obtain total current during the second period:

$$i = i' + i'' = 2(1 - \epsilon^{-0.5t}) - 4(1 - \epsilon^{-0.5(t-1)}) \qquad (437)$$

When $t = 2$ a third voltage is introduced. The response to it alone is

$$i''' = \frac{E}{R}(1 - \epsilon^{\lambda(t-2)}) \qquad (438)$$

During the third period the total current has three components:
$i = i' + i'' + i'''$

$$= 2(1 - \epsilon^{-0.5t}) - 4(1 - \epsilon^{-0.5(t-1)}) + 4(1 - \epsilon^{-0.5(t-2)}) \qquad (439)$$

For later periods of time, more terms may be added to the series of Eq. (439) by inspection.

Computation from Eq. (439) is quite straightforward. Let us determine current when $t = 3$. From Eq. (439),

$$\begin{aligned} i_3 &= 2(1 - \epsilon^{-1.5}) - 4(1 - \epsilon^{-1.0}) + 4(1 - \epsilon^{-0.5}) \\ &= 1.554 - 2.528 + 1.572 = 0.598 \end{aligned} \qquad (440)$$

The amount of calculation required to find i_3 by the method of superposition, in Eq. (440), is somewhat less than that needed to find the same value of i_3 by the previous method, in Eq. (434).

11. Square-wave Response. A square wave of voltage is often applied to a circuit or network for analyzing circuit behavior. An electronic "square-wave generator" is connected to the network, and a cathode-ray oscilloscope is used to depict the resulting voltage across some element or combination of elements of the network. The response to a steadily applied square wave is studied, not the disturbance at the moment of first connecting the square-wave generator.

The circuit's response to each jump of voltage in the square wave is similar to the response to a suddenly applied battery voltage, as considered in Sec. 10. If the duration of the transient is short compared to the period of the square wave, the similarity is evident, as in the first column of oscillograms in Fig. 52. If, on the contrary, the period of the square wave is short compared to the time constant of the circuit (high-frequency square wave, third column of the figure), the similarity to a simple transient current is obliterated by the rapid superposition.

Various typical output wave forms appear in this kind of square-wave testing. By observing the response of a circuit to square waves of various frequencies, it is possible to deduce a good deal of information about the circuit with very little trouble. Time constants and natural frequencies, for instance, are readily approximated. Theoretically the data from the square-wave test could yield exact and detailed information about the circuit, but precise interpretation is too difficult to be entirely practical.

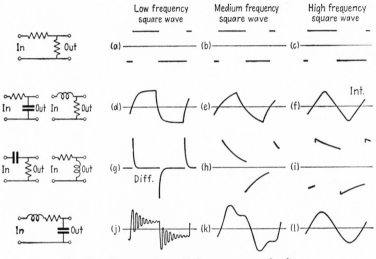

FIG. 52.—Response to applied square wave of voltage.

Some examples of results obtained from simple circuits at low, medium, and high frequencies are shown in Fig. 52. For the second and third rows of diagrams, "medium frequency" means that the half-period of the square wave (the duration of the flat top of the wave) is of the order of magnitude of the time constant of the circuit; the time constant of an inductive circuit is L/R, and the time constant of a capacitive circuit is RC. In the fourth row, "medium frequency" is about half the natural frequency of oscillation; it will be seen that the third harmonic is rather prominent although the frequency is too high for third-harmonic resonance. (These waves were traced from the screen of a cathode-ray oscilloscope.) "High frequency" is greater than the medium frequency by a factor of 5 to 10, and "low frequency" is as much less.   The reader may estimate for himself the ratio of low to medium frequency in each case by study of the curves.

It is often helpful to consider the Fourier components of the square wave.   A square wave contains a fundamental frequency and all odd harmonics.   When the output voltage in response to a square wave is also square, as in Fig. 52*a*, *b*, or *c*, there is no distortion in the circuit.   A response as in Fig. 52*i* indicates that high frequencies in the output voltage are retarded in phase relative to low frequencies.   If the top of the output wave sloped the other way it would indicate greater retardation of low than of high frequencies.   Figure 52*j* indicates oscillation in the circuit, and a sine-wave output, as in Fig. 52*l*, indicates that either the fundamental has been emphasized by resonance or that the third and all higher harmonics have been suppressed (as happens if the third-harmonic frequency is above cut off of an amplifier or filter circuit).

Interpretation of square-wave tests is essentially a study of the transient response of a circuit.   Square-wave testing is quite commonly used in checking the performance of amplifiers and other communication circuits.

12. Integrating and Differentiating Circuits.   The voltage across a condenser is the integral of condenser current.   The *R-C* circuit in row 2 of Fig. 52 is called an "integrating circuit" because the output voltage is approximately the integral of the input voltage.   The approximation is good only if the period of the applied voltage is much shorter than the time constant of the circuit, for it is good only as long as the condenser voltage is a small part of the input voltage.   *R* and *C* must both be large. Most of the applied voltage must be across the resistance.   Current will then be nearly proportional to input voltage, and since condenser voltage is the integral of condenser current, it is also the integral of input voltage.   Figure 52 shows good integration in *f*, poor integration in *d* and *e*.

The current through a pure inductance is the integral of applied voltage.   The *R-L* circuit in row 2 of Fig. 52 is therefore an integrating circuit also.   Like the *R-C* circuit, it must have a long time constant relative to the applied frequency.   *L* must be large and *R* small, but if *R* is too small there will be little output.

Row 3 of Fig. 52 shows two "differentiating circuits."   The

current through a condenser is proportional to the derivative of
the applied voltage; this is the principle of operation of the *R-C*
circuit. The voltage across an inductance is proportional to the
derivative of current; this is the principle of operation of the *R-L*
circuit. Both of these circuits must have *short* time constants
(relative to the frequency of the applied voltage) to give accurate
differentiation of input voltage, as may be seen in Fig. 52. The
impulsive response shown in Fig. 52*g* is a fair approximation of
the derivative of a square wave, whereas the curves of Fig. 52*h*
and *i* are meaningless as derivatives.

Integrating and differentiating circuits are used to operate on
applied waves of all shapes. The square wave is used here for
illustration, as in practice the square wave is used for testing,
because it makes the circuit's inexactness of response quite
evident.

Problems

1. Connect inductance, capacitance, and resistance in series, as in the
circuit diagram of Fig. 48. Record on an oscillograph the current that
flows when alternating voltage is suddenly applied, and record also the
applied voltage. Measure the circuit parameters, the amplitude and
frequency of the applied voltage, and the amplitude of the steady-state
current.

The circuit will be composed of a condenser and a coil; no resistance
except that of the coil need be used, and the ratio of resistance to inductance
in the coil should be as low as possible. Do not use a coil with an iron core.

Select values of inductance and capacitance to give the circuit a natural
frequency about 30 per cent higher than the frequency of the applied voltage.
The condenser must be able to withstand, momentarily, five times the
applied voltage.

The applied voltage should be sinusoidal, with no harmonic components
apparent in the recorded wave. Amplitude, form, phase, and frequency of
the applied voltage must in no way be affected by connection to the test
circuit. This is a very important condition, but usually presents no
difficulty.

Transfer the recorded curve of current from the oscillogram to a sheet
of cross-section paper, and determine from the oscillogram the angle of the
voltage wave at the initial instant (the angle θ). On another sheet plot
the transient and steady-state components of current, and the total current,
as computed from network parameters. Compare the computed curve
with the experimentally observed curve.

If it is not convenient to make an oscillogram, that which is reproduced as
oscillogram 6 may be used. The upper curve of this record is current, the
lower is applied voltage. Near the right-hand end of the current wave a
single cycle of steady-state current has been superimposed, by means of a

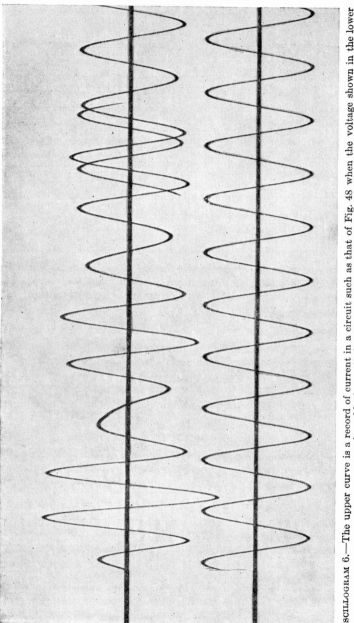

OSCILLOGRAM 6.—The upper curve is a record of current in a circuit such as that of Fig. 48 when the voltage shown in the lower curve is suddenly applied.   For use with Prob. 1 of Chap. VI.

separate exposure, after the steady state was well established; this is for calibration. The *effective* (r.m.s.) value of the steady-state current is 1.33 amp. A record of time is given by the 60-cycle voltage wave. Circuit parameters are:

$$R = 5.56 \text{ ohms.}$$
$$L = 0.322 \text{ henry.}$$
$$C = 12.67 \ \mu f.$$

Effective amplitude of applied voltage $= 117.8$ volts.

2. What form of alternating voltage can be applied to a circuit of inductance, resistance, and capacitance (the circuit being initially at rest) without necessarily producing a transient component of current?

3. Certain frequency meters have a number of reeds whose natural frequencies of mechanical vibration are equal to the electrical frequencies to be measured. Adjacent reeds have natural frequencies that differ by one cycle per second, or some simple fraction of a cycle. Watch the reeds in such a meter just after connecting it to a voltage within its range. Observe the transient behaviour of the reeds. To what extent is this behaviour analogous to the current of oscillogram 6?

4. Consider the ballistic galvanometer described in Prob. 4 of Chap. IV. What is the maximum deflection of the galvanometer if a constant current flows through it for 0.05 sec., exerting a moment of 0.10 g. cm. during this time? There is no current either before or after this interval. What is the maximum deflection if one-tenth as much current flows for 10 times as long a period? Note that electric charge through the galvanometer is the same in both cases.

5. An electrical device is proposed for use in comparing the acceleration characteristics of an automobile using various gasolines.[1] A direct-current generator with constant field excitation is driven by the engine, or by one of the wheels. In series with the armature of the generator is a condenser and an ammeter. Prove whether or not the reading of the meter is proportional to the acceleration of the automobile. Is the device feasible? Can it be designed with practicable parameters? Rapid acceleration of an automobile is about 4 per cent of its maximum speed per second.

6. Discuss whether or not the following statement is true: "Alternating voltage is applied to a circuit of capacitance and resistance in series. When the elapsed time after closing the switch is equal to the time of one cycle of the applied voltage, the transient component of current will be small compared to the maximum of the steady-state component." Is this true for all values of R and C, and for any applied frequency and any instant of closing the switch?

[1] GARDNER, G. T., *Gen. Elec. Rev.*, **37**, 148, 1934.

CHAPTER VII

COUPLED RESONANT CIRCUITS

1. A Special Network. The discussion of coupled resonant circuits belongs, logically, in Chap. V, for the circuits constitute a network that can be treated in the same manner as other networks. This is pointed out in Sec. 22 of that chapter, in which the procedure for an exact solution is outlined. But for two reasons qualitative discussion of the transient current and consideration of approximate solutions have been reserved for the present chapter: first, because the practical importance of coupled resonant circuits is great enough to justify a separate chapter; second, because the action of coupled circuits is related to the behaviour of a circuit to which alternating voltage is applied, and Chap. VI serves as an introduction.

When two circuits are coupled, as in Fig. 53*b*, and a source of voltage is applied to the first circuit, circuit 2 can obtain energy only at the expense of circuit 1. Transfer of energy takes place through the mutual parameter; in Fig. 53, where the mutual parameter is inductance, the first circuit gives energy *to* the magnetic field, and the second circuit then receives energy *from* the magnetic field. The rate of transfer of energy depends on the value of the mutual parameter relative to the other parameters of the network. This relation is expressed as the **coefficient of coupling**: when the coupling is inductive, the coefficient of coupling is defined as

$$\text{Coefficient of coupling} = \frac{L_{12}}{\sqrt{L_{11}L_{22}}}$$

When circuits are loosely coupled, and the coefficient is small, the transfer of energy is relatively slow. But with close coupling, and with the coefficient approaching its maximum value of unity, the circuits exchange energy rapidly.

2. Oscillograms of Current. Figure 53 shows a number of oscillograms of current in the pair of coupled circuits. Figure

220

53a shows the current in circuit 1 when circuit 2 is open; it is therefore merely the familiar damped sinusoidal wave of a single circuit. It has a certain natural frequency. When circuit 2 is

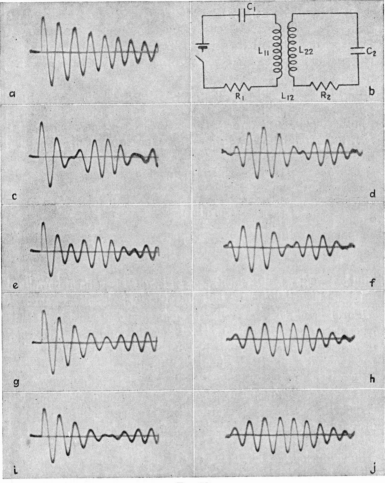

Fig. 53.

allowed to carry current, it will receive energy through its inductive coupling with circuit 1. The natural frequency of circuit 2 is approximately equal to the natural frequency of circuit 1. In Fig. 53, c and d show current in circuits 1 and 2, respectively, with complete transfer of energy in the course of five half-cycles.

The first half-cycle of current in c is quite similar to the first half-cycle of current in a, but energy of circuit 1 is rapidly drained away, and at the end of five half-cycles circuit 2 has received all the energy (except that which has been lost in resistance). The amplitude of current in circuit 1 has reached zero, whereas the amplitude of i_2 has reached a maximum. During the directly following five half-cycles the process is reversed and circuit 1 regains all of the energy that was transferred to circuit 2—except, of course, that which is meanwhile lost in resistance. The tenth half-cycle of c has the same amplitude as the tenth half-cycle of a; it is, however, reversed in sign. Another complete transfer of energy to circuit 2 and a partial return to circuit 1 are accomplished before the end of the oscillographic record.

It is approximately true that complete transfer of energy from one circuit to the other occurs if the natural frequencies of the two individual circuits are equal. As will be seen later, however, the effect of mutual inductance is such that if the closeness of coupling is changed, the circuit parameters must be adjusted slightly to maintain such a condition. To observe the effect of altering the self-parameters independently of the mutual inductance, and the mutual inductance independently of the self-parameters, we may refer again to Fig. 53.

Parts e and f of Fig. 53 differ from c and d because of a small change in the value of the capacitance in circuit 2. The value of C_2 was increased about 20 per cent, changing the natural frequency of that circuit by about 10 per cent, and the currents shown in e and f resulted. It will be seen that the transfer of energy is not complete, and the amplitude of current in circuit 1 does not reach zero, although it goes through a minimum at the fifth half-cycle. The maximum amplitude of current is correspondingly less in f than in d, for part of the total energy is retained in circuit 1. The current in the fifth half-cycle of e is about one-third the current in the corresponding half-cycle of a, showing that the energy retained in circuit 1 is about one-ninth the total energy; the secondary circuit is given eight-ninths the total energy, making the amplitude of current in f about 95 per cent of its amplitude in d.

In the network that produces the currents e and f, as well as the network which gave c and d, the mutual inductance was

0.1 henry, while L_{11} and L_{22} were each 0.5 henry. The coefficient of coupling was therefore 0.2.

The effect of reducing the coefficient of coupling is shown in curves g and h. The mutual inductance is only about half as great, and it will be seen that the maximum transfer of energy has not been accomplished until the ninth half-cycle. It is at this time that current in circuit 1 becomes minimum and current in circuit 2 maximum. Because of the smaller value of mutual inductance, and the consequent looser coupling, transfer of energy from one circuit to the other is slower. Except for the change of mutual inductance the network for g and h was identical with the network for c and d.

It might seem, at first thought, that close coupling of the circuits would be necessary to transfer energy efficiently from one to the other. It is quite true that close coupling permits a faster transfer of energy, but it does not make the transfer any more complete. This may be seen in curves i and j; while recording these last two oscillograms, the mutual inductance was unchanged from the value used for curves g and h, but the capacitance of circuit 2 was raised about 7 per cent (making C_2 slightly greater than it was for c and g, but less than its value for e). In this final case the transfer of energy is complete at the end of the ninth half-cycle, and during the remaining eight half-cycles of the oscillographic record the energy is being returned to circuit 1 from circuit 2. If the oscillogram had continued for another cycle the amplitude of i_2 would have fallen to zero, but the length of the record is insufficient to show the complete return of energy.

Let us now summarize the information obtained from Fig. 53: electromagnetic energy can be repeatedly transferred between two coupled resonant circuits; when the circuits are properly adjusted, the transfer of energy can be complete, as in c and d. When the adjustment of one of the circuits is changed, the transfer of energy is incomplete, as in e and f. When mutual inductance is decreased, the transfer of energy is slower, as in g and h; moreover, it is not quite complete unless the self-parameters are readjusted. But the transfer, although slower, may be made complete as in i and j. There is much more to be learned from a careful study of Fig. 53 that cannot be included in this summary.

3. Coupled Circuits without Loss.   The complete analytical solution for current in two coupled circuits is very lengthy. Moreover, when the solution is finished it does not make plain the circuit's behavior, for it is too complex to be comprehensible. But if resistance in the two circuits is neglected, the solution is very greatly simplified, and although the result does not exactly correspond to a physical network, it is nevertheless quite helpful and illuminating.   Let us, therefore, neglect resistance.

The voltage equations for the network of Fig. 53b are

$$\left(R_1 + L_{11}p + \frac{1}{C_1p}\right)i_1 - L_{12}pi_2 = E \tag{441}$$

$$-L_{12}pi_1 + \left(R_2 + L_{22}p + \frac{1}{C_2p}\right)i_2 = 0 \tag{442}$$

When R_1 and R_2 are zero these become

$$\left(L_{11}p + \frac{1}{C_1p}\right)i_1 - L_{12}pi_2 = E \tag{443}$$

$$-L_{12}pi_1 + \left(L_{22}p + \frac{1}{C_2p}\right)i_2 = 0 \tag{444}$$

Substituting λ for p, according to the method explained in Sec. 4 of Chap. V, and making the left-hand member of Eq. (443) equal zero, we obtain a pair of equations which may be solved for λ:

$$\left(L_{11}\lambda + \frac{1}{C_1\lambda}\right)i_1 - L_{12}\lambda i_2 = 0 \tag{445}$$

$$-L_{12}\lambda i_1 + \left(L_{22}\lambda + \frac{1}{C_2\lambda}\right)i_2 = 0 \tag{446}$$

Simultaneous solution of these equations gives

$$(L_{11}L_{22} - L_{12}{}^2)\lambda^4 + \left(\frac{L_{11}}{C_2} + \frac{L_{22}}{C_1}\right)\lambda^2 + \frac{1}{C_1C_2} = 0 \tag{447}$$

From this equation values of λ may be obtained.

Although Eq. (447) is a quartic equation, it is peculiar in that it contains only even powers of λ; it is of the form known as biquadratic.   The biquadratic form is due to the neglect of resistance in the network, for a similar expression obtained from the general voltage equations (441) and (442) will contain also the first and third powers of λ. The general quartic equation is quite difficult to handle, but the biquadratic is readily solved by treating it as a quadratic in λ^2. An expression for λ^2 is thereby obtained, and the square root will give values of λ. Solution of Eq. (447) gives

$$\lambda = \pm \sqrt{\frac{-\left(\frac{L_{11}}{C_2} + \frac{L_{22}}{C_1}\right) \pm \sqrt{\left(\frac{L_{11}}{C_2} + \frac{L_{22}}{C_1}\right)^2 - 4\frac{L_{11}L_{22} - L_{12}^2}{C_1 C_2}}}{2(L_{11}L_{22} - L_{12}^2)}} \quad (448)$$

It is at once evident that there will be four values of λ, corresponding to the four combinations of algebraic signs. They will, moreover, be in pairs of equal and opposite values. All four values will be purely imaginary, for the quantity under the principal radical will always be real and negative.[1] They may therefore be written in pairs as

$$\begin{matrix} \lambda_1 = j\omega_1 & \lambda_3 = j\omega_3 \\ \lambda_2 = -j\omega_1 & \lambda_4 = -j\omega_3 \end{matrix} \Bigg\} \quad (450)$$

If resistance had been included in the solution there would have been two pairs of roots, but they would have been conjugate complex pairs instead of purely imaginary pairs.

From the four values of λ we may write the form of the currents:

$$i_1 = K_{11}\epsilon^{\lambda_1 t} + K_{12}\epsilon^{\lambda_2 t} + K_{13}\epsilon^{\lambda_3 t} + K_{14}\epsilon^{\lambda_4 t} \quad (451)$$
$$i_2 = K_{21}\epsilon^{\lambda_1 t} + K_{22}\epsilon^{\lambda_2 t} + K_{23}\epsilon^{\lambda_3 t} + K_{24}\epsilon^{\lambda_4 t} \quad (452)$$

There is no steady-state component of current in either circuit. Since the λ's are imaginary, the exponential terms may be combined into sinusoidal terms:

[1] It is real because the quantity under the inner radical must always be positive; this is shown by writing the quantity under the inner radical as

$$\left(\frac{L_{11}}{C_2} - \frac{L_{22}}{C_1}\right)^2 + 4\frac{L_{12}^2}{C_1 C_2} \quad (449)$$

and since the first term is squared the expression must be positive. The quantity under the principal radical is always negative because the value of the inner radical must always be numerically less than

$$\frac{L_{11}}{C_2} + \frac{L_{22}}{C_1}$$

$$i_1 = A_{11} \sin (\omega_1 t + \phi_{11}) + A_{13} \sin (\omega_3 t + \phi_{13}) \qquad (453)$$
$$i_2 = A_{21} \sin (\omega_1 t + \phi_{21}) + A_{23} \sin (\omega_3 t + \phi_{23}) \qquad (454)$$

In either the exponential or the sinusoidal equations there are eight coefficients to be determined from initial conditions. To complete the solution, eight initial conditions must be determined.

Since the circuits are inductive we have, first, that when

$$t = 0, \qquad i_1 = 0 \qquad\qquad (455)$$
$$i_2 = 0 \qquad\qquad (456)$$

Since the integral terms of the voltage equations (443) and (444) are initially zero, it follows that when

$$t = 0, \qquad \begin{array}{l} L_{11}pi_1 - L_{12}pi_2 = E \\ -L_{12}pi_1 + L_{22}pi_2 = 0 \end{array} \Big\} \qquad (457)$$

and simultaneous solution gives

$$t = 0, \qquad pi_1 = E \frac{L_{22}}{L_{11}L_{22} - L_{12}{}^2} \qquad (458)$$

$$pi_2 = E \frac{L_{12}}{L_{11}L_{22} - L_{12}{}^2} \qquad (459)$$

The second derivative must next be found. As it does not appear in the voltage equations, they must be differentiated by operating throughout with p:

$$\left(L_{11}p^2 + \frac{1}{C_1}\right)i_1 - L_{12}p^2i_2 = pE = 0$$
$$-L_{12}p^2i_1 + \left(L_{22}p^2 + \frac{1}{C_2}\right)i_2 = 0 \qquad\qquad (460)$$

The initial current being zero, these become, when

$$t = 0, \qquad \begin{array}{l} L_{11}p^2i_1 - L_{12}p^2i_2 = 0 \\ -L_{12}p^2i_1 + L_{22}p^2i_2 = 0 \end{array} \Big\} \qquad (461)$$

Simultaneous solution of the Eqs. (461) leads to the expression

$$(L_{11}L_{22} - L_{12}{}^2)p^2i_1 = 0$$

and since it is impossible for the quantity in parentheses to be zero (except in the special case that makes the coefficient of coupling unity), it follows that when

$$t = 0, \qquad p^2 i_1 = 0 \qquad\qquad (462)$$

and also
$$p^2 i_2 = 0 \qquad\qquad (463)$$

To find the initial value of the third derivative of current, it is necessary to differentiate the voltage equations a second time:

$$\left.\begin{aligned}
L_{11}p^3 i_1 + \frac{1}{C_1}p i_1 - L_{12}p^3 i_2 &= 0 \\
-L_{12}p^3 i_1 + L_{22}p^3 i_2 + \frac{1}{C_2}p i_2 &= 0
\end{aligned}\right\} \qquad (464)$$

The initial values of $p i_1$ and $p i_2$ are known from Eqs. (458) and (459); merely to simplify the algebra it is desirable to designate these initial values by the symbols X_1 and X_2:

$$\left.\begin{aligned}
X_1 &= E\frac{L_{22}}{L_{11}L_{22} - L_{12}{}^2} \\
X_2 &= E\frac{L_{12}}{L_{11}L_{22} - L_{12}{}^2}
\end{aligned}\right\} \qquad (465)$$

Furthermore, let us designate the initial values of $p^3 i_1$ and $p^3 i_2$ by the symbols Y_1 and Y_2. The Eqs. (464) may now be written, for the instant when $t = 0$, in terms of these four symbols:

$$\left.\begin{aligned}
L_{11}Y_1 - L_{12}Y_2 &= -\frac{1}{C_1}X_1 \\
-L_{12}Y_1 + L_{22}Y_2 &= -\frac{1}{C_2}X_2
\end{aligned}\right\} \qquad (466)$$

Simultaneous solution of Eqs. (466) gives

$$Y_1 = \frac{-\dfrac{L_{22}}{C_1}X_1 - \dfrac{L_{12}}{C_2}X_2}{L_{11}L_{22} - L_{12}{}^2} = -E\frac{L_{22}{}^2 C_2 + L_{12}{}^2 C_1}{C_1 C_2(L_{11}L_{22} - L_{12}{}^2)^2} \qquad (467)$$

$$Y_2 = \frac{-\dfrac{L_{11}}{C_2}X_2 - \dfrac{L_{12}}{C_1}X_1}{L_{11}L_{22} - L_{12}{}^2} = -E\frac{L_{11}L_{12}C_1 + L_{22}L_{12}C_2}{C_1 C_2(L_{11}L_{22} - L_{12}{}^2)^2} \qquad (468)$$

The eight necessary initial conditions have now been found; they are the initial current and the first, second, and third derivatives of current in each circuit.

Next, the formal current equations must be differentiated. The first, second, and third derivatives of current are found by repeated differentiation of Eqs. (453) and (454). To obtain the *initial* values of current and its derivatives we then let $t = 0$ in the resulting expressions. By this process we find that when

$$t = 0, \qquad i_1 = A_{11} \sin \phi_{11} + A_{13} \sin \phi_{13} = 0 \qquad (469)$$

$$p i_1 = A_{11} \omega_1 \cos \phi_{11} + A_{13} \omega_3 \cos \phi_{13} = X_1 \qquad (470)$$

$$p^2 i_1 = -(A_{11} \omega_1^2 \sin \phi_{11} + A_{13} \omega_3^2 \sin \phi_{13}) = 0 \qquad (471)$$

$$p^3 i_1 = -(A_{11} \omega_1^3 \cos \phi_{11} + A_{13} \omega_3^3 \cos \phi_{13}) = Y_1 \qquad (472)$$

Simultaneous solution of these four equations, which have been equated to the previously determined initial values of current and its derivatives, will evaluate the four coefficients in the expression for i_1. A similar group may be written for i_2. As the first step in the solution we solve Eqs. (469) and (471) together; solving for ϕ_{11} and ϕ_{13} we find that they both equal zero. This fortunate result makes it possible to eliminate ϕ from the other two equations, giving

$$A_{11} \omega_1 + A_{13} \omega_3 = X_1 \qquad (473)$$

$$-A_{11} \omega_1^3 - A_{13} \omega_3^3 = Y_1 \qquad (474)$$

The coefficients are found from this pair of equations to be

$$A_{11} = \frac{-X_1 \omega_3^3 - Y_1 \omega_3}{\omega_1^3 \omega_3 - \omega_1 \omega_3^3} \qquad (475)$$

$$A_{13} = \frac{X_1 \omega_1^3 + Y_1 \omega_1}{\omega_1^3 \omega_3 - \omega_1 \omega_3^3} \qquad (476)$$

The solution for the coefficients of i_2 is similar and yields similar equations:

$$A_{21} = \frac{-X_2 \omega_3^3 - Y_2 \omega_3}{\omega_1^3 \omega_3 - \omega_1 \omega_3^3} \qquad (477)$$

$$A_{23} = \frac{X_2 \omega_1^3 + Y_2 \omega_1}{\omega_1^3 \omega_3 - \omega_1 \omega_3^3} \qquad (478)$$

When values of these coefficients have been determined by using the above equations (together with Eqs. (465), (467), and (468) which define X and Y) they are substituted in the following expressions for current, which result from (453) and (454). Knowing that the ϕ's are all zero we have

$$i_1 = A_{11} \sin \omega_1 t + A_{13} \sin \omega_3 t \qquad (479)$$

$$i_2 = A_{21} \sin \omega_1 t + A_{23} \sin \omega_3 t \qquad (480)$$

This completes the solution for currents in the ideal network that contains no resistance. The final expressions are simple, and numerical evaluation is not difficult.   The entire solution is straightforward and follows the same course as have previous solutions of other networks.   If resistance had been included, the sinusoidal terms of the current expressions would be multiplied by exponential damping factors, and values of ϕ would appear as in Eqs. (453) and (454).   The values of ϕ would be small if resistance were small and would have little effect on the physical shape of the current wave, but they would not drop out of the mathematical solution.   Moreover—and it is for this reason that the complete solution is not given here—the evaluation of coefficients, of initial derivatives, and of natural angular velocities in networks containing resistance is quite laborious without being particularly lucid.

The current in each circuit is shown by Eqs. (479) and (480) to be composed of two sine waves of different frequencies.   It is not entirely erroneous to associate one of these frequencies with circuit 1 and the other with circuit 2, for if the coupling is very loose the frequencies will approach the natural frequencies of the two circuits individually. This can be seen from Eq. (448), the expression for the natural angular velocities, for

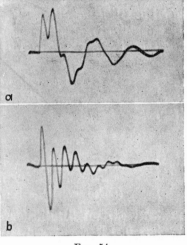

Fig. 54.

if L_{12} is allowed to approach zero, the values of ω approach $1/\sqrt{L_{11}C_1}$ and $1/\sqrt{L_{22}C_2}$.   But whenever there is coupling between the two circuits (as there must be if the circuits are to form a network) the natural frequencies of the network will differ slightly from the natural frequencies of the independent circuits because of the effect of the mutual inductance.

4. Widely Different Natural Frequencies.   Figure 54 shows oscillographic records of the current in circuits 1 and 2 when the natural frequencies of the network are quite different. The natural frequency of circuit 1 is about 100 cycles per sec., the natural frequency of circuit 2 is about 400 cycles, and the two natural frequencies of the network do not differ greatly from these values. The result is that each record shows a complex wave with two damped sinusoidal components, one having about four times the frequency of the other. But in i_1 (Fig. 54a) the low frequency, which is the natural frequency of circuit 1, is predominant over the high-frequency ripple; while in i_2 (Fig. 54b) the high frequency, natural to circuit 2, overshadows the low-frequency component.

Each circuit is disturbed at the initial instant by the sudden application of voltage in circuit 1, and each begins to carry current of its own natural frequency. But, at the same time, the current in each circuit induces a voltage in the other circuit so that there is a relatively small component of the natural frequency of each circuit in the other. From this point of view the current is not unlike the response of a single circuit to which alternating voltage is applied; this case was discussed in the previous chapter, and Fig. 54 may be compared with Fig. 48 *a* and *b*. Voltage applied to the second of two coupled circuits is, in fact, an alternating voltage, although its amplitude is not constant but decreases as the current in circuit 1 is damped. Equation (442), the voltage equation for circuit 2, shows that the driving voltage in circuit 2 is $L_{12}pi_1$, and if that equation is written

$$R_2i_2 + L_{22}pi_2 + \frac{1}{C_2p}i_2 = L_{12}pi_1 \qquad (481)$$

it may be compared with Eq. (394) of the previous chapter. The driving voltage in circuit 2 is evidently not a purely sinusoidal voltage, but if the coefficient of coupling is small, the approximation is close and the concept is helpful.

5. Approximately Equal Natural Frequencies. A special case of importance is one that has already been mentioned: the network of two circuits that are tuned to very nearly the same frequency. A set of oscillograms for such a circuit is shown in Fig. 53. The primary current shown in Fig. 53c, and the secondary current in Fig. 53d are just as truly composed of two damped sinusoidal components as are the curves of Fig. 54. But owing to the fact that the two sinusoidal components are of nearly the same frequency, they combine to give a curve that has the appearance of being a modulated wave. This effect is also comparable to the combination of components in the single circuit to which alternating voltage is applied, and Fig. 53*d* should be compared with Fig. 48*c*.

The transfer of energy from circuit 1 to circuit 2, and then its return to circuit 1, and so on, has already been discussed. A careful comparison of oscillograms will show that as long as the current in circuit 1 is inducing a voltage in circuit 2 that has a component in phase with i_2, there will be energy added to circuit 2; at the same time the voltage being induced in circuit 1 by the current in circuit 2 has a component in opposition to i_1, and energy is being removed from circuit 1. This action continues, in Fig. 53 *c* and *d*, until all energy is lost from circuit 1, but immediately thereafter a new current is induced in circuit 1 by the current in circuit 2. The new current in circuit 1 has an exactly opposite phase relationship: it receives energy from the induced voltage while circuit 2 now loses energy. The reversal of phase in i_1 is very clearly shown in Fig. 53 *c* and *i*; after each point of zero energy in circuit 1 is passed the current grows again but with a reversal of sign. Then, when all energy has been lost by circuit 2, there is a similar reversal of sign of i_2; this appears in Fig. 53*d* and *f*.

A change of any one of the network parameters will prevent complete transfer of energy from circuit 1 to circuit 2. When C_2 is changed, for example, Fig. 53*e* results. The current in *e* does not show the same reversal of phase that was typical of the point of zero energy in *c*; in fact, no point of zero energy is reached. But an exactly similar effect is occurring, although it is less obvious, for there is a gradual phase shift in *e* which controls the transfer of energy in the same manner as the sudden phase reversal of *c*.

The relation of the transfer of energy and the phase of the driving voltage is considered in more detail in Sec. 6 of Chap. VI.

6. Complete Transfer of Energy. Mathematically, the necessary condition for a complete transfer of energy is that the coefficients of the two components of current must be equal. Let us neglect resistance, for simplicity, and use Eq. (479) for i_1:

$$i_1 = A_{11} \sin \omega_1 t + A_{13} \sin \omega_3 t \qquad (479)$$

If ω_1 and ω_3 do not differ by more than about 25 per cent, it is more convenient to change the trigonometric form to that of a modulated wave.   Equation (479) may be rewritten as

$$i_1 = A_{11} \sin \left(\frac{\omega_1 t + \omega_3 t}{2} + \frac{\omega_1 t - \omega_3 t}{2} \right)$$
$$+ A_{13} \sin \left(\frac{\omega_1 t + \omega_3 t}{2} - \frac{\omega_1 t - \omega_3 t}{2} \right)$$

The sine terms may now be expanded as the sum and difference of two angles, and when terms are collected after expansion the result is

$$i_1 = (A_{11} + A_{13}) \sin \left(\frac{\omega_1 + \omega_3}{2} t \right) \cos \left(\frac{\omega_1 - \omega_3}{2} t \right)$$
$$+ (A_{11} - A_{13}) \cos \left(\frac{\omega_1 + \omega_3}{2} t \right) \sin \left(\frac{\omega_1 - \omega_3}{2} t \right) \quad (482)$$

Now, if A_{11} and A_{13} are equal, the second term of the right-hand member becomes zero, and current is described by the first term alone; it is a sine wave whose frequency is the average, or half the sum, of the natural frequencies of the network, and it is modulated by the cosine factor at a frequency equal to half the difference of the natural frequencies.   This (aside from the inevitable damping) is a perfect description of the curve of Fig. 53c; maximum amplitude of current corresponds to unity value of the cosine factor, while zero amplitude appears when the cosine is zero.

On the other hand, if the coefficients are of equal magnitude but opposite sign, the first term of Eq. (482) will disappear and the second term alone will define the current.   This term, a cosine wave modulated by a sine wave, is a description of Fig. 53d, which is the current in circuit 2.

It follows, then, that when transfer of energy is complete, the coefficients of Eqs. (479) and (480) are related:

$$\left. \begin{aligned} A_{11} &= A_{13} \\ A_{21} &= -A_{23} \end{aligned} \right\} \quad (483)$$

If the conditions of Eq. (483) are not met, there will be two components in the total current; there will be a component with sine modulation added to a component with cosine modulation, and since one component is of maximum amplitude when the other is zero, it follows that the amplitude of the total current will not periodically become zero.   This condition is particularly evident in curves *e* and *g* of Fig. 53, in which the current reaches a minimum amplitude but does not become zero.

The values of the coefficients for Eqs. (483) are given in Eqs. (475) to (478).   Unfortunately, the algebraic complexity is too great to permit an explicit solution for conditions to satisfy Eqs. (483).   But computation of specific numerical examples is not difficult, and it will be found that if the natural frequencies of the two circuits individually are equal, and the coefficient of coupling is small, the coefficients derived from Eqs. (475) to (478) will come very close to satisfying the conditions of Eqs. (483).   See Prob. 3, page 238.

An oscillographic study, as in Fig. 53, should whenever possible supplement the mathematical study of a network.

7. Approximate Computation.   *Frequency.*   Sometimes it is necessary to compute the complete and exact form of transient currents, such as those recorded in Fig. 53, but much more frequently it is enough for the engineer to know the frequencies of the transient components of current and the maximum amplitude to be expected.   The duration of the transient current may also be needed.   Approximate computations will quite readily determine these essential factors with a degree of accuracy that depends on the network conditions.

If resistance in the network is low enough to allow the currents to be freely oscillatory, their natural frequencies can be determined with very good precision from Eq. (448).   Although this expression for the natural angular velocities was derived for a network without resistance, it is an excellent approximation for a network with low resistance.   This is particularly fortunate, because most coupled circuits in which the transient current is of engineering importance have rather low resistance and so are amenable to approximate treatment of this kind.

If the coefficient of coupling is small, it is possible to consider the two natural frequencies of the network equal to the natural frequencies of the two individual circuits.   This approximation is useful if the coefficient of coupling is not greater than 0.1 or 0.15.   The amount of error due to this approximation is of the order of half the coefficient of coupling.   But Eq. (448) takes into account the mutual inductance and is the better approximation to use if it is applicable.

8. Approximate Amplitude.   Maximum current in circuit 1 may sometimes be found quite accurately by adding A_{11} and A_{13} as determined in Eqs. (475) and (476); however, these equations do not consider resistance and may not be used if the loss is so great that either current of the network is strongly damped.   But when Eq. (448) leads to satisfactory values for natural frequencies, Eqs. (475) and (476) are sufficiently accurate for amplitude.

Maximum current in circuit 2 may be found by adding A_{21} and A_{23} under the same restriction as to moderately low resistance, provided also that the two natural frequencies are quite different.   If one natural frequency is several times the other, the simple sum of coefficients is adequate to give the maximum amplitude.   But if the two natural frequencies are nearly equal, the maximum amplitude may come so long after the initial instant that much of the initial energy has been lost in resistance.   This is illustrated in Fig. 53j, for, although the entire energy of the system is transferred to circuit 2 by the time of the ninth half-cycle, it has been so attenuated by loss that the maximum amplitude of the current in circuit 2 is considerably reduced. In such a case, it is necessary to make some approximation of the amount of damping; this will be discussed a little later.

An even simpler approximation of the maximum current in circuit 1 is possible if the coefficient of coupling is small; with loose coupling, the transfer of energy to circuit 2 during the first half-cycle is small, and the initial current is almost unaffected by the presence of the second circuit.   So initial amplitude may be computed as if circuit 1 existed alone and the result will be a good approximation for a network in which the coefficient of coupling does not exceed 0.2 or 0.3.   If, at the same time, resistance is small, the initial amplitude is approximately equal to $\sqrt{C_1/L_{11}}$.   As an example, this value is adequate for any of the curves of i_1 in Fig. 53, but it is a rather poor approximation for Fig. 54a, because of the relatively close coupling in the latter case.

9. Approximate Duration.   The rate of damping of the current waves in a network of two circuits is due to loss in both circuits. However, if the natural frequencies of the circuits are so different and the coupling so loose that each circuit carries current of substantially one frequency only, we are justified in considering that the chief component of current is attenuated exponentially, the decrement factor being R/L for that circuit alone.   By this means the approximate duration of the transient current may be obtained.

If, however, the energy of the transient current is being transferred completely from one circuit to the other, as in the examples of Fig. 53 c and d, and i and j, the conditions are entirely different; in such a case there is loss first in one circuit and then in the other as the current flows in the two circuits alternately.   The maximum current in circuit 2 may be found as follows, if damping is negligibly small: At first all of the energy is in circuit 1, and when it is in magnetic form the current is the square root of twice the energy divided by the self-inductance.   When all of the energy has been transferred to the second circuit the same relation of current and energy is true with reference to the self-inductance of circuit 2.   The maximum currents, therefore, are in inverse proportion to the square roots of the self-inductances, or

$$\frac{\text{Maximum } i_2}{\text{Maximum } i_1} = \sqrt{\frac{L_{11}}{L_{22}}} \tag{484}$$

But when there is appreciable damping, as there will almost always be, the maximum value of i_2 obtained from Eq. (484) is too large and must be reduced by a factor that is dependent on the rate of loss and on the elapsed time.   The fact that the rate of loss is, in general, different in the two circuits must be taken into account.   If the two circuits have equal ratios of R/L they will have the same rate of energy loss, and if the ratios differ, an approximate damping factor may be obtained by finding an arithmetic mean:

$$\text{Approximate damping factor} = \epsilon^{-\frac{R_1 L_{22} + R_2 L_{11}}{2 L_{11} L_{22}} t} \tag{485}$$

Finally, then, if the transfer of energy is complete, the maximum amplitude of current in circuit 2 may be approximated by multiplying the value obtained from Eq. (484) by the factor expressed as (485), in which the value of time is that corresponding to complete transfer of energy.   This time is seen from Eq. (482) to be $\pi/(\omega_1 - \omega_3)$.

If the transfer of energy is not complete, it is possible to determine from the expression for i_1, Eq. (482), the fraction of energy that remains in circuit 1.   From this, the amount of energy transferred to circuit 2 is found, and, from the energy, the current is determined.

It is evident that the various approximate methods of computation that have been suggested do not cover all possible networks of coupled circuits. Particularly, those networks with large resistance are not easily attacked in even an approximate manner. But it is fortunate that the circuits that may be most readily handled are also those most often encountered in electrical engineering. And there remains always, as a last resort, the exact solution of the complete network.

10. The "Quenched Gap." It is interesting to consider again the operation of a spark transmitter for radiotelegraphy. The current in the initial circuit is discussed in Chap. IV, Sec. 17. But the effect of the coupled antenna circuit was neglected. The solution for current in the initial circuit was of the form shown in Fig. 53a: a damped sinusoid. We may now consider the form when the antenna circuit is effective; when the two circuits are correctly tuned, the result may be a wave of the form of Fig. 53 c or i, in the primary circuit, with a current such as d or j in the antenna. Complete transfer of energy from the primary circuit to the secondary circuit is highly desirable in the radio transmitter, for only energy in the antenna can be useful.

Operation of the transmitter is improved if energy is transferred to the antenna circuit and is not allowed to return to circuit 1. This can be accomplished by opening circuit 1 when the amplitude of i_1 becomes zero. See, for example, Fig. 55a; the upper record is current in the secondary, and the lower record is current in the primary of two coupled circuits. Energy was totally transferred from circuit 1 to circuit 2 in five cycles, and at the end of that time the switch in circuit 1 was opened. The total energy of the system was thereby trapped in circuit 2, and the current i_2 died away exponentially thereafter.

Contrast this to Fig. 55b, for which the primary circuit was not opened at the end of the first transfer of energy. It will be seen in the oscillogram that the energy was transferred from one circuit to the other five times, finally being trapped in circuit 2 at the end of 25 cycles. Remembering that current in circuit 2 is useful in radiating telegraph signals, whereas current in circuit 1 serves no useful purpose, it is plain that there is great advantage in the procedure that keeps the energy in circuit 2 with no unnecessary transfers of energy.

The oscillograms of Fig. 55 are not records of radio-frequency oscillations. The frequency of their wave is only about 300 cycles per sec. But the principle of the "quenched gap" is very clearly shown. In a radio transmitter, the trapping of

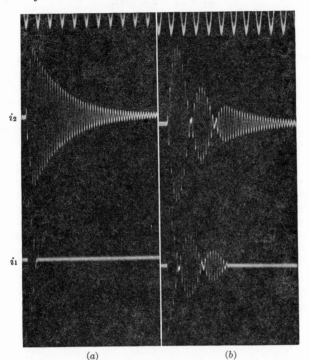

(a)   (b)

FIG. 55.—Current in tuned circuits, illustrating in (a) the effect of interrupting i_1, as by a "quenched gap." In (b) the interruption occurs at a later time. (*Oscillograms by T. A. Rogers, University of California.*)

energy in the antenna circuit is accomplished by quenching the spark in circuit 1 at the proper instant; current in circuit 1 is thereby interrupted as effectively as if a switch in the circuit were opened. Figure 25 in Chap. IV shows how the spark operates as a switch, and, if the gap is properly designed, it will be automatically quenched as the amplitude of current through it—that is, amplitude of i_1—becomes small.

As a matter of fact, all types of spark transmitters for radio-telegraphy are obsolete since the introduction of vacuum tubes.

Problems

1. A two-section filter for the keying circuit of a radiotelegraph transmitter is shown in the figure. This network provides better filtering than the one-section filter described in Prob. 8 of Chap. V. Network parameters are as follows:

$$L_1 = L_2 = 2 \text{ henrys.}$$
$$C_1 = C_2 = \quad 1 \text{ } \mu\text{f.}$$
$$R_1 = R_2 = \quad 100 \text{ ohms.}$$
$$r = 5000 \text{ ohms.}$$

Assuming R_1 and R_2 to be zero and r to be infinite, compute the voltage across S_1 and r as a function of time after closing S_2.

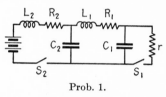

Prob. 1.

2. Taking into account the actual resistances of the filter network of Prob. 1 and with S_2 closed, find a good approximation of voltage across r after S_1 is closed.

3. Two circuits, each containing inductance and capacitance, but not resistance, would each individually have the same natural frequency. They are inductively coupled, and the charged condenser of one is suddenly allowed to discharge, the other circuit being until that instant at rest. Prove that the charge on the condenser in each circuit can be expressed as a function of time that is simply the product of a sine term and a cosine term. Show that this is nearly, but not quite, the condition to satisfy Eq. (483).

CHAPTER VIII

CIRCUITS WITH VARIABLE PARAMETERS

1. Flux. When the nature of inductance was considered in Sec. 3 of the first chapter, it was defined as a factor of proportionality between rate-of-change of current and induced voltage. In making use of inductance, it has been tacitly assumed that a constant factor of proportionality existed; it now becomes necessary to consider the behavior of networks in which the proportionality is not constant, inductance, therefore, being a variable quantity. When inductance is variable, its relationship to current is best expressed in terms of flux.

Magnetic flux is a physical concept that may be used as a mental steppingstone between rate-of-change of current and induced voltage; it may be considered that current produces flux and rate-of-change of flux induces voltage. This concept is particularly helpful when there is iron present and magnetic saturation results, for in such a case it is usual to consider that induced voltage is still proportional to the rate-of-change of flux, but that flux is no longer proportional to current. Written symbolically, with flux denoted by ϕ, and with N the number of times the flux links the circuit, the induced voltage is

$$e = N \frac{d\phi}{dt} \tag{486}$$

If there is no iron in the neighborhood of the circuit in which current flows, and no ferromagnetic alloy, flux is proportional to current; if iron is present in the magnetic field, and particularly if the iron becomes magnetically saturated, flux is not proportional to current but may be described as a function of current:

$$N\phi = f(i) \tag{487}$$

The relation expressed by this equation is most commonly and most satisfactorily represented by the magnetization curve, as in Fig. 56. Inductance of a circuit in which $N\phi$ flux linkages are produced by current i may now be expressed as

$$L = N \frac{d\phi}{di} \qquad (488)$$

In the equations that involve flux linkages, there may or may not be numerical coefficients, depending on the electric and magnetic units employed. If voltage, current, and inductance are in volts, amperes, and henrys, the flux may be expressed in webers, and there will be no need for numerical quantities other than the number of turns of the circuit. If, however, the flux is expressed in maxwells it is necessary to include also the factor 10^{-8} (this being the ratio of one maxwell to one weber).

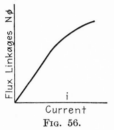

Current

Fig. 56.

Equation (488) is not a new definition of inductance, for even variable inductance is adequately defined by Eq. (1):

$$e = L \frac{di}{dt} \qquad (1)$$

It is permissible, however, to accept Eq. (488) as the definition of flux and, by combining it with Eq. (1), derive Eq. (486):

$$e = L \frac{di}{dt} = N \frac{d\phi}{di} \frac{di}{dt} = N \frac{d\phi}{dt} \qquad (489)$$

The fundamental magnetization curve is a plot of magnetic-flux density as a function of magnetic intensity: B as a function of H. With a given circuit, however, a similar curve will represent flux linkages as a function of current, and this is a more useful relation for purposes of the present discussion. For it may be seen from Eq. (488) that the slope of a curve of flux linkages as a function of current is inductance. When flux is directly proportional to current, as it is, practically, in the absence of ferromagnetic material, the magnetization curve is a straight line through the origin. In such a case the slope is constant, and the inductance is constant. When iron is present and the magnetization curve has the typical shape shown in Fig. 56, the inductance may be found (as a function of current) by measuring the slope at each point of the curve.

2. Voltage Equations with Variable Inductance. When inductance varies as a function of current the analytical methods of Chap. I cannot be applied. The voltage equation of a circuit with *variable* inductance is obviously not a differential equation with *constant* coefficients, and no other kind of differential equation has yet been considered. Analytical solutions for currents in such circuits are sometimes possible, and as the first step it is necessary to find an analytical expression to describe the magnetization curve. There are many combinations of functions which may be fitted to an experimentally determined magnetization curve. The most common and, because of its simplicity, the best, is known as Fröhlich's equation:

$$N\phi = \frac{ai}{b + i} \tag{490}$$

This equation[1] was originally supposed to be rational, but is now generally used as an empirical expression in which a and b are selected to give good agreement between the equation and an experimentally determined magnetization curve. By means of Fröhlich's equation, flux may be eliminated from Eq. (489), leaving induced voltage expressed in terms of current and time.

In the simplest circuit, of resistance and inductance only, with constant voltage suddenly applied, a solution can be obtained by separation of the variables as in Sec. 6 of Chap. I. The voltage equation for such a circuit is

$$Ri + Lpi = E$$

By means of Eq. (488), inductance may be expressed in terms of flux linkages:

$$Ri + N \frac{d\phi}{di} \frac{di}{dt} = E \tag{491}$$

or

$$Ri + N \frac{d\phi}{dt} = E \tag{492}$$

By simple transposition

$$dt = \frac{N \, d\phi}{E - Ri}$$

[1] The fundamental form of Fröhlich's equation is

$$B = \frac{aH}{b + H}$$

but $N\phi$ is proportional to B and i to H.

and by integration

$$t = \int \frac{N \, d\phi}{E - Ri} \qquad (493)$$

Performance of the integration indicated in Eq. (493) would complete the solution for current as a function of time. To make this integration possible it is necessary either to express ϕ in terms of i or i in terms of ϕ. Fröhlich's equation (490) gives the necessary relation, and the analytical solution is accomplished by substituting Fröhlich's equation in (493) and integrating. The mathematics encountered in the solution is slightly involved.

3. Graphical Solution. The integration indicated in Eq. (493) may be done graphically, and this is often the better means of solution. The graphical solution makes direct use of the magnetization curve, and Fröhlich's equation is not needed. The essential steps in the graphical solution are as follows.

First, plot the magnetization curve as determined experimentally. The standard method of plotting the magnetization curve is based on measurements with a ballistic galvanometer. Simultaneous oscillographic records of current and voltage also contain the necessary data for plotting the magnetization curve, and the convenience of the oscillographic method will usually outweigh the disadvantage of lesser accuracy. The cathode-ray oscillograph is particularly adapted to presenting the magnetization curve directly on its screen, by means of a special circuit.[1] The magnetization curve of the field circuit of a motor or generator is readily plotted from measurements of field current and induced voltage at constant speed, provided the necessary information is available for converting induced voltage to flux. However it is obtained, the curve may be plotted as in Fig. 56.

If the magnetization curve is a loop, due to hysteresis, the problem can still be solved if the proper loop is followed in the proper direction. It must be known whether the current during the transient period will be increasing or decreasing, and the initial condition of magnetization of the core must also be known. If the core is soft iron and has an air gap, it is usually possible to neglect hysteresis.

[1] See, for example, Johnson, J. B., A Braun Tube Hysteresigraph, *Bell System Tech. Jour.*, **8**, 286, 1929.

For graphical integration, it is somewhat more convenient to plot the curve as in Fig. 57a, with the axes interchanged from their usual positions.

Second, a curve, Fig. 57b, of $1/(E - Ri)$ is plotted. Select in a a value of flux linkages, such as $N\phi_1$, and locate on the magnetization curve the corresponding value of current i_1. Project $N\phi_1$ downward as the abcissa of Fig. 57b and compute $i/(E - Ri_1)$ to be the corresponding ordinate. Compute enough points in this manner to make it possible to draw the curve of Fig. 57b.

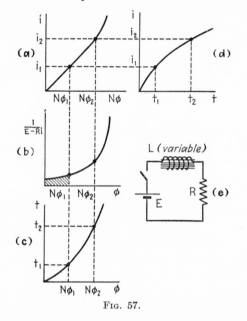

Fig. 57.

The ordinates will become large without limit as the steady-state condition is approached and Ri approaches E, but the practical computation can be carried as near to the steady state as is desired. Equation (493) shows that area under this curve is proportional to time.

Third, determine the area under the curve between the vertical axis and $N\phi_1$. This area is crosshatched in Fig. 57b. This area is a measure of time and is plotted in Fig. 57c as the ordinate t_1 corresponding to $N\phi_1$. Area under the curve as far as $N\phi_2$ is t_2. When enough such points have been plotted, the curve of t as a function of ϕ can be drawn. It should be recognized that 1 sec.

of time is represented in Fig. 57b by the area of a rectangle 1 weber wide and 1 reciprocal volt high; this relation provides the time scale for Fig. 57c. The integration has now been accomplished, and flux is known as a function of time.

Finally, to find current as a function of time, the values of flux are referred back to the magnetization curve. The value $N\phi_1$, for instance, is projected up to Fig. 57a, and the corresponding current i_1 is carried over to Fig. 57d. But t_1 is the time at which flux linkages are $N\phi_1$; it is therefore the time at which current is i_1. So t_1 is the abcissa and i_1 the ordinate of a point on the current curve in Fig. 57d.

This curve is the solution of the problem. It may be determined without great difficulty and with as much accuracy as the data in any case may warrant. Although the graphical method is illustrated here by a single example only, it may be used for the solution of any voltage equation in which the variables—time and current—can be separated for integration. The necessity for separation of the variables is seen in Eq. (493), for only with time on one side of the equation and current on the other side can a solution be obtained by integration.

4. Other Variable Parameters. Inductance is not the only quantity that may vary. Certain crystalline materials, such as carborundum, galena, and others, have the unusual property of high electrical resistance when current density is low and low resistance when current density is high. Electric discharge in gas shows a similar variation of resistance between electrodes, and some porous materials also have lowered resistance to high current densities. The ability to pass large current with relatively small increase of voltage makes such materials useful in lightning arresters. The transient behaviour of circuits containing elements of variable resistance is therefore of great importance. If the circuit consists of inductance and resistance only, or of capacitance and resistance only, the method of graphical integration is readily available.

It is not usual for capacitance to vary as a known function of current, but if it should, and if current and time could be separated in the voltage equation, a graphical solution would be readily possible.

It is necessary to distinguish between variation of parameters that is related in a definite manner to current, such as the change of inductance with iron and the change of resistance of lightning-arrester material, and variation that is controlled by some other factor. An example of the latter sort of variation is the change of inductance of a magnetically operated mechanism, as the armature of the magnet moves and shortens the air gap. The time required to close a solenoid-operated oil switch is influenced by this sort of change. Another example is the variation of resistance of an electric-light filament with temperature. It is evident that it is not possible to take changes of this kind into account in the graphical solution, for their amounts are not known without that time relation whose determination is the object of the solution.

The most important kind of variation that is precluded from the problem is change of applied voltage as a function of time. With alternating voltage, for instance, it is not possible to solve by separation of the variables. In Fig. 57b, the ordinate $1/(e - Ri)$ cannot be found if the voltage varies with time, for to find e it is necessary to know time and to find Ri it is necessary to know current, and it is not possible to know both.

The arrangement of curves for graphical solution can be varied to suit the problem. There are many ways of grouping the variables and of plotting the curves, and certain attacks are specially advantageous in special cases. But all are fundamentally the same; separation of the variables, followed by graphical integration, is the basis of each, and the details can best be arranged in accordance with the conditions of specific problems.

5. An Example of Graphical Solution. The magnetization curve of a certain 55-kva. alternating-current generator is shown in Fig. 58, field current being plotted as a function of field flux linkages. (To determine this curve a temporary exploring coil was threaded through the air gap of the machine. The exploring coil had four turns, and 16.3 volts was induced in it at 40 amp. field current. An oscillograph showed the air-gap flux to be practically sinusoidal. From the induced voltage, the rate-of-change of flux, and hence the maximum flux, is easily computed. The field winding has 440 turns, which, multiplied by flux, gives linkages. This method is not exact, as it neglects leakage flux from the field and neglects various other minor factors, but for many purposes it is satisfactory.) The resistance of the field circuit is 3.03 ohms, and the machine is equipped with a field-discharge resistor of 7.00 ohms.   The connection is as in Fig. 7b, page 26, so that when the field switch is opened the energy of the field is absorbed by the total resistance of 10.03 ohms.

The field switch is opened to the discharge position when the field current is 40 amp.   Plot the diminishing field current as a function of time.

Solution: First, the magnetization curve that corresponds to Fig. 57a is given as one of the curves of Fig. 58 (*i vs. Nϕ*).

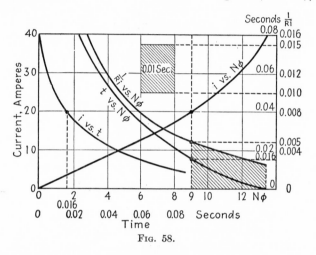

Fig. 58.

Second, a curve of $1/Ri$ is plotted; this takes the place of the curve of $1/(E - Ri)$ of Fig. 57b, for in this special problem there is no applied voltage and E is zero.   The voltage equation for the field-discharge circuit is

$$Ri + L\frac{di}{dt} = 0 \tag{6}$$

which leads to

$$t = -\int \frac{1}{Ri} N \, d\phi \tag{494}$$

so that integration of $1/Ri$, with proper attention to sign, gives time.   The following illustration will serve to show the means of locating points on the $1/Ri$ curve: when current is 20 amp. the flux linkages are 9.0; resistance is 10.0 ohms, so $1/Ri$ is 0.0050; a point on the curve, at 9.0 flux linkages and 0.0050 reciprocal volts is thereby located.   When enough such points are found the curve is drawn through them. This curve is superimposed on the magnetization curve in Fig. 58, using the same horizontal scale of flux linkages.

Third, the integration of Eq. (494) is done graphically by measuring area under the curve. Integration begins at the initial point, which corresponds to 40 amp. field current and 13.5 flux linkages, and, since it proceeds from right to left, the integral is negative, and time, from Eq. (494), is positive. The area under the curve between the limits (of flux linkages) of 13.5 and 9.0 is crosshatched in the figure and represents time required for flux linkages to diminish from 13.5 to 9.0. A rectangular area is shown in the upper part of the figure for comparison; it is 2 units (flux linkages) wide and 0.005 units (reciprocal volts) high, so its area is 0.01 sec. Since the crosshatched area under the curve is six-tenths greater than this, it represents 0.016 sec., and the first point on a time curve is determined. When enough such areas are measured and the corresponding times plotted, there results the curve of time versus flux linkages, which is also superimposed upon the other curves of Fig. 58.

Finally, the curve of current as a function of time is plotted. Since the time versus flux linkages curve shows that when time is 0.016 sec. there are 9.0 flux linkages, and since the magnetization curve shows that when there are 9.0 flux linkages there is a current of 20 amp., it follows that when time is 0.016 sec. the current is 20 amp. This gives a point on the curve of current versus time, and enough such points are found to determine the curve. Note that for convenience this latter curve is drawn with a horizontal time scale, whereas flux linkages are plotted against a vertical time scale; the only purpose of the horizontal time scale is to bring the current curve into its usual orientation.

As would be expected from the behavior of the saturated iron in the circuit, current falls very rapidly at first, while current is large and inductance low. As inductance becomes greater, the current diminishes much more gradually. After the straight part of the magnetization curve is reached, the current diminishes according to a simple exponential law, for inductance has become constant.

6. Point-by-point Solution. When all other attacks fail, there is available the point-by-point method of solution. In

Chap. I for the inductive circuit, and in Chap. II for the capacitive circuit, we considered in a qualitative way how a circuit must behave from moment to moment as current changes. Figures 2 and 9 were used for illustration. It will be recalled that in Fig. 2 the current at time t_2 was found from conditions at the slightly earlier moment t_1; and current at t_3, in turn, was found from conditions at t_2, and so on. By continuing thus, in finite steps, the current-time relation can be progressively developed.

It is mentioned in those early chapters that the use of intervals of time from t_1 to t_2 and from t_2 to t_3 in steps of finite length is inexact, but that the solution becomes precise if the steps are infinitesimal. To handle infinitesimal variations, the use of calculus is introduced, and differential equations are developed.

Now, however, it is found that in many cases the differential equations cannot be solved. Several situations that do not admit of exact solution have arisen in the present chapter. So, to avoid mathematical difficulties, let us return to the use of finite intervals. A methodical procedure may be developed, which will yield quantitative values of current as a function of time.

Let us attempt a point-by-point solution of a circuit of inductance and resistance, with constant voltage suddenly applied. The circuit equation is

$$Ri + Lpi = E \qquad (495)$$

This may be written

$$pi = \frac{E - Ri}{L} \qquad (496)$$

At the initial instant, when time is zero, current is zero, and $pi = E/L$. This initial derivative is correct for an instant only. But let us assume that it remains correct during a period of time that is short, yet of finite duration. Then at the end of the period there will be current equal to the product of the initial derivative and the incremental time. If, in a specific circuit, $R = 10$ ohms, $L = 1$ henry, and $E = 100$ volts, the initial derivative will be 100 amp. per sec. Assuming that this rate of increase continues during 0.02 sec., the current at the end of that interval will be 2.0 amp.

A second increment of time is now considered. At the beginning of this second time interval the current is 2.0 amp., so the resistance drop is 20 volts, and the voltage across the inductance is 80. The rate of change of current is therefore 80, and during 0.02 sec. there is an increase of current of 1.6 amp. (assuming the same rate of change to continue during the interval). This, added to the current at the beginning of the second interval, gives 3.6 amp. as the current at the end of the second interval. Tabulation of results, as the solution progresses, is practically necessary, and the following table is a convenient one for the problem under consideration.

(1)	(2)	(3)	(4)	(5)	(6)	(7)	(8)
t	i	Δt	L	$E - Ri$	$pi = \dfrac{E-Ri}{L}$	$\Delta i = \Delta t \cdot pi$	$i' = i + \Delta i$
0	0	0.02	1.0	100	100	2.0	2.0
0.02	2.0	0.02	1.0	80	80	1.6	3.6
0.04	3.6	0.02	1.0	64	64	1.28	4.9
0.06	4.9	0.02	1.0	51	51	1.02	5.9
0.08	5.9						

The first column, t, gives the time at the beginning of each increment; the second column gives the corresponding current. The third column gives the length of the increment of time. The fourth column, L, is for the inductance of the circuit. The fifth column is computed from known values of E and R, together with the value of i from column 2. For the sixth column, pi is computed from the two preceding columns, and for the seventh column the increment of current is found by assuming the derivative of current to remain constant during the interval. Finally, the current at the end of the interval, i', is found by adding the increment of current to i. Since the current at the end of one interval is the current at the beginning of the next, i' of one tabular row becomes i of the next row.

In our problem, when time is zero, i is zero. We have selected 0.02 as the length of Δt. L is given as 1.0, and the initial inductance voltage, current derivative, current increment, and final current are entered in their respective columns. In the second row, time is 0.02 sec. Current, from the last column of the

previous row, is 2 amp.   The same increment of time is used
again. $E - Ri$ is now 80.   The derivative is therefore 80, the
increment of current is 1.6, and the current at the end of the
interval is 3.6.   During the next interval the current increases
1.28 amp. to 4.88, and so on.   The solution is continued in this
way, step by step, until the significant part of the transient current has been determined.   The result is in the first two columns
of the tabulation, which give current as a function of time.

The accuracy of the point-by-point solution is evidently
dependent upon the length of the increment of time employed.
Some error is inherent in the method, but the error may be
reduced to a negligible amount by taking sufficiently short steps
from point to point.   The length of step to be used is a matter
for careful judgment, for if steps are too short the labor is greatly
increased, whereas if steps are too long the error is too great to
be neglected.   As a guide in selecting the best increment of time
it should be remembered that error arises from assuming constant
rate-of-change of current during a finite time; the best increment
of time is the longest interval for which this assumption is substantially true.   When the rate-of-change of current is changing
rapidly, and the curve of current is sharply bent, the steps must
be short, but the gently sloping parts of the current curve may
be covered rapidly with increments of time that are relatively
few and long.

There is no limit to the adaptability of the point-by-point
method.   It makes possible a solution for current in any network.
Any or all of the parameters may vary.   The voltage may change
in any manner.   Mechanical motion of the circuits, as in generators, or of the magnetic parts, as in relays, may be taken
into account.   There is but one restriction: whatever takes place
must be related to the network's behavior in a known *quantitative* manner.

If inductance changes, it must be a known function of current,
of time, or of some other quantity that, in turn, is related to
current or time.   In the above tabulation, a column was included
for inductance, to be used if inductance were not constant.
Since, in the numerical example for which the table was used,
inductance was constant, there was no need for such a column.
But if inductance had varied, its value at the beginning of each
increment of time would have been entered in that column.

It would have been necessary, therefore, to know the value of inductance that corresponded to each particular time or to each particular value of current. It is quite common for inductance to vary as a function of current, as it does when iron in the magnetic system becomes saturated, and in such a case its value for use in the point-by-point tabulation may be taken from the magnetization curve.

If resistance varies as a known function of current, its value for use in computation should be determined at each step. Sometimes, however, resistance varies in a manner that is very difficult to take into account. The resistance of the filament of an electric light, for instance, varies with temperature. The temperature is due to the current, but can be related to it only by proper consideration of thermal capacity and radiation of heat.

7. An Example of Point-by-point Solution. An alternating-current generator is described in Sec. 5 of this chapter, with the object of determining the rate of discharge of its field circuit after opening the field switch. We will now repeat the determination of field current as a function of time, using the point-by-point method of solution. The magnetization curve of the generator appears in Fig. 58, and the solution is facilitated by plotting a curve of inductance. Inductance is

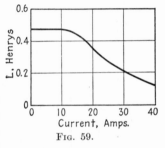

Fig. 59.

the derivative of the magnetization curve with respect to current, and it is plotted in Fig. 59.

Solution: When the voltage equation of the field-discharge circuit is adapted to the point-by-point method of solution, it becomes

$$pi = -\frac{Ri}{L}$$

A tabulation shown on page 252 is now prepared to include the necessary computations, organized on the basis of assumed constant rate-of-change of current during short but finite periods.

It will be seen that the size of the time increment is changed several times during the course of the solution; the best size is determined partly by judgment and partly by trial. If pi, in the sixth column, changes very greatly from one step to the next, it is an indication that there will be appreciable error in the result, for the basic assumption of the method is that there is negligible change in pi during any one period. In this particular solution the accuracy could be improved by taking more steps of length 0.002 sec. But it is not reasonable to attempt a greater accuracy in the result than existed in the original data, and that consideration must limit the effort to be expended on computation.

(1)	(2)	(3)	(4)	(5)	(6)	(7)	(8)
t	i	Δt	L	Ri	$pi = -\dfrac{Ri}{L}$	$\Delta i = \Delta t \cdot pi$	$i' = i + \Delta i$
0	40.0	0.001	0.118	400	−3380	−3.4	36.6
0.001	36.6	0.001	0.14	366	−2610	−2.6	34.0
0.002	34.0	0.001	0.17	340	−2000	−2.0	32.0
0.003	32.0	0.001	0.19	320	−1680	−1.7	30.3
0.004	30.3	0.001	0.21	303	−1440	−1.4	28.9
0.005	28.9	0.002	0.22	289	−1310	−2.6	26.3
0.007	26.3	0.002	0.25	263	−1050	−2.1	24.2
0.009	24.2	0.002	0.28	242	− 865	−1.7	22.5
0.011	22.5	0.004	0.31	225	− 725	−2.9	19.6
0.015	19.6	0.005	0.36	196	− 545	−2.7	16.9
0.020	16.9	0.005	0.41	169	− 413	−2.1	14.8
0.025	14.8	0.005	0.44	148	− 336	−1.7	13.1
0.030	13.1	0.010	0.46	131	− 285	−2.8	10.3
0.040	10.3	0.010	0.475	103	− 217	−2.2	8.1
0.050	8.1	0.010	0.475	81	− 170	−1.7	6.4
0.060	6.4	0.010	0.475	64	− 135	−1.3	5.1
0.070	5.1	0.010	0.475	51	− 107	−1.1	4.0
0.080	4.0						

Data from the first two columns of the tabulation are used to plot current as a function of time in Fig. 60. The solution of the same problem by graphical integration is included in Fig. 60 for comparison. The graphical solution, if accurately done, will give a result that is exact, rather than approximate, so the divergence between the two curves may be considered as the error of the point-by-point method.

8. A Revised Point-by-point Method. The accuracy of the point-by-point solution can be increased by determining a sort of average value of pi, instead of assuming that its initial value continues throughout each interval. The value of pi at the beginning of each time interval is obtained as before, and it is multiplied by the increment of time to obtain an approximate increment of current. An approximate value of i' is thereby found, which is used to compute a new value of pi. The new value of pi may be considered to be the derivative of current at the end of the interval, whereas the former value of pi was the derivative of current at the beginning of the interval. By taking an average of these two derivatives a value is obtained that is more nearly correct, over the entire interval, than either derivative alone, and the increment of current during the interval is recomputed by using the average derivative. Each successive step is performed in this manner.

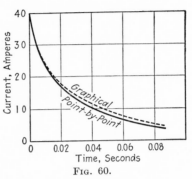

Fig. 60.

The accuracy is far greater than with the simple point-by-point method, for the approximation of constant derivative of current during an interval has been partially corrected.

Let us illustrate the use of the revised method by solving again for current in a circuit which consists of 1 henry inductance in series with 10 ohms resistance, to which 100 volts is suddenly applied. This same circuit is considered in Sec. 6 of this chapter, and the solutions may be compared. The tabulation must be

t	i	Δt	Init. pi	First approx.		Final pi	Aver. pi	Δi	i'
				Δi	i'				
(1)	(2)	(3)	(4)	(5)	(6)	(7)	(8)	(9)	(10)
0	0	0.02	100.0	2.00	2.00	80.0	90.0	1.80	1.80
0.02	1.80	0.02	82.0	1.64	3.44	65.6	73.8	1.48	3.28
0.04	3.28	0.02	67.2	1.34	4.62	53.8	60.5	1.21	4.49
0.06	4.49	0.02	55.1	1.10	5.59	44.1	49.6	.99	5.48
0.08	5.48								

changed to accommodate the revised method, as shown on page 253, adding columns for the first approximate values of current derivative and current increment.

The use of this table needs little explanation. The first six columns correspond to the previous table, and values of Δi and i' as first approximation are computed as before. For "Final pi," use i' from column six in the equation $pi = (E - Ri)/L$, and average with "Init. pi" to obtain "Aver. pi." The last two columns are then computed by multiplying the average derivative of time by the increment of time, and adding the initial current i.

The much greater accuracy obtained by use of the revised method is shown in the following table.

Time	Exact value of current	Revised pt.-by-pt. method with $\Delta t = 0.02$	Revised pt.-by-pt. method with $\Delta t = 0.04$	Simple pt.-by-pt. method with $\Delta t = 0.02$
0	0	0	0	0
0.02	1.81	1.80	...	2.0
0.04	3.30	3.28	3.2	3.6
0.06	4.51	4.49	...	4.9
0.08	5.51	5.48	5.4	5.9

The exact value of current, for the table, is computed from Eq. (19) of Chap. I. It will be seen that the error of the revised method is less than one-tenth the error of the simple method when the same time increment is used. In another column of the table, there appear values computed by the revised point-by-point method with time increments of double length; this column is of interest because the labor of computation is about the same as when using the simple method with shorter steps, and the accuracy is considerably greater.

9. Solution for Oscillatory Current. Circuits that contain condensers are also amenable to the point-by-point solution. The tabulation must be extended to include columns for charge on the condenser. Charge is determined at each point as the integral of current, and condenser voltage is found by dividing charge by capacitance.

As an illustration, consider a circuit of inductance, resistance, and capacitance. The voltage equation is

$$Lpi + Ri + \frac{1}{Cp}i = E \tag{147}$$

Charge on the condenser, q, is the integral of current:

$$q = \frac{1}{p}i$$

The derivative of current is obtained from Eq. (147) as

$$pi = \frac{1}{L}\left(E - Ri - \frac{q}{C}\right) \tag{497}$$

Let the suddenly applied voltage E be 100 volts, inductance 1 henry, resistance 1 ohm, and capacitance 0.1 farad. A convenient tabular form for the computation is shown below, and the first rows of computed values have been entered.

(1)	(2)	(3)	(4)	(5)	(6)	(7)	(8)	(9)	(10)
t	i	q	Δt	pi	$\Delta i =$ $pi \cdot \Delta t$	$i' =$ $i + \Delta i$	Aver. i	$\Delta q =$ (Av. i)Δt	$q' =$ $q + \Delta q$
0	0	0	0.2	100	20	20	10	2.0	2.0
0.2	20	2.0	0.2	60	12	32	26	5.2	7.2
0.4	32	7.2	0.2	− 4	− 1	31	32	6.3	13.5
0.6	31	13.5	0.2	− 66	−13	18	24	4.9	18.4
0.8	18	18.4	0.2	−102	−20	− 2	8	1.6	20.0
1.0	− 2	20.0	0.2	−102	−20	−22	−12	−2.4	17.6
1.2	−22	17.6							

It must be emphasized at once that the increments of time in this computation are much too great. The error is excessive. Figure 61 shows the results of the computation plotted as a function of time, and it is evident that the assumption of constant derivative of current throughout each increment of time is in no way justified by the facts. The sharp corners on the current curve are a sign of trouble. It happens that current in this circuit of constant parameters can be determined exactly by solution of the differential equation, and the current so obtained is plotted in Fig. 61 as a dash-line. The point-by-point method with such extravagantly long steps is in error at the current crest by more than 20 per cent. This is no reflection on the point-by-point method, however, for with 20 times as many steps (with increments of time reduced to 0.01 sec.) the accuracy is good; it is, rather, a warning against the use of unrestrained increments of time.

Computation is based on Eq. (497); a derivative of current is computed and is then used to determine increments of current and charge. Let us consider specifically the step from 0.2 to 0.4 sec. This corresponds to the second row of the tabulation. The first column is for the time at the beginning of the interval, 0.2. Current and charge at this instant are copied from i' and q' of the previous row, and appear in the second and third columns. In the fourth column is the increment of time, and the fifth column contains the derivative of

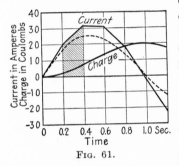

Fig. 61.

current as computed from Eq. (497). Assuming this derivative to continue through 0.2 sec., the increment of current is determined to be 12 amp. Since current at the beginning of the interval was 20 amp., current at the end of the interval is 32 amp., and this value occupies the seventh column. The charge accumulated on the condenser during

this interval is the integral of current; graphically, it is the area under the current curve during the interval and is indicated by cross-hatching in Fig. 61. The area of this trapezoidal figure is found by multiplying the base by the average altitude, which, in this case, means the time increment by the average current. For this purpose the average of i, 20 amp., at the beginning of the interval, and i', 32 amp., at the end of the interval, is entered as "Aver. i" in the eighth column; it is 26 amp. When multiplied by the time increment, it gives the increment of charge, 5.2, as in the ninth column, and charge at the end of the interval is found by adding to it the charge at the beginning of the interval. That value of final charge, 7.2, and the final current, 32, are then transferred to the next row of the tabulation. In this manner the computation may be continued indefinitely.

The chief error in the computation is due to the fact that charge on the condenser is not taken into account as it gradually accumulates but is taken all in one lump at the end of each step. Only at the end of the time interval is a new derivative of current determined. The result is that charge is not taken into account until some time after it has actually appeared on the condenser; there is a time lag between the appearance of charge and its effect on the computed action of the circuit. The same fallacious lag is in the computed condenser voltage. In the computation, therefore, the condenser voltage is not in quadrature with the current, as it properly should be; instead, there is a computed component of condenser voltage in phase with the current that is in reality nonexistent but which affects the computations as if it were a source of energy. The point-by-point computation will yield a damped sine wave that is damped less than it ought to be. In an extreme case the computation may even lead to a cumulative oscillation that increases with time, instead of dying away. In the computation for Fig. 61 the effect of the spurious component of condenser voltage is just great enough to balance the true damping of the circuit's resistance, and the point-by-point solution with time increments of 0.2 sec. gives an oscillatory current that is practically undamped.

10. Mechanical Solution. Like other errors of the point-by-point solution, this error is greatly reduced by use of shorter steps. The ideal computation would require an unlimited number of steps, each of infinitesimal length. Only in this way could changes in current and charge be immediately reflected in the computation. But this ideal can never be attained in the point-by-point method.

Machines have been devised for the solution of differential equations and operate on the same fundamental principle as the point-by-point method—that is, they develop a solution gradually, as does the point-by-point method, determining the result at each instant by means of the accumulated, integrated, results of previous instants. They employ mechanical integration. In the "Differential Analyzer"[1] for example, a series of integrating machines is interconnected, and it can be so arranged that input is continuously responsive to output. The Analyzer is superior, therefore, in this respect, to point-by-point solution, for in the latter the input (that is, rate of change of current) is responsive to output (that is, current and charge) only at the end of each finite increment of time.

---

[1] For a discussion of the Differential Analyzer see V. Bush, *J. Franklin Inst.*, **212**, 447–488, 1931.

But despite the inherent inaccuracy of the point-by-point solution, it is an extremely valuable tool in the solution of non-linear circuits and, furthermore, of all nonlinear physical systems. The error can always be reduced to an insignificant amount, although at the expense of increasing the arithmetical labor of the solution. When other expedients have failed, it is well to remember the point-by-point solution, for its range of application is very wide.

Problems

1. Compute the starting current in a magnetic relay, a magnetic holding coil, or some similar device. Assume that sinusoidal alternating voltage is

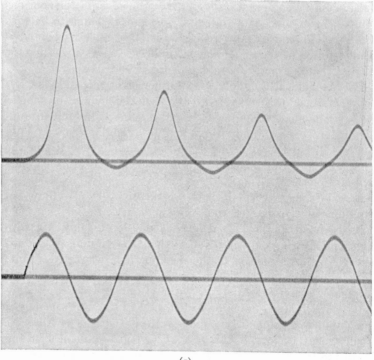

(a)

OSCILLOGRAM 7.—Starting current in a coil with an iron core when alternating voltage is applied. Record *a* shows transient current and voltage; record *b*, page 259, shows steady-state current and voltage with abnormally high applied voltage. For use with Prob. 1 of Chap. VIII.

applied when the voltage is instantaneously zero and that the amplitude of the voltage is sufficient to produce marked saturation of the magnetic circuit. Determine experimentally the magnetization curve of the magnetic circuit of the relay and the resistance of its winding.

Record an oscillogram of current under the same conditions, and compare the experimentally determined curve of current with a curve of computed results.

The magnetic device used must be selected with certain conditions in mind. Its iron core must be laminated, and there must be no metallic path about all or any part of the core. This is necessary to prevent flow of current in paths that would constitute additional circuits in the network

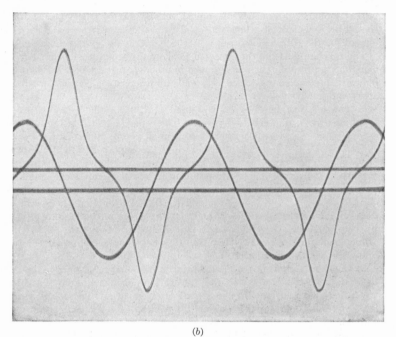

(b)

OSCILLOGRAM 7.—For descriptive legend see page 258.

being tested. The problem is greatly simplified if hysteresis is negligible; for this reason it is better to use a device with an air gap in the magnetic circuit than one (such as a transformer) with an unbroken iron core. The winding must be such that it is possible to saturate the magnetic circuit.

Should it be inconvenient to do the necessary laboratory work, the following example may be used. The holding coil of a standard commercial motor-starting compensator was tested, with the armature of the holding coil in the fully closed position. The "shading" ring, designed to prevent chattering, was removed.

To obtain the magnetization curve, oscillogram 7b was recorded; this has two curves. The upper curve is current through the coil, the lower curve is the sinusoidal applied voltage. The applied voltage had an effective (r.m.s.) value of 342 volts. To avoid confusing the record, no line was recorded on the photograph for calibration of the current wave, but by measurement on the ground-glass screen of the oscillograph it was found that the crests of the current wave were 1.90 amp.

The transient record is reproduced as oscillogram 7*a*. Transient current is the upper curve; it has the same vertical scale as current in oscillogram 7*b*. Applied voltage appears as the lower curve. The effective (r.m.s.) value of applied voltage was 207 volts (rated voltage is 220) and steady current through the coil at this voltage was 0.222 amp. The resistance of the coil was 24.1 ohms. Frequency of applied voltage was 60 cycles per sec. A special arrangement of relays was used to close the switch at the correct instant for the transient record.

The solution must not be expected to show the accurate agreement with experimental results that was obtained in other chapters, unless it is carried out with meticulous care. In case of large discrepancy, explain where it arises and how it could be avoided.

2. The network here shown was used for testing the behaviour of a lightning-arrester material (Thyrite).[1] The capacitance C_1, of the impulse generator, was given an initial charge of known voltage. Breakdown of the gap G permitted the capacitor to discharge through the network, and through the test specimen S. Cathode-ray oscillograms of voltage across the specimen and of current through it were obtained. It is known that the specimen does not have constant resistance and that its current and voltage are related by the equation $e = Ki^{\frac{1}{2}}$, the constant K being about 700. Write the voltage equations of the two circuits. How could one solve for current and voltage in the test specimen?

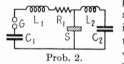

Prob. 2.

3. Consider initial current and initial rate-of-change of current in the network of Prob. 2. Remembering that the specimen is a perfect insulator when there is no current through it, will there be any initial voltage across it? Any initial current through it? Any initial rate of change of current through it?

4. If there were appreciable hysteresis in the magnetic device used in Prob. 1, as there would be in a transformer, what additional data would be needed in the solution of the problem?

5. Explain the effect of both saturation and hysteresis in producing a large initial surge of current when voltage is suddenly applied to a transformer.

6. The crankshaft of a Diesel engine, equipped with a vibration damper, is represented in the diagram. The large flywheel A is considered to have infinite moment of inertia. The small flywheel B represents the relatively small moment of inertia of the crankshaft and moving engine parts. The

[1] Nuttall, A. K., D. R. Hartree, and A. Porter, The Response of a Non-linear Electric Circuit to an Impulse, *Proc. Cambridge Phil. Soc.*, **32**, part 2, 304, 1936.

elastance of the shaft S between A and B is the elastance of the actual crankshaft. Driving force of the pistons, exerted on the crankshaft at B, has a sinusoidal component that produces torsional vibration of the flywheels B and C and the shaft S. If the frequency of the input torque is near the natural frequency of vibration, stress in the shaft is dangerous. C is the damper; it is not rigidly keyed to the shaft, but is held by friction; the friction is capable of exerting a certain torque on the damper flywheel, but if that torque is exceeded the flywheel slips on the shaft. This occurs if vibration becomes excessive. When the damper is slipping, its torque is constant, independent of velocity of slip. Elastance of the shaft S' is negligible.[1]

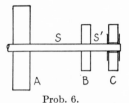

Prob. 6.

Write the differential equation of motion of the system when the damper is not slipping, and find an electric circuit with an analogous differential equation. Write the differential equation that applies while the damper is slipping. Define the properties of an electric network that would be analogous. Is such an analogous system practicable?

7. Plot motion of the damper described in Prob. 6. Assume any desired starting conditions, and plot until the steady operation of the damper, including slipping, is determined.

[1] Skilling, H. H., An Electric Analog of Friction, *Trans. A.I.E.E.*, **50**, 1155, September, 1931.

CHAPTER IX

TRAVELING WAVES

1. Transmission Lines. When an electric circuit or network is contained within the walls of a single room, it is often possible to neglect the inductance and capacitance of interconnecting wires. There is a magnetic field around every such wire, and an electric field between such wires, but the inductance and capacitance are small. The distributed inductance and capacitance of the wires will have little effect on the current-time relationships of the network, for they are overshadowed by the lumped inductance of coils and the lumped capacitance of condensers. However, if connecting lines are relatively long, their distributed parameters must be taken into account.[1]

Because the importance of distributed parameters is relative, it is only by consideration of the entire network that one can know whether or not the distributed inductance and capacitance are negligible. At the higher frequencies of radio communication a few feet of wire will constitute a very long transmission line, while on the other hand the transient phenomena of large electric generators are substantially unaffected by many miles of connected line.

Sometimes it is necessary to consider the inductance of a transmission line even though, for the phenomena being considered, the capacitance is negligible. In such a case, the inductance may be treated as if it were a lumped inductance, for the same current flows through all of it. This is also true of the distributed resistance of a transmission line. It is only when the distributed capacitance of a line by-passes an appreciable part of the entering current that the peculiar phenomena of traveling waves appear.

2. An Approximate Network. Let us consider that the inductance and capacitance of a transmission line, instead of being

[1] Specifically, if the length of line is an appreciable fraction of the wavelength of the electric oscillations, the parameters of the line must be considered to be distributed.

truly distributed, are gathered into small but finite lumps as in
Fig. 62a. Resistance will, for the present, be neglected. A
battery voltage E is suddenly applied to the sending end of the
line by closing the switch. Current immediately begins to flow
through inductance L_1 into condenser C_1. As C_1 becomes
charged, so that there will be voltage across it, current starts to
flow through L_2 into C_2. C_2 becomes charged, and current then
flows through L_3 into C_3, and this action continues on down the
line. First C_1 is charged to voltage E, then C_2 is charged to
voltage E, then C_3 is charged to voltage E, and so on. There
is a voltage wave traveling along the line; it starts at the sending
end and travels at a certain velocity, and all of the line that it
has reached is charged to voltage E, while the line beyond the

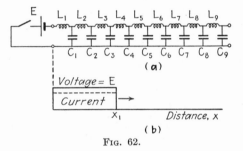

FIG. 62.

front of the wave is yet uncharged. This is shown graphically
in Fig. 62b, in which voltage is plotted as a function of distance
along the line. The wave has traveled to the point x_1, so that
the line to the left of x_1 is charged to voltage E, and the front
of the wave is continuing toward the right as indicated by the
arrow.

The voltage wave is accompanied by a current wave. While
C_1 is being charged, current flows through L_1. When C_1 becomes
charged, current starts to flow through L_2, and the current to
L_2 is supplied through L_1. Then current is extended into L_3
and continues to flow through L_1 and L_2. A current wave progresses along the line in this way, coincident with the voltage
wave. Each is necessary to the other. In fact, the current
and voltage are not separate waves; they are merely different
aspects of the same wave of energy. They are analogous, in a
water wave, to the height of the wave and to the motion of the

water. To consider a voltage wave without current would be as meaningless as to consider a water wave without water.

For easier visualization of the action of distributed parameters, this discussion has been based on a mental picture of a line in which inductance and capacitance are collected into small but finite lumps. But the discussion has been simplified by neglecting certain effects that are inseparable from lumped parameters. When voltage is applied to the artificial line of Fig. 62a, current will begin to flow in L_1, but gradually and not instantaneously. C_1 will charge gradually, and current will begin in L_2 as soon as there is any voltage across C_1, not waiting for C_1 to reach voltage E. Moreover, the voltage of C_1 will not rise abruptly to E and then continue at that value thereafter; instead, it will rise in a finite time and will increase to a value greater than E, finally approaching E as a limit. But all these differences from ideal behavior are due to "lumpiness" of the line, and become of less magnitude as the number of lumps is increased and the size of the individual lumps is decreased; and in the limiting case of the actual transmission line with truly distributed parameters, the differences disappear.

3. Proportionality of Current to Voltage. When a wave of electric energy travels along a line, the subsidiary waves of voltage and current travel along together at the same velocity, and they are related in magnitude by a factor of proportionality that is characteristic of the transmission line. Current must be great enough to charge the line capacitance to the voltage E as rapidly as the wave travels. If the capacitance of the line per unit length (per mile) is c, the charge required to raise the voltage on unit length (1 mile) of line is cE. If the wave is traveling along the line with a velocity v (miles per second), it is necessary to charge v (miles) of line every second, requiring a charge in 1 sec. equal to cEv. This charge is supplied by current flowing into the line at a uniform rate, and to supply charge cEv in 1 sec. requires a current

$$I = cEv \tag{498}$$

From this the proportionality between voltage and current is obtained as either

$$\frac{E}{I} = \frac{1}{cv} \quad \text{or} \quad \frac{I}{E} = cv \tag{499}$$

To complete the solution it is necessary to find v, the velocity of propagation of the wave.

4. Velocity. As the traveling wave of Fig. 62 proceeds along the line, energy is imparted to the electric and magnetic fields of the line, and we can find the speed of the wave from the rate at which the line is supplied with energy. When the wave has progressed a distance x (miles) along the line it has charged a total capacitance equal to cx. The electrostatic energy in this section of line is then $\frac{1}{2}cxE^2$. At the same time, current in this section of line has become I. If l is the inductance per unit length (per mile), the total inductance that carries current is lx, and the magnetic energy of the section of line is $\frac{1}{2}lxI^2$. Since the battery at the sending end is the only source of energy, we may equate the energy that has left the battery to the energy stored in the line. If the time required for the wave to travel the distance x (miles) is t (seconds), so that the wave has been traveling at a velocity $v = x/t$ (miles per second), the energy which has left the battery is EIt. Equated to the stored energy, this gives

$$EIt = \tfrac{1}{2}cxE^2 + \tfrac{1}{2}lxI^2 \tag{500}$$

Dividing each side by t,

$$EI = \tfrac{1}{2}cvE^2 + \tfrac{1}{2}lvI^2 \tag{501}$$

Solution for velocity gives

$$v = \frac{2EI}{cE^2 + lI^2}$$

$$= \frac{2}{c\dfrac{E}{I} + l\dfrac{I}{E}} \tag{502}$$

Voltage and current are now eliminated by substituting Eq. (499) in the denominator of (502):

$$v = \frac{2}{\dfrac{1}{v} + lcv} \tag{503}$$

Finally, solving for velocity,

$$v^2 = \frac{1}{lc} \quad \text{or} \quad v = \pm\frac{1}{\sqrt{lc}} \tag{504}$$

Equation (504) shows that velocity is determined by the inductance and capacitance of the line and is independent of the magnitude of the wave being transmitted. The plus or minus option of the square root in the equation corresponds to the two possible directions of travel along the line, the speed of propagation being the same in either direction.

On an ordinary overhead transmission line, the speed of propagation is very slightly less than the speed of light. Light is an electromagnetic wave (of extremely high frequency) whose electric and magnetic fields are not restricted by wires. Energy travels along a transmission line as an electromagnetic wave, also, but with electric and magnetic fields restricted by the metallic conductors. On an overhead line the restriction is not great and the velocity is nearly the velocity of light.

Let us compute the velocity along a wire. For greatest simplicity we will assume that the return conductor is a hollow metal cylinder surrounding the wire and concentric with it, like the sheath of a single-phase cable. The capacitance between wire and cylinder is

$$c = \left(0.03883\, \frac{k}{\log \dfrac{R}{r}}\right)10^{-6}$$

farads per mile; r is radius of the wire, R is the inner radius of the surrounding cylinder, and k is the dielectric constant (relative to vacuum) of the region between the wire and cylinder. The inductance is

$$l = \left(0.7411 \log \frac{R}{r} + 0.08047\mu\right)10^{-3}$$

henrys per mile; μ is the magnetic permeability of the wire. The formula for inductance consists of two parts: the first term gives inductance due to the magnetic field outside of the wire, and the second term gives inductance due to the magnetic field within the wire.

Let us now assume that the surrounding cylinder is large beyond all limit. The second term of the inductance formula is then negligible, and only the logarithmic term remains. Velocity is found from Eq. (504); with the above assumption

$$v = \frac{1}{\sqrt{(0.7411)(0.03883)k \cdot 10^{-9}}} = 186{,}400\frac{1}{\sqrt{k}}$$

If $k = 1$, as in vacuum, the velocity is $v = 186,400$ miles per second, which is also the velocity of light in vacuum.

The same velocity will be found for a wave on an ordinary parallel-wire transmission line if the magnetic fields within the wires are neglected and if the wires are far apart compared to their radii. In fact, under most conditions of practical operation, the velocity of propagation of waves on open-wire lines is practically the velocity of light in vacuum.

It should be noticed that any change from the ideal condition (which corresponds to a velocity equal to that of light) will reduce the speed of propagation. Under no circumstances can a wave travel faster than light. If, for example, the complete expression for inductance is used, there will be some additional inductance due to the field within the conductors; an increase of inductance will give a larger value to the denominator of Eq. (504), and velocity will be reduced. For the same reason, if the wire has a magnetic permeability greater than unity, the velocity will be reduced. If the dielectric material between conductors has a dielectric constant greater than vacuum, the capacitance will be increased, and velocity will be reduced. This latter condition is met, in practice, in a cable with solid or liquid dielectric, in which the wave velocity may be only a fraction of the velocity of light.

5. Characteristic Impedance. Equation (499) expresses the ratio of voltage to current in terms of velocity of propagation of the wave; and since the velocity of the wave is characteristic of the line, and independent of the wave form, so also is the ratio of E to I. In fact, this ratio is called the **characteristic impedance** or surge impedance of the line, denoted by Z_0, and when v is eliminated from Eq. (499) by means of Eq. (504) it becomes

$$Z_0 = \frac{E}{I} = \sqrt{\frac{l}{c}} \tag{505}$$

When voltage is applied to the end of a long transmission line, the current is proportional to the voltage, so the line acts just as if it were a resistance in the circuit. This is assuming that there is no loss and that the line is so long that the wave continues on indefinitely without reaching the other end of the line or encountering any other obstruction.

6. Energy. One further property of the transmission line is of interest: the electric energy of the wave is equal to its magnetic energy. By squaring Eq. (505) we find that

$$lI^2 = cE^2 \qquad (506)$$

But the magnetic energy in unit length of line is $\frac{1}{2}lI^2$, and the electric energy in the same length is $\frac{1}{2}cE^2$, so the two forms of energy are equal.

7. The Differential Equations. It is not safe to proceed any further on the insecure foundation of reasoning from the "lumpy" line of Fig. 62. The conclusions that have been reached, however, are correct, and they may be rigorously derived from the differential equations of the transmission line. To obtain the differential equations, consider a section of line, as in Fig. 63, so short that current i does not vary appreciably from one end of the section to the other. The length of the section is Δx. If l and r are inductance and

Fig. 63.

resistance of the line per unit length, $l \cdot \Delta x$ and $r \cdot \Delta x$ are the inductance and resistance of the short section.[1] Due to this inductance and resistance there is a drop of voltage through the section of line; as current travels from left to right, the voltage that must be *added* to e_1 to get e_2 is

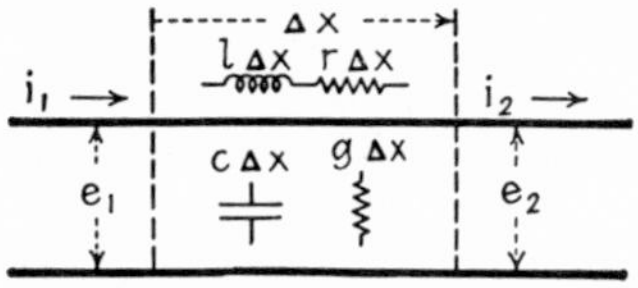

$$-ri \cdot \Delta x - l \frac{\partial i}{\partial t} \cdot \Delta x \qquad (507)$$

The first term of this expression is resistance drop, and the second term—the product of inductance and rate of change of current—is voltage drop due to inductance as the current changes with time. It should be noted that current in the line may vary, at a given instant, from place to place and also, at a given point, from time to time. For this reason, current is mathematically a function of both place and time and is written in functional notation as $i(x, t)$. Because current is a function

---

[1] Consideration of a short section of line as an independent unit, unaffected by current or voltage in the rest of the line through mutual electric or magnetic fields, requires justification. It would seem reasonable that voltage and current in one section of the line would induce voltage in another section. That such is not the case can be shown by *assuming* that each line section produces a magnetic and electric field surrounding that section only; the resulting field distribution is then compared to Maxwell's equations, and it is found to be correct *provided there is no energy loss* along the line. For most practical lines it is a very close approximation.

of two variables, the derivative with respect to time, in Eq. (507), is a partial derivative.

Let us call the change of voltage through the short section of line Δe. Then

$$\Delta e = -ri \cdot \Delta x - l\frac{\partial i}{\partial t} \cdot \Delta x \qquad (508)$$

Divide each side of this equation by the length of the section, Δx, to get the change of voltage in the section *per unit length:*

$$\frac{\Delta e}{\Delta x} = -ri - l\frac{\partial i}{\partial t} \qquad (509)$$

Finally, let the length of the section of line become shorter and shorter; as the length becomes infinitesimal, Eq. (509) becomes

$$\frac{\partial e}{\partial x} = -ri - l\frac{\partial i}{\partial t} \qquad (510)$$

There is also a change of current from one end of the section to the other. It is so small a change that it could be neglected while finding the change of voltage, for in Eq. (510) it would lead only to infinitesimals of the second and higher orders. But since there is capacitance between one line and the other and also, perhaps, some leakage current from one wire to the other, there will be a small difference between i_1 and i_2 (of Fig. 63). If c is the capacitance per unit length of the line, and g is the conductance from wire to wire per unit length of line, the amount of current that will be shunted across the section of length Δx will be composed of two parts: the leakage current will be $ge \cdot \Delta x$ and the charging current to the capacitance of the line[1] will be $c\frac{\partial e}{\partial t} \cdot \Delta x$. The amount of current that must be *added* to i_1 to get i_2 is therefore

$$\Delta i = -ge \cdot \Delta x - c\frac{\partial e}{\partial t} \cdot \Delta x \qquad (511)$$

Dividing through by the length of the section, Δx, and letting the length of the section become infinitesimal,

$$\frac{\partial i}{\partial x} = -ge - c\frac{\partial e}{\partial t} \qquad (512)$$

---

[1] The form of this expression may be compared to the similar relation between current and rate of change of voltage in Eq. (316).

Equations (510) and (512) are the differential equations of the transmission line.

The simultaneous solution of these equations is possible, but not easy. However, if energy loss along the line is neglected, so that r and g are both zero, the solution is perfectly simple. Then the equations become

$$\frac{\partial e}{\partial x} = -l\frac{\partial i}{\partial t} \tag{513}$$

and

$$\frac{\partial i}{\partial x} = -c\frac{\partial e}{\partial t} \tag{514}$$

By differentiating Eq. (513) again, with respect to x,

$$\frac{\partial^2 e}{\partial x^2} = -l\frac{\partial}{\partial x}\left(\frac{\partial i}{\partial t}\right) = -l\frac{\partial}{\partial t}\left(\frac{\partial i}{\partial x}\right) \tag{515}$$

The order of differentiation is immaterial in the second partial derivative. It is now possible to substitute Eq. (514) for $\frac{\partial i}{\partial x}$ in (515). This gives a second-order differential equation in which e is the only variable:

$$\frac{\partial^2 e}{\partial x^2} = lc\frac{\partial^2 e}{\partial t^2} \tag{516}$$

In an exactly parallel manner, e may be eliminated from Eq. (514) to give an equation in i only:

$$\frac{\partial^2 i}{\partial x^2} = lc\frac{\partial^2 i}{\partial t^2} \tag{517}$$

The solutions of these Eqs. (516) and (517) must now be considered. In functional notation they are, respectively,

$$e(x, t) = e(x - vt) \tag{518}$$

and

$$i(x, t) = i(x - vt) \tag{519}$$

in which

$$v = \frac{1}{\sqrt{lc}} \tag{520}$$

Equation (518) can be expressed in words as follows: *any* expression for voltage will satisfy the transmission-line equation

(516), provided that where time and distance appear in the expression they appear together as the quantity $(x - vt)$. Physically this means that any voltage distribution is possible on a transmission line, but that the voltage must be a traveling wave. For Eq. (518) is the equation of a wave that travels with velocity v.

8. Equations of Traveling Waves. To show that Eq. (518) describes a traveling wave, consider an example. Since any sort of function may be chosen for the example, let us select one that is mathematically simple and yet physically possible: let us consider the traveling wave

$$e(x, t) = -(x - vt)\epsilon^{(x-vt)} \tag{521}$$

This satisfies Eq. (518) because wherever x or v appears, x and v are together as $(x - vt)$.

Since Eq. (521) is a traveling wave it will be interesting to see how it looks at different instants of time. First, let time equal zero, and substitute zero for t in Eq. (521). The result is a mathematical snapshot of the wave at that instant:

$$-x\epsilon^x$$

This expression, which tells how voltage is distributed along the transmission line at the particular instant, is plotted in Fig. 64a. (In plotting, only the positive part of the curve is drawn, for in this way it can represent most readily a physical wave.)

A short period of time is allowed to pass, and another snapshot of voltage distribution is taken. The elapsed time is enough to make $vt = 1$, and this value is substituted in Eq. (521) to give

$$-(x - 1)\epsilon^{x-1}$$

The curve of this distribution is plotted in Fig. 64b; it is similar to the curve of Fig. 64a, but moved one unit of distance to the right. In other words, during the elapsed time, the voltage wave has traveled one unit toward the right. It is evident from the mathematical expression that, at the later instant, x must be everywhere greater by one to give the same value to the function.

Figure 64b also shows the wave when $vt = 2$, the wave having traveled two units, and when $vt = 3$ after travel of three units.

Each of the curves of Fig. 64*b* is found by selecting a value of time and plotting the function; this corresponds to examining the space-distribution of voltage at a given instant. We may also examine the time-distribution of voltage at a given point. For example, to find how voltage varies at the point $x = 0$,

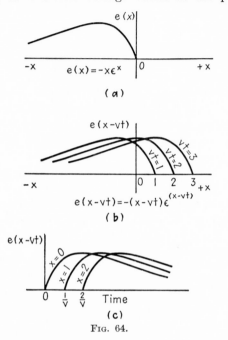

Fig. 64.

substitute that value of x in Eq. (521). The resulting expression is

$$vt\epsilon^{-vt}$$

This is voltage, as a function of time, at that particular point on the line. The same method will give voltage at point $x = 1$, and at point $x = 2$, as

$$-(1 - vt)\epsilon^{(1-vt)} \qquad \text{and} \qquad -(2 - vt)\epsilon^{(2-vt)}$$

respectively. Curves of voltage at these three points are plotted in Fig. 64*c*. It will be seen that the only difference between them is a time delay equal to the time required for the wave to travel; where the distance is one unit, the time required is $1/v$, and where the distance is two units the time lag is $2/v$.

The time curves of Fig. 64c have the same general shape as the space curves of Fig. 64b, but turned about. Similarity of shape between space curves and time curves results whenever a wave travels with constant velocity and without attenuation or distortion.

An expression that describes a stationary distribution of voltage on a line can be changed into an expression for a traveling wave of the same shape by substituting $(x - vt)$ for x. That is, it is changed from a function $e(x)$ to a function $e(x - vt)$, and the wave then travels with velocity v. This may be illustrated by the function of Fig. 64a; when $(x - vt)$ is substituted for x in the expression $-x\epsilon^x$ it becomes the traveling wave formula of Eq. (521). When the same substitution is made in the expression $-(x - 1)\epsilon^{x-1}$ the result is also a traveling wave, but it is a traveling wave that is already displaced one unit at zero time and that is always one unit ahead of the wave of Eq. (521).

A similar sort of substitution will change a time function into a traveling wave. The time function, which tells how voltage varies at a specified point, is changed into an expression for a traveling wave by substituting $\left(t - \dfrac{x}{v}\right)$ for t. This rule can be illustrated by making the substitution in the time function $vt\epsilon^{-vt}$, and the result is again the traveling wave expression of Eq. (521).

So, by these rules, a function of either time or distance can be made to travel. The resulting waves travel with constant velocity v, and they are not attenuated or distorted as they travel.

9. A Traveling-wave Solution of the Differential Equations. It has been stated that $e(x - vt)$ is a solution of the transmission-line Eq. (516). To prove this, we differentiate the voltage $e(x, t) = e(x - vt)$ with respect to x, and regardless of the form of the function the result is[1]

$$\frac{\partial e}{\partial x} = \frac{\partial}{\partial x} e(x - vt) = \frac{d}{d(x - vt)} e(x - vt) \qquad (522)$$

A second differentiation with respect to x gives

[1] See discussion of differentiation of composite functions in any calculus book.

$$\frac{\partial^2 e}{\partial x^2} = \frac{d^2}{d(x - vt)^2}e(x - vt) \tag{523}$$

The voltage is next differentiated twice with respect to t, giving first

$$\frac{\partial e}{\partial t} = \frac{\partial}{\partial t}e(x - vt) = -v\frac{d}{d(x - vt)}e(x - vt) \tag{524}$$

and second

$$\frac{\partial^2 e}{\partial t^2} = v^2 \frac{d^2}{d(x - vt)^2}e(x - vt) \tag{525}$$

Comparison of the right-hand members of Eqs. (523) and (525) shows that

$$\frac{\partial^2 e}{\partial x^2} = \frac{1}{v^2}\frac{\partial^2 e}{\partial t^2}$$

This is Eq. (516), which is shown therefore to be satisfied by any function $e(x - vt)$.

The physical meaning of the statement that any function of $(x - vt)$ is a solution of the transmission-line equation is that the line will propagate, as a traveling wave, any voltage that is applied to its terminals. The form of the wave is determined by the form of the applied voltage, whereas the manner of propagation is determined by the line itself. This is another case in which the solution of a differential equation cannot be completed until the boundary conditions are defined; the boundary in this case is the end of the line, and the condition that must be known is the applied voltage. When a battery voltage is applied to the line, as in Fig. 62, the traveling wave is the flat-topped wave that is shown in the figure. No other wave could satisfy both the differential equations and the boundary condition, for no other simple traveling wave would have a constant voltage at the sending end where the battery is connected.

When a varying voltage is applied to the transmission line, the form of the traveling wave is similar to the form of the terminal voltage. The wave on the line is a record of past values of terminal voltage. It is helpful to picture, in analogy, a pencil that marks upon a sheet of paper; the pencil does not move, but the paper slides beneath the pencil point. The paper is a long sheet that moves at constant speed from left to right, and a long straight line is traced upon it by the stationary pencil. Now, as the paper moves sidewise, allow the pencil to move up and down, thus marking a wave upon the sheet. The resulting pencil mark is a traveling wave, and the position of the pencil is analogous to applied voltage. This analogy is subject, of course, to the same limitations and assumptions as are the differential equations (513) and (514).

An example of a wave produced by varying terminal voltage is shown in Fig. 64. Consider that a transmission line begins at the origin in Fig. 64*b* and extends toward the right. A pulse of voltage described by $vt\epsilon^{-vt}$ is applied at the terminal of the line, and the traveling wave of Eq. (521) is propagated along the line. The applied voltage as a function of time is shown in Fig. 64*c* by the curve at $x = 0$. The traveling wave is shown in Fig. 64*b*. Only that part of the wave to the right of the origin has any physical existence, however, for the transmission line extends only to the right, and it is at the origin that the wave is produced.

10. The Complete Solution of the Differential Equations. A function of $(x - vt)$ is not the only solution of the differential Eq. (516). That equation is also satisfied by any function of $(x + vt)$, so that

$$e(x, t) = e(x + vt)$$

is also a solution. Proof of this is exactly parallel to the proof that leads to Eqs. (523) and (525). Physically, $e(x + vt)$ describes a voltage wave that travels toward the left, just as $e(x - vt)$ describes a voltage wave that travels toward the right.

Finally, the complete solution of Eq. (516) is the sum of the two partial solutions:

$$e(x, t) = e_1(x - vt) + e_2(x + vt) \qquad (526)$$

In this expression, e_1 and e_2 may be any two functions, either the same or different. The physical meaning of the complete solution is simply that a transmission line can carry traveling waves in either direction, or in both directions at the same time.

11. The Solution for Current. Equation (517) is a differential equation in terms of current, distance, and time. Its solution is obviously of the same form as the solution of the voltage equation (516); it is satisfied by any traveling wave of current $i(x - vt)$, or $i(x + vt)$, or in general by any combination of traveling waves of current such that

$$i(x,\ t)\ =\ i_1(x\ -\ vt)\ +\ i_2(x\ +\ vt) \qquad (527)$$

The velocity v is the same as the velocity of the voltage wave:

$$v\ =\ \frac{1}{\sqrt{lc}} \qquad (520)$$

It has been shown physically, and it will be seen mathematically, that the voltage and current waves are not by any means independent of each other. Voltage and current are, indeed, everywhere proportional. This fact may be shown from either Eq. (513) or (514). Let us use Eq. (514), integrating both sides. Integration of the left-hand member gives current:

$$\int \frac{\partial i}{\partial x} dx\ =\ i\ =\ -c \int \frac{\partial e}{\partial t} dx \qquad (528)$$

We see from Eq. (524) that the right-hand member of (528) equals

$$-c \int \frac{\partial e}{\partial t} dx\ =\ -c \int \left(-v\frac{de}{d(x\ -\ vt)} \right) dx$$

From Eq. (522) the total derivative of voltage with respect to $(x\ -\ vt)$ equals the partial derivative with respect to x, so

$$i\ =\ cv \int \frac{de}{d(x\ -\ vt)} dx\ =\ cv \int \frac{\partial e}{\partial x} dx\ =\ cve \qquad (529)$$

Finally, therefore,

$$\frac{e}{i}\ =\ \frac{1}{cv}\ =\ \sqrt{\frac{l}{c}} \qquad (530)$$

This result, which shows that there is a constant ratio of voltage to current at all points along the line, is the same that was obtained in Eq. (505). It is less restricted, however, for it applies to a wave of any shape as well as to a flat-topped wave, and it tells us that as a voltage wave of any shape travels along the line it is accompanied by a current wave of the same shape. Since Eq. (530) applies at any point along the line, it applies at the sending-end terminal, so, for any form of applied voltage, the current entering the line is at each instant proportional to the voltage. Indeed, if only the terminals are exposed, it is impossible to tell whether they are terminals of a transmission line of unlimited length, or of a simple resistance of magnitude $\sqrt{l/c}$.

12. Reflection of Waves at Open End of Line.   The discussion so far has been limited to waves traveling without loss of energy along a perfectly uniform and unlimited transmission line.   At the speed of light, however, it will not take long for a wave to reach the distant end of any actual line.   Nearly 200 miles is traversed in 0.001 sec.   When a wave arrives at the end of the line its orderly progress is interrupted.

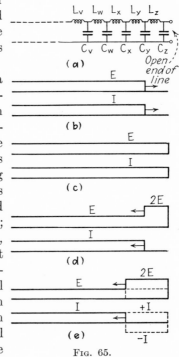

(a)

(b)

(c)

(d)

(e)

Fig. 65.

Figure 65 shows the action of a wave on arriving at the open-circuited end of a line—a smooth line, if the inductances and capacitances shown are considered to be infinitesimal.   Figure 65b shows the flat-topped wave approaching the end of the line.   The two parts of the energy wave, voltage and current, are progressing together; L_y is carrying current but L_z is not, and C_y is charged to voltage E but C_z is not.   There is voltage, however, across C_y, so current will immediately begin to flow through L_z, and since L_z will carry as much current as L_y, the charge on C_y will increase no further.   The voltage of C_y will therefore become and remain E.   Current entering L_z will flow into the capacitance C_z, charging it to voltage E.

The energy wave, at this instant, has reached the end of the line, as shown in Fig. 65c.   All capacitance is now charged to voltage E, and all inductance is now carrying current I.   But the procedure by which the wave has progressed along the line can not be continued here: L_z is carrying current to C_z, and there is no inductance beyond C_z to act as an outlet for current as C_z becomes charged.   The result is that C_z becomes overcharged, for L_z cannot stop carrying current until its magnetic energy is exhausted. L_z will continue to drive current into C_z, and, because of its magnetic energy, the current cannot be stopped until the voltage of C_z has been raised to double its normal value, or $2E$. When the voltage across the last element of capacitance is $2E$, current will stop flowing in the last element of inductance. This condition is illustrated in Fig. 65d; the voltage of C_z is now $2E$, and current in L_z has dropped to zero.

When L_z has ceased to carry current, all current carried by L_y is driven into C_y. This doubles the voltage of C_y, and current in L_y is forced to stop. At the same time, voltage is equalized at the two ends of L_z, and the overcharge on C_z cannot escape. When this has happened conditions are as shown in Fig. 65e: voltage is $2E$ across C_y and C_z, and current is zero in L_y and L_z. This procedure continues progressively along the line; from right to left the voltage becomes doubled and the current drops to zero.

It appears that when the original traveling wave reached the open end of the line, something of the nature of reflection took place. A traveling wave was reflected from the end and started to progress in the opposite direction. The reflected wave is shown by dash lines in Fig. 65e. It is a wave of voltage traveling toward the left, of magnitude E, which adds to the previously existing voltage. It makes the total voltage, as far as the reflected wave has progressed, $2E$. It is accompanied by a reflected wave of current that travels in the same direction at the same speed, but the reflected current wave is a negative wave, $-I$, and where it is added to the current of the original wave the total current becomes zero.

The front of the current wave as shown in Fig. 65e is progressing toward the left. It should be specially emphasized that this does not imply any reversal of flow of current. The current was originally flowing from the battery toward the open end of the line, and it still does so, after reflection, in that part of the line which continues to carry current. It is only the propagation of the wave front, and not the actual total current, that reverses direction when the wave is reflected. Current flows from left to right as the wave travels outward to charge the capacitance of the line to voltage E, and it continues to flow from left to right as the reflected wave returns, doubling the charge on the line as the voltage is raised to $2E$.

The possibility of a reflected wave was included in the mathematical solution of the line differential equations, although it may not have been recognized as such. The reflected wave travels from right to left, and therefore is a function of $(x + vt)$ as in the last term of Eq. (526). Its velocity $-v$ corresponds to the negative option of the square root of Eq. (520). But when velocity is negative in Eq. (530), and $-\dfrac{1}{\sqrt{lc}}$ is used instead of $+\dfrac{1}{\sqrt{lc}}$, the sign of the ratio of voltage to current is also changed; a reflected wave, traveling from right to left, has

$$\frac{e}{i} = -\sqrt{\frac{l}{c}} \tag{531}$$

The physical meaning of a negative current is a current flowing from right to left, whereas a positive current flows from left to right by definition. If positive voltage is being built up by positive charge on a transmission-line wire, and it is being supplied by current flowing from the left, that will be a positive current. If the same charge is supplied by current from the right, the current will be negative. That is why a positive voltage wave traveling from the left is accompanied by a positive current, whereas the same wave traveling from the right requires a negative current.

When a traveling wave arrives at the end of a transmission line, it has reached another boundary, and the polarity and magnitude of the reflected wave are determined by boundary conditions. When the wave of Fig. 65 reached the open end of its line the boundary condition that determined the nature of the reflection was that, at the open end, there could be no current. At that point it must always be true that

$$i = 0 \tag{532}$$

From this fact we may find the reflected wave.

Equation (527) describes the current at all points on the line, including a point just at the open end where the current is zero. If the length of the line is D, and voltage and current are given the subscript r at the open end of the line (the receiving end), the current

$$i_r = i_1(D - vt) + i_2(D + vt) = 0 \tag{533}$$

Equation (533) is a function of time alone, for it describes the current at only one point: that is, at the receiving end of the line. It is made up of two parts; the first is due to the incident wave and the second to the reflected wave. Since the two terms must always add to zero,

$$i_2(D + vt) = -i_1(D - vt) \qquad (534)$$

The two waves, in other words, must be equal and opposite at the terminating point of the line. The function i_2 must therefore describe the same shape of wave as the function i_1, but it must be of negative polarity, it must travel in the opposite direction, and it must leave the receiving end of the line at the instant of arrival of the incident wave.[1]

[1] Although i_2 and i_1 describe waves of the same shape, they are not the same function for two reasons: first, the i_2 wave is turned around and headed in the other direction, and second, it does not start at the sending end of the line when time is zero, but at the receiving end when time is D/v. The wave i_2, however, is the same function of the quantity $[2D - (x + vt)]$ that i_1 is of the quantity $(x - vt)$. Substitution of the former quantity for the latter in the expression for the incident wave gives the reflected wave—a wave that travels from right to left [for it is a function of $(x + vt)$], that may be thought of as having originated at a point as far beyond the receiving end of the line as the receiving end is beyond the sending end (at $x = 2D$). The reflected wave is, of course, negative.

Analytically, the reflected wave must satisfy both Eqs. (532) and (527). The total current on the line is

$$i(x, t) = i_1(x - vt) + i_2(x + vt) \qquad (527)$$

If, and only if, i_2 is the function

$$i_2(x, t) = -i_1(2D - (x + vt)) \qquad (535)$$

can both Eqs. (527) and (532) be satisfied. This satisfies (527) because it is a function of $(x + vt)$, and it satisfies (532) because, when D is substituted for x, (527) becomes

$$i(t) = i_1(D - vt) - i_1(2D - D - vt) = 0$$

Equation (535) is therefore the reflected wave.

This means, for example, that if the incident wave is of the form

$$i_1 = -(x - vt)\epsilon^{x-vt}$$

the reflected wave must be

$$i_2 = +[2D - (x + vt)]\epsilon^{2D-(x+vt)}$$

This is shown in Fig. 66. If, as another example, the incident wave is

$$i_1 = \sin (x - vt)$$

the reflected wave is

$$i_2 = -\sin [2D - (x + vt)]$$

The voltage of the reflected wave is related to the current of the reflected wave by Eq. (531); since the current of the reflected wave is opposite to the current of the incident wave, the voltage of the reflected wave is equal to the voltage of the incident wave.   Total line voltage is the sum of the two waves, as in Eq. (526).

So, by mathematical reasoning, the results of Fig. 65 are substantiated and are generalized to apply to waves of any shape. Figure 66 shows the result of reflection of a wave that is not flat.   The wave of Fig. 64 is approaching the end of the line in

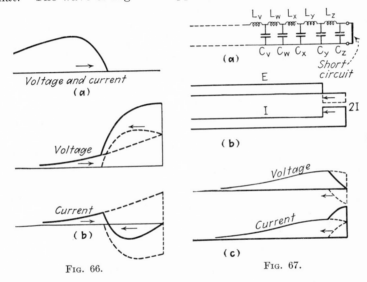

Voltage and current
(a)

Voltage

Current
(b)

Fig. 66.

(a)

(b)

E

I   21

(c)

Voltage

Current

Fig. 67.

Fig. 66a.   A short time later, as shown in Fig. 66b, the front part of the wave has been reflected.   The voltage wave is reflected as if it had been folded back on itself, and total voltage is the sum of the two waves; voltage at the end is always twice the voltage of either wave alone.[1]   The current wave is reflected with reversal of sign, and the current at the end is always (as it must be) zero.

13. Reflection at Short-circuit.   If the end of the line had been short-circuited instead of open, the action would have been entirely different.   Figure 67a is a diagrammatic representation

---

[1] It is convenient, if inelegant, to say that the wave turns about and crawls over its own back.

of a short-circuited line.   As a traveling wave approaches the end of it, C_x becomes charged through L_x, and then L_y begins to carry current to C_y; C_y is charged to a voltage E, and L_z begins to carry current.   But C_z can take no charge; it is short-circuited. Current will flow freely from L_z through the short-circuit and into the return wire, like water from the open end of a pipe.   So more and more current flows through L_z until the charge on C_y becomes exhausted.   The current through L_z and through the short-circuit becomes $2I$ or twice as great as its normal value, and the voltage across C_y falls to zero.   Current and voltage at this instant are plotted in Fig. 67b.   A reflected wave reduces the voltage from E to zero, and increases current from I to $2I$, as the wave travels from right to left.

This is evidently a different kind of reflected wave than the one reflected from the open end of a line; it is natural that it should be, for the boundary condition with a short-circuited line is entirely different.   The short-circuit allows unlimited current at the end of the line, but it does not allow any voltage, so the boundary condition   is

$$e_r = 0 \qquad\qquad (536)$$

Hence, from Eqs. (526) and (536),

$$e_2(D + vt) = -e_1(D - vt) \qquad\qquad (537)$$

This means that at the terminal point the reflected voltage wave will be at all times equal and opposite to the incident voltage wave.   It will travel from the terminal point toward the sending end of the line as a wave with the same shape[1] as the incident wave.   The negative reflected voltage wave will be accompanied by a positive reflected current wave, in accordance with Eq. (531).

The total result of reflection at the short-circuited end of the line will be elimination of voltage at the end, and doubling of current.   This effect is shown for a flat-topped wave in Fig. 67b, and for a rounded wave in Fig. 67c.   This type of reflection is, in a sense, the inverse of that which occurs at the open end of a line, and the voltage waves in one case are exactly like the current waves in the other.

14. Reflection from Terminal Resistance.   If the transmission line is neither open nor short-circuited, but has resistance con-

---

[1] It will have the same functional form as the current of Eq. (535).

nected between the receiving-end terminals, the boundary condition at the receiving end will determine the magnitude of the reflected wave.   The voltage across the terminating resistance is e_r and the current through the resistance is i_r, so if R is the amount of resistance it must always be true that

$$\frac{e_r}{i_r} = R \tag{538}$$

The amount of the terminating resistance is the factor that determines, physically, the size of the reflected wave, and must therefore do so mathematically.   We know that current and voltage are related in the incident wave by

$$e_1 = Z_0 i_1 \tag{539}$$

and in the reflected wave by

$$e_2 = -Z_0 i_2 \tag{540}$$

We know further that the total voltage and current are the sums of the incident and reflected waves:

$$e = e_1 + e_2 \tag{541}$$

and

$$i = i_1 + i_2. \tag{542}$$

At the receiving end of the line these total values of voltage and current are e_r and i_r of Eq. (538), and by substituting in that equation we obtain

$$\frac{e_1 + e_2}{i_1 + i_2} = R$$

Current is eliminated from this expression by means of Eqs. (539) and (540):

$$\frac{e_1 + e_2}{\dfrac{e_1}{Z_0} - \dfrac{e_2}{Z_0}} = R$$

and this equation can be solved for the reflected voltage as a function of the incident voltage:

$$e_2 = e_1 \frac{R - Z_0}{R + Z_0} \tag{543}$$

Equation (543) relates the voltage of the two waves, at the receiving end, at each instant of time. Since it is true at every instant, it is true of the functions as a whole, and it tells us that, in general, the reflected wave from a terminal resistance will be a function of time of the same form as the incident wave, but smaller by the factor of proportionality of Eq. (543).

It tells us, further, that if the terminating resistance is greater than the characteristic impedance Z_0, the reflected voltage will be of the same sign as the incident voltage. The limiting case is an open-ended line, for which $R = \infty$, making $e_2 = e_1$. If, on the other hand the terminating resistance is less than the characteristic impedance, the reflected voltage wave will be negative, subtracting from the incident wave. A short-circuit is the extreme case, with $R = 0$, which makes $e_2 = -e_1$.

There is a very interesting and important intermediate case, which appears if $R = Z_0$. When resistance has this value there can be no reflected wave, for $e_2 = 0$, and the only wave on the transmission line is the incident wave.

When a transmission line is open at the receiving end there is no consumption of energy at the terminal point, nor is there when the line is short-circuited; in both cases, therefore, the reflected wave has just as much energy as the incident wave. If the reflected wave did not carry energy away from the end of the line as rapidly as it is brought by the incident wave, there would be an accumulation of unused energy—an impossible condition. When the resistance is either more or less than Z_0, the dissipation of energy in the resistance is less rapid than the arrival of energy of the incident wave, so there must be a reflected wave of proper magnitude. But if resistance is equal to the characteristic impedance, the energy of the wave is used as it arrives and there is no excess to produce reflection.

Because this critical value of resistance, equal to Z_0, will prevent reflected wave-trains, and incidentally because complete absorption of energy means high efficiency, it is general practice in telephone engineering to terminate each line with apparatus whose resistance is equal to the characteristic impedance of the line. The result is that any wave that comes along the line, regardless of its magnitude or length or form, simply disappears into the terminal equipment and so passes out of existence so far as the line is concerned.

The wave of voltage reflected from a resistance load will of course be accompanied by a reflected wave of current. Since the reflected current is related to the reflected voltage by Eq. (540), it will be related to the incident current by

$$i_2 = -i_1 \frac{R - Z_0}{R + Z_0} \qquad (544)$$

When resistance is equal to the characteristic impedance of the line, there is no reflected current wave, just as there is no reflected voltage wave.

15. Reflection from Terminal Inductance. If a transmission line is terminated at the receiving end with a circuit or network other than pure resistance, the differential equation of the terminating equipment must be taken into account in computing the reflected wave on the line. Consider, as a first simple example, a line with pure inductance across the receiving terminals.

Figure 68a shows such a line. A traveling wave arrives at the

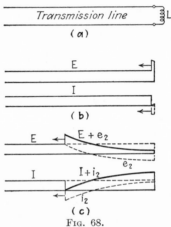

FIG. 68.

end and is reflected. It is reflected exactly as if the line were open at the receiving end, for at the very first instant the inductance can carry no current. The terminal voltage is therefore twice the wave voltage, momentarily, and the terminal current is zero for an instant. This condition is shown in Fig. 68b.

But there is voltage across the terminal inductance from the instant of arrival of the wave, so the inductance will begin to carry current. It will carry current more and more freely, as time passes, until at last it is practically equivalent to a short-circuit and carries steady current with no terminal voltage. When the voltage across the inductance has become zero, the current through it has become twice the current of the incident wave, as in the case of the short-circuited line. This condition and the transition period are shown in Fig. 68c.

As the inductance changes from an element that carries no current (and so reflects voltage with a positive sign) to an element that supports no voltage (and so reflects voltage with a negative sign), it passes through all intermediate stages and the reflected voltage changes gradually. As the reflected voltage changes, the terminal voltage across the inductance is reduced, and the rate-of-change of voltage is reduced also. The short-circuit condition at the terminals is therefore approached asymptotically, but never quite reached; it is reasonable to suppose that the voltage decreases according to an exponential law, and such is indeed the case.

The mathematical determination of the wave reflected from terminal inductance is quite similar to the determination when the line is ended in pure resistance. And in the more general case, with inductance and resistance in series across the end of the line, the method is still similar. In every case the reflected wave is found by simultaneous solution of the transmission-line equations (539) to (542) with the equation that expresses the boundary, or terminal, conditions. When the line is terminated in resistance, the boundary condition is expressed by Eq. (538); that is,

$$e_r = Ri_r \qquad (545)$$

When there is inductance in series with the resistance, the boundary condition becomes

$$e_r = Ri_r + Lpi_r \qquad (546)$$

Operating characteristics of the transmission line are now brought into the computation by substituting in Eq. (546) the group of Eqs. (539) to (542); this gives the following equation which applies at the receiving end of the line:

$$e_1 + e_2 = R\left(\frac{e_1}{Z_0} - \frac{e_2}{Z_0}\right) + Lp\left(\frac{e_1}{Z_0} - \frac{e_2}{Z_0}\right) \qquad (547)$$

Solution for e_2 in terms of e_1 gives:

$$(R + Z_0)e_2 + Lpe_2 = (R - Z_0)e_1 + Lpe_1 \qquad (548)$$

Equation (548) is a differential equation, and its solution is not difficult. The voltage e_1, as a function of time, is presumably known, for e_1 is the incident wave that is arriving from the sending end of the line. The right-hand member of Eq. (548) may therefore be treated as $f(t)$, a known function of time, and the equation is recognized as a first-order linear differential equation with constant coefficients. Its general solution is treated in Chap. III, Eq. (89).

To investigate the action of the line in a special case, let us consider that the incident wave is a flat-topped wave of constant voltage E. This is similar to the incident wave of Fig. 68. E is now substituted for e_1 in the right-hand member of Eq. (548), and since E is constant with respect to time, the derivative term is zero. The equation therefore becomes

$$(R + Z_0)e_2 + Lpe_2 = (R - Z_0)E \qquad (549)$$

This differential equation may be solved by means of the formulas established in Chap. III, or, since it is relatively quite simple, it can be solved by separation of the variables.

Write $\dfrac{d}{dt}$ for p in Eq. (549) and transpose in order to obtain t on one side of the equation and e_2 on the other:

$$\frac{L}{(R - Z_0)E - (R + Z_0)e_2} de_2 = dt \qquad (550)$$

Integration of each member gives

$$\frac{L}{-(R + Z_0)} \ln\left[(R - Z_0)E - (R + Z_0)e_2\right] = t + C \qquad (551)$$

C is a constant of integration in this equation. By changing from the logarithmic form to the exponential form, and at the same time writing as K the exponential factor that contains the constant of integration, Eq. (551) becomes

$$(R - Z_0)E - (R + Z_0)e_2 = K\epsilon^{-\frac{R + Z_0}{L}t} \qquad (552)$$

The coefficient K must next be evaluated by means of known boundary conditions that relate e_2 and t. Characteristics of the terminating circuit of inductance and resistance must be considered. At the instant of arrival of the oncoming wave, the terminal circuit cannot carry finite current because of its inductance; consequently, the wave is fully reflected, and the voltage of the reflected wave (at that instant) is equal to the voltage of the incident wave. Symbolically, when

$$t = 0, \qquad i = 0$$

and therefore   (553)

$$e_2 = E$$

It should be particularly noted that in this discussion we have arbitrarily chosen the reference time, $t = 0$, as the time of arrival of the incident wave at the receiving end of the line. Heretofore the reference time has been the instant of closing a switch, or the instant of starting a wave from the sending end of a line; all such choices are arbitrary, and for every problem the best choice is the one that is easiest to use. In the present case, the best reference time is the instant of arrival of the incident wave, for that is the instant of application of voltage to the terminal circuit and the time of origin of the reflected wave.

Having introduced Eq. (553) into (552), the latter becomes

$$-2Z_0 E = K \tag{554}$$

Finally, this value of K is substituted in Eq. (552), and solution for e_2 gives

$$e_2 = E \frac{R - Z_0 + 2Z_0 \epsilon^{-\frac{R+Z_0}{L}t}}{R + Z_0} \tag{555}$$

It must be remembered that e_2 in Eq. (555) is not a traveling wave. It is voltage, as a function of time, at the receiving end of the line. But it generates a traveling wave, which must be a function of $(x + vt)$. In accordance with Sec. 8, an expression can be derived from Eq. (555) to describe the traveling wave by substituting $\left(t + \dfrac{x}{v}\right)$ for t, provided the *receiving* end of the line is selected as the reference point at which $x = 0$.

In general, Eq. (555) describes a wave whose initial height is E, for this value appears when $t = 0$. As in Fig. 68, the reflected wave then changes exponentially until, with very large values of t, it approaches the value of Eq. (543). Since Eq. (543) describes the reflection with pure resistance at the receiving end, it will be seen that in time the effect of the inductance disappears.

If there were no resistance at the receiving end, but only inductance, as in Fig. 68, the result would be found from Eq. (555) by letting $R = 0$. The reflected wave would vary from E, initially, to $-E$, finally, as is shown in that figure.

It is interesting to notice that the reflected waves from all terminations that have been discussed (open, short-circuit, resistance, and inductance) can be found as special cases of Eq. (555).

16. Reflection from Terminal Capacitance. If there is a condenser connected to the terminals of the line, it acts as a short-circuit at the moment of arrival of the incident wave. At this instant, the reflected voltage wave is negative, for the terminal voltage is momentarily zero, and the current of the incident wave is, momentarily, doubled. As the condenser becomes charged, the terminal voltage rises. Finally the condenser becomes fully charged; it then behaves as an open circuit, for the terminal current is zero and the voltage of the incident wave is doubled. The curves of Fig. 68b and c illustrate this case perfectly if the "current" curves are taken to illustrate voltage and the "voltage" waves are taken to illustrate current.

The mathematical solution for the capacitive termination is so like the solution for the inductive case that it will not be given. It introduces no new ideas.

There is more practical importance in the case of a line with terminal condenser than might appear at first sight, owing to the paradox that for lightning waves a transformer acts as a capacitance rather than as an inductance. Lightning voltage arrives at a transformer as a traveling wave, and the front of the wave is so steep, and rises so suddenly to a maximum, that there is practically no time for current to start to flow through the large inductance of the transformer winding. But there is some small capacitance in the transformer from turn to turn, and from winding to core, and it is largely this capacitance, rather than the inductance, that determines the transformer's reaction to lightning.

17. Transmission-line Junctions. There must be some reflection of energy whenever any irregularity interferes with the propagation of a wave. The end of the line is an inevitable irregularity, but many others may be encountered also. When the dimensions of a transmission line are changed, for instance, or two dissimilar lines are joined, there will be reflections as waves pass the junction.

Figure 69a represents the junction of a line with wide spacing and a line with narrow spacing; the former has parameters l and c, and the latter l' and c'. Since these are different, their ratios

Z_0 and Z_0' will also be different.   Let us assume that a wave of energy comes from the left; it enters, that is, on the widely spaced line.   It has a certain ratio of voltage to current, equal to Z_0.

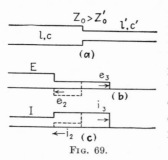

(a)

(b)

(c)

Fig. 69.

It cannot pass the junction smoothly, for a wave on the narrowly spaced line must have a different ratio of voltage to current.   So when the incident wave arrives at the junction there are two new waves formed; part of the incident energy is propagated on toward the right, and part is reflected back toward the left.

Solution for the magnitudes of the transmitted and reflected waves is possible in either of two ways.   Voltage and current of the waves on one side of the junction point can be equated to voltage and current of the wave on the other side, and since ratios of voltage to current are known from the characteristic impedances it is not difficult to solve for the unknown currents and voltages.   But use may be made of a previous solution by considering that, as far as the incident wave is concerned, the second section of line could be replaced by a resistance equal to Z_0'.   This is possible because the current that enters the second line will be proportional at every instant to the voltage at the junction, just as it would be in a resistance.   So the magnitude of the reflected voltage wave can be found from Eq. (543), which was derived for a terminal resistance, with Z_0' replacing R.   Reflected current can be found in the same way from Eq. (544).   Transmitted voltage is then equal to the sum of the incident and

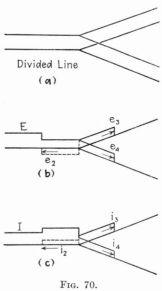

Divided Line

(a)

(b)

(c)

Fig. 70.

reflected waves at the junction point, and transmitted current to the sum of the incident and reflected current waves.   An example is shown in b and c of Fig. 69.

When a line divides, as in Fig. 70a, the same methods of reasoning can be applied. The two parts of the divided line will affect the incident wave as if they were two resistances in parallel at the junction, thereby determining the reflected wave. There will be two transmitted waves, with the same voltage, but different currents as required by the different characteristic impedances. An example appears in Fig. 70b and c.

Other combinations of apparatus can be handled in the same manner. Always, the requirements of all lines and circuits must be satisfied simultaneously.

18. Repeated Reflections. Only one reflection of an incident wave has been considered in the discussion thus far, but that initial reflection is in reality only the first of an infinite series. The incident wave is reflected on arrival at the receiving end of the line, and the reflected wave is reflected again at the sending end. Like a ray of light between two mirrors, the electric wave goes repeatedly from end to end of the line until its energy is exhausted.

It will be well to trace one or two typical cases.[1] Let us first

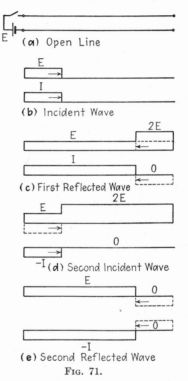

(a) Open Line

(b) Incident Wave

(c) First Reflected Wave

(d) Second Incident Wave

(e) Second Reflected Wave

FIG. 71.

consider a transmission line, open at the receiving end, to which a constant battery voltage E is suddenly applied at the sending end. The line is shown in Fig. 71a, and the incident wave in Fig. 71b. At the receiving end the current must always be zero, so when the incident wave of current reaches the end of the line it must necessarily produce a reflected wave with negative current. The wave of negative current, when traveling toward

[1] Traveling waves on lines without loss are thoroughly treated by L. V. Bewley, "Traveling Waves on Transmission Systems," John Wiley & Sons, Inc., New York, 1933.

the left, must be accompanied by a wave of positive voltage. Distribution of voltage and current shortly after reflection are shown in Fig. 71c; the solid line shows total voltage and current, and the dash line indicates the traveling wave.

When the first reflected wave arrives at the sending end of the line it produces an unstable condition: it charges the line, as it travels, to voltage $2E$, while the sending end of the line is connected to the battery and can have no voltage other than the battery voltage E. On arrival of the wave at the sending end, the line, charged to $2E$, immediately starts to discharge again into the battery, and a traveling wave of voltage $-E$ is sent out onto the line. It must be accompanied by a current wave, and since it moves with positive velocity the current will be of the same sign as the voltage, or $-I$. Conditions shortly after reflection at the sending end are shown in Fig. 71d. For the first time, current on the line has become negative, indicating that charge is now flowing toward the battery instead of from it.

This second incident wave soon reaches the receiving end, and is again reflected. The second incident wave is a negative wave, producing negative current as it passes. But, again, there can be no current at the receiving end, so on the arrival of the second incident wave with negative current a second reflected wave with positive current must start toward the sending end. The positive current of the second reflected wave must be accompanied by a negative voltage wave (because the direction of travel is negative), and Fig. 71e shows the components of the second reflected wave. As the second reflected wave travels it makes both total voltage and total current zero all along the line.

Just as the first reflected wave produced conditions at the sending end of the line incompatible with the boundary condition of the connected battery, so the second reflected wave leaves the line in a condition that cannot continue to exist. It leaves the sending end voltage zero, but the sending end voltage must be E, so an incident wave with positive voltage is sent along the line. This is the third incident wave.

The behavior of the wave need be traced no further, for the third incident wave is identical with the first incident wave; a cycle of operation has been completed, and Fig. 71b can illustrate the third incident wave, or the fifth incident wave, or the seventh, and so on. If it were true, as has been assumed, that the wave could travel without loss of energy, it would never cease to surge up and down the line.

A line short-circuited at the receiving end reflects waves in a different manner. Its action, neglecting energy loss, is shown in Fig. 72. Reflected waves are made necessary by the following boundary conditions: sending end voltage is always E and receiving end voltage is always zero.

The first reflected wave must have negative voltage and will therefore have positive current. On reaching the sending end it makes necessary a second incident wave of positive voltage, accompanied by a wave of positive current. The voltage of the line is cyclic in this simple manner: a positive wave goes out from the battery, and a negative wave returns. The current, however, is not cyclic at all, but continues to increase without limit as each reflection adds to its magnitude.

If there is resistance in the short-circuited transmission line the current will increase, but not without limit. It will approach a final value of E/rD, where r is resistance per unit length and D the length of the line. The quantity rD is merely the direct-current resistance of the line, and so it obviously limits the current in the steady state. When a wave travels along a line with resistance, it becomes smaller as it travels. If it is a wave due to the sudden application of battery voltage, as in Figs. 71 and 72, the front of the wave decreases with time according to an exponential law; the wave is therefore not flat-topped, but sloping, and slightly curved, as in Fig. 73b. Reflections of such a wave must satisfy the same terminal conditions as before: at the short-circuited receiving end, $e = 0$; at the sending end,

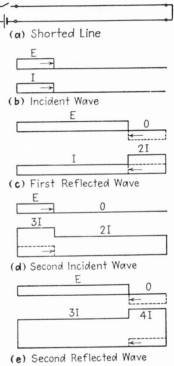

(a) Shorted Line

(b) Incident Wave

(c) First Reflected Wave

(d) Second Incident Wave

(e) Second Reflected Wave

Fig. 72.

$e = E$. A general indication of the shape of the waves and the effect of multiple reflections is given in Fig. 73, although detailed discussion must await a more careful consideration of the effect of energy loss.

It will be observed that Fig. 73 differs from Fig. 72 (which was drawn for the nondissipative line) primarily in that the travel-ing wave diminishes, and after several traverses of the line it becomes almost negligible. Each traverse of the line, moreover, brings the current and voltage distribution closer to the steady-state conditions, as shown in Fig. 73*e*.

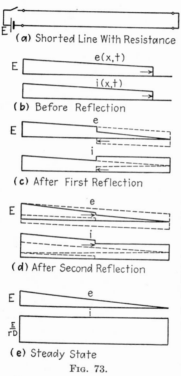

(*a*) Shorted Line With Resistance

e(x,t)

(*b*) Before Reflection

e

i

(*c*) After First Reflection

e

i

(*d*) After Second Reflection

e

i

(*e*) Steady State

Fig. 73.

The manner in which the wave changes as it travels is, in general, quite complicated. But there is one special case—the so-called "distortionless line"—in which the attenuation of the traveling wave is quite simple.

19. The Distortionless Line. If r, l, c, and g—the resistance, inductance, capacitance, and conductance per unit length, respectively—are so propor-tioned that

$$\frac{r}{l} = \frac{g}{c} \tag{556}$$

a special case of wave transmission results. On such a line a traveling wave from a battery will proceed outward, as in Fig. 73*b*, diminishing exponentially, and the voltage at a specific point will rise to a specific value and will remain at that value thereafter—or until the reflected wave returns. This would seem to be the natural behavior of a line when our study of the nondissipative line is considered, but it must be remembered that the nondissipative line is itself a special case that satisfies Eq. (556). In general the contrary is true: the voltage and cur-rent at a point will rise suddenly as the head of a wave passes and will continue to change gradually thereafter as functions of time.   Figuratively, the energy wave (except in the distortionless case) writhes as it crawls.

When a wave travels out upon a distortionless line from a battery of voltage E, the voltage at any point on the line that has been reached by the wave is

$$e = E\epsilon^{-\frac{r}{l}\frac{x}{v}} \qquad (557)$$

It will be seen that this voltage is a function of x, but not of time, indicating that after the arrival of the wave the voltage does not change.   If battery voltage is applied to the sending end of a line for 0.001 sec. and is then removed, a wave is started out along the line.   The traveling wave is shown in Fig. 74a after the front of it has progressed some 250 miles.   In Fig. 74b the applied voltage at the sending end, as a function of time, is plotted as the rectangle marked $x = 0$.   If the line is distortionless, so that Eq. (557) applies, the voltage at a point 100 miles along the line will also be rectangular, when plotted with respect to time, but less in magnitude.

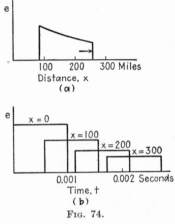

Fig. 74.

It appears in the figure as the curve $x = 100$.   The same may be said of the voltage where x equals 200, or 300, or at any other point.   At points more distant along the line the voltage as a function of time is smaller, *but it is the same function.*   This statement is not limited to waves of battery voltage, but may be applied to any sort of wave whatever; it is because of this distinctive property that the line is called **distortionless.**

Another aspect of the absence of distortion is seen in the fact that the traveling wave itself (as a function of x) remains the same shape as it travels.   It is important to notice that a flat-topped wave as a function of time (in Fig. 74b) is not produced by a flat-topped wave as a function of distance, but by a wave whose top is an exponential curve (Fig. 74a).   As this exponential wave travels it retains the same shape but becomes uniformly smaller with time. This, also, is true of all traveling waves on distortionless lines.

An analytical expression for voltage along a line after connection of a battery to the sending end was given in Eq. (557). It is of course accompanied by a current wave

$$i = \frac{E}{Z_0} \epsilon^{-\frac{r}{l}\frac{x}{v}} \tag{558}$$

Proof of the correctness of Eqs. (557) and (558) is found on introducing them into the fundamental transmission-line equations (510) and (512). From Eq. (557),

$$\frac{\partial e}{\partial x} = -\frac{Er}{lv} \epsilon^{-\frac{r}{l}\frac{x}{v}}$$

and from (558),

$$\frac{\partial i}{\partial t} = 0$$

and

$$-ri = -\frac{Er}{Z_0} \epsilon^{-\frac{r}{l}\frac{x}{v}}$$

Simply by definition

$$lv = l\sqrt{\frac{1}{lc}} = Z_0.$$

When these values are substituted in Eq. (510), which is

$$\frac{\partial e}{\partial x} = -ri - l\frac{\partial i}{\partial t} \tag{510}$$

it becomes an identity. From Eqs. (557) and (558),

$$\frac{\partial i}{\partial x} = -\frac{Er}{Z_0 lv} \epsilon^{-\frac{r}{l}\frac{x}{v}}$$

$$\frac{\partial e}{\partial t} = 0$$

$$-ge = -gE\epsilon^{-\frac{r}{l}\frac{x}{v}}$$

From Eq. (556) for the distortionless line,

$$\frac{r}{l} = \frac{g}{c}$$

and by definition

$$cv = \frac{1}{Z_0}$$

When these values are substituted in Eq. (512) it also is reduced to an identity:

$$\frac{\partial i}{\partial x} = -ge - c\frac{\partial e}{\partial t} \qquad (512)$$

Therefore Eqs. (557) and (558) are a solution of the transmission-line equations.

When the applied voltage is other than a constant battery voltage, it is not possible to have any simple equations like (557) and (558) to describe the wave. But the functional equations

$$e(x, t) = \epsilon^{-\frac{r}{l}t}e_1(x - vt) \qquad (559)$$

$$i(x, t) = \frac{e(x, t)}{Z_0} \qquad (560)$$

contain the information that the wave travels without distortion (although it is attenuated exponentially) and that the voltage is accompanied by a proportional wave of current. Proof of this pair of equations is also found on substituting them in the differential equations of the transmission line. They describe a wave traveling toward the right; there is another equally valid solution containing a function of $(x + vt)$ instead of $(x - vt)$ that describes a wave traveling, on a distortionless line, toward the left; and the complete solution of the differential equations is the sum of these two partial solutions.

The complete solution is necessary to describe formally both incident and reflected waves. It is more practical, however, to compute a wave for as much time as may be needed, and then to take reflections into account by folding it back on itself in whatever way is made necessary by terminal conditions. This is permissible on a distortionless line, as it was on a line without loss.

20. The General Transmission Line. If the transmission line is not distortionless, its transient behavior is quite intricate. The advantages of the distortionless line in telephone communication were pointed out by Heaviside many years ago. He showed that it would give maximum efficiency of transmission as well as greatest fidelity, and this knowledge has had an important influence on the design of telephone lines. Few modern telephone lines, however, and no power lines are distortionless. In general r/l is greater than g/c, and on power lines the conductance between lines is usually negligible. A traveling wave, therefore, will usually be distorted as well as attenuated as it travels.

Sometimes the distortion can be neglected. In Fig. 73, curves were drawn for a line with resistance but no leakage—a line that is consequently not without distortion. They were drawn as if the voltage at each point of the line changed only as the head of the wave passed that point—an assumption that is contrary to fact except on a distortionless line. But in many cases the distortion is so small that the assumption does not lead to a large degree of error, and this is most likely to be true if r and g are small compared to l and c.

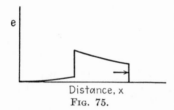

Distance, x

Fig. 75.

When there is distortion of a traveling wave, its shape, as a function of distance, is changed as it travels. A rectangular wave does not remain rectangular; a wave with exponential top, as in Fig. 74a, does not continue in quite the same form. The effect of distortion is to take energy from the head of the wave and spread it back along the line, adding to the rear part of the wave and giving it a "tail." Figure 75 shows how the wave of Fig. 74, sent out from a battery on a line that is not distortionless, will leave energy behind as it travels.[1]

The main wave loses energy, on a line with distortion, not only in the resistance and leakance of the line, but also because energy is sent back along the line. As spray is driven from the front of an ocean wave by an opposing wind, to fall behind the wave or be blown back across the water, so energy is driven back from an electric wave on a line with distortion. It is only the very front of the wave that is diminished in a simple exponential manner as it travels, for it is only the front that cannot gain energy at the

---

[1] Motion pictures have been made by Prof. L. F. Woodruff of the Massachusetts Institute of Technology, showing traveling waves on an artificial transmission line. The pictures are based on cathode-ray oscillograms. See Woodruff, L. F., *Elec. Eng.*, **54**, 1045, 1935.

expense of a preceding portion of the wave. The front of a wave will always (according to the differential equations of the transmission line) travel with exactly the velocity $v = 1/\sqrt{lc}$, regardless of loss; it will be diminished in a simple exponential manner with time, and the voltage and current at the wave front will always be related by the ratio $Z_0 = \sqrt{l/c}$.

The fact that the front of a wave travels as it does, in the same manner as if the line were distortionless, suggests the reason for distortion of the rest of the wave. Let us first consider the distortionless case of Fig. 74a. Select some fixed point on the line, which the wave will pass; at the instant of arrival of the wave the voltage at that point becomes some value that may be designated by e_x, and the current becomes $i_x = e_x/Z_0$. Energy is consumed at that point of the line in proportion to the resistance r and the leakance g. Current and voltage at the specified point would necessarily become less, with the passage of time, if the loss were not replenished, current being reduced by resistance and voltage by leakance. New energy, however, is supplied to the point where the loss occurs, for the wave itself, having an exponential top, brings a continuous supply of energy to each point that the wave is passing. The wave is, of course, becoming smaller as it travels, because it is supplying energy to replace the losses in the line.

Now finally (and this is the distinguishing feature of the distortionless wave) the current of the traveling wave and the voltage of the traveling wave are so proportioned that they replenish losses due to leakance and resistance in exactly the right relative amounts, and thereby maintain the voltage and current at each point constant as the wave passes (see Fig. 74b). From Eqs. (556) and (560),

$$\frac{r}{g} = \frac{l}{c} = \frac{e^2}{i^2}$$

By cross multiplication,

$$ri^2 = ge^2 \tag{561}$$
$$li^2 = ce^2 \tag{562}$$

Equation (561) tells us that, on the distortionless line, the resistance loss at a point is equal to the leakance loss at that point; whereas from Eq. (562) it may be seen that the new supply of magnetic energy to replace resistance loss is equal to the new supply of electric energy that replaces leakance loss. [That the new energy will be just adequate to replace the loss is not shown; that depends on the shape of the traveling wave, which is not taken into account in Eqs. (561) and (562).]

When the line is not distortionless, Eq. (561) is not true. On the ordinary line, therefore, energy is supplied to a point of the line by a passing wave in proportions that are different from the line's consumption. Either magnetic or electric energy is brought in larger amounts than can be used. When this happens, the behavior at the point is the same that has already been studied at the line terminals: when energy is brought in proportions that cannot be used, some must be reflected.

So each point on the line, as the wave passes, reflects continuously a small amount of energy—*every* point of the line that the wave has reached is contributing to the reflection—and the effect is distortion of the main wave and the growth of a "tail."

Derivation of the equations of traveling waves on transmission lines that involve distortion is too specialized a procedure to be given here, and the resulting equations, whether as integrals, infinite series, or Bessel functions, are not very useful unless their derivations are understood. Many of the more comprehensive books on electromagnetic theory treat the subject quite fully and may be used as reference.[1]

21. Factors Not Included in the Differential Equations. It was implied in the preceding section that the travel of a wave on a transmission line is not in precise accordance with the differential equations. This is certainly true, although the discrepancies are very small; too small, in fact, for study by experiment and too complex for mathematical analysis.

One factor not included in the differential equations is "skin effect." The equations are derived with an assumption of constant resistance and inductance of the line, regardless of the behaviour of the current flowing, and this is not quite the physical nature of a transmission line. When current in a wire is changing rapidly, whether owing to high frequency or to the steep front of a traveling wave, current is concentrated near the

---

[1] References suggested for engineers are V. Bush, "Operational Circuit Analysis"; L. F. Woodruff, "Electric Power Transmission and Distribution"; *loc. cit.*

surface of the wire. This is called skin effect. It is due to
the greater inductance of current paths near the center of the
conductor. It has the effect of increasing the effective resistance
of the wire, and decreasing slightly its inductance. The greater
the rate-of-change of current, the greater the skin effect.

The front of a traveling wave therefore encounters, because of
skin effect, a higher resistance and lower inductance than does
the tail of the same wave. The result is a minor distortion of
the wave that has not, as yet, been amenable to mathematical
treatment. But its nature can be predicted. Sharp corners will
become rounded on a traveling wave, and steep wave fronts will
become slightly less steep. Any abrupt changes will tend to be
smoothed out, and energy loss will increase slightly.

Other physical facts that are not taken into account by the differential equations are losses in near-by conductors, notably
ground, and distortion of the electric and magnetic fields near the
ends of transmission lines and at junctions and corners. Radiation of energy into space is not considered, nor is mutual effect
between one part of a conductor and another part of the same
conductor. But, ordinarily, the effects of these phenomena are
all negligible. It is only in very special cases that the differential
equations are not adequate.[1]

22. Speed of Wave Travel. It has been stated in this chapter
that traveling waves have a definite velocity, determined by the
parameters of the line, equal to $1/\sqrt{lc}$. This seems, at first, to
be at variance with the well-known fact that, in the steady state,
sinusoidal waves of low frequency appear to travel more slowly
than sinusoidal waves of high frequency. But the lower speed in
the steady state is merely apparent, not real, for it is the combined result of true velocity and distortion. If there is no distortion, r, g, l, and c being properly related, the velocity of all
waves is $1/\sqrt{lc}$.

When a sinusoidal wave of a steady-state wave-train is distorted as it travels, the distortion takes a very special and
peculiar form. Energy is removed from the front of the wave,
and added to the back of the wave, by the distortion, in such a
way that the distorted wave is still sinusoidal but appears not

---

[1] See BEWLEY, L. V., Attenuation and Distortion of Waves, *Elec. Eng.*,
52, 876, 1933; discussion by J. Slepian, **53,** 472, by C. L. Fortescue, 596, and
closure by the author, **597.**

to have progressed as far as a square wave, for example, would obviously have done.

This type of distortion, which does not appear to be distortion but does appear to be a change of velocity, can take place only in the steady state.   Moreover, it can take place only in a sinusoidal wave.   If the steady-state wave is not sinusoidal, it will be distorted in such a way that each sinusoidal component will appear to have a different speed.   A single traveling wave will never appear to have reduced velocity, for it is not subject to this type of distortion.

23. The Cause of Traveling Waves.   The flat-topped traveling waves of this chapter have been ascribed to the application of a battery or some other source of constant potential at one end of the transmission line.   This is the most satisfactory assumption for analysis, but the application of constant potential does not often occur in practice.   Most traveling waves of practical importance are due either to switching operations, or to lightning, or to induction from a wave on some nearby circuit.

On power lines it is most probable that waves due to switching will result from the sudden application of sinusoidal voltage to a transmission line.   The frequency of the applied voltage will probably not exceed 60 cycles, however, and, in the time required for several reflections of the wave on a line of moderate length, the applied voltage will not change greatly.   If a line is 93 miles long, a traveling wave will reach the receiving end, be reflected, and return to the sending end in 0.001 sec.   For comparison, a half-cycle of voltage at the rate of 60 cycles per sec. occupies more than 0.008 sec.   This is so much longer, that for many purposes it is a good approximation to assume that the applied voltage is constant during the life of the traveling wave. The sine wave of voltage changes quite slowly near the instant of maximum, and the assumption is then particularly good. On very long lines, especially if several reflections are considered, it will be necessary to take into account the actual form of the applied voltage and the resulting shape of the traveling wave.   Three-phase transient disturbances are computed for each phase separately, and the resulting currents and voltages are then superimposed.

When a wave is caused by lightning, it may result from a direct stroke of lightning to the transmission line, or it may result from the release of bound charge on the line as lightning strikes nearby.   A direct stroke is of course the most destructive. In either case a traveling wave will proceed along the line and when it arrives at the end of the line it will be reflected.   If reflection takes place at a switch, where the line is open, the voltage will be doubled by reflection (see Fig. 66); if the line is terminated by a transformer or a generator, the voltage will be practically doubled, for equipment of this sort is so highly inductive that no current can pass through it during the short duration of the lightning wave.   In fact, the distributed capacitance of a transformer makes it act as a condenser as far as lightning surges are concerned.   The latter case is one of great practical importance, for the doubled voltage at the transformer terminals is dangerous and may easily damage the transformer insulation. Lightning arresters are widely used at transformers to help prevent such trouble by carrying the lightning wave to ground.   As another precaution, it is very helpful to have the distributed capacitance of the transformer winding so proportioned that voltage stress due to the lightning wave is applied with a fair degree of equality across the entire insulation of the transformer, instead of being concentrated in the insulation of the first few turns.   Such electrostatic shielding is quite useful in avoiding damage from waves so short-lived that it is the capacitance rather than the inductance of a transformer that determines its internal voltage distribution.

A traveling wave on a power line will do no damage unless its voltage materially exceeds the normal operating voltage of the line.   On a high-voltage line, a wave that greatly exceeds the operating voltage will produce corona about the line as it travels, and the resulting loss of energy will very rapidly attenuate the wave.   Corona will be produced by the front of the wave, and as energy is lost from the wave its front will slope continually less steeply.[1]   The crest of a traveling wave will be rapidly reduced by corona, particularly if the wave is of short duration, and any lightning wave will be reduced in a few miles of travel to a voltage below the corona-forming voltage of the line.   On lines which normally operate at low voltage this may still be a dangerous value.

[1] See Skilling, H. H., and P. de K. Dykes, Distortion of Traveling Waves by Corona, *Elec. Eng.* (*Trans. A.I.E.E.*), **56**, 850, 1937.

Problems

1. When longitudinal force is applied to the end of a long steel bar a compression wave is propagated along the bar. Write the partial differential equations of motion and solve for the equations of wave propagation, in terms of density and elasticity of steel. (Note: To simplify the problem and to make the equations analogous to those of the electric transmission line, neglect transverse strain. This is equivalent to assuming Poisson's ratio, the factor of lateral contraction, to be zero.)

2. A surge due to switching travels along two conductors of a power line. Each conductor is 1 in. in diameter, and they are spaced 22 ft. apart. What is the velocity of propagation of the surge? Transmission-line parameters may be determined from tables, or they may be computed from the formulas of Sec. 4 of this chapter. The formulas of Sec. 4 apply to parallel-wire lines of practical dimensions if R is interpreted as spacing between lines; capacitance and inductance are given by the formulas in farads and henrys, respectively, per mile, *to neutral.*

3. A surge due to a suddenly applied voltage travels along two conductors of a telephone line. Each conductor is 0.1 in. in diameter, and they are spaced 8 in. apart. What is the velocity of propagation of the surge?

4. What is the velocity of a surge on a cable in which a $\frac{3}{4}$-in. conductor is separated from its metallic sheath by 1 in. of insulation? Dielectric constant of the insulation is 3.5, and both conductor and sheath are copper. Neglect magnetic-flux linkages within the material of the conductor and sheath. Repeat, taking into account linkages within the inner conductor on the basis of a uniform distribution of current. Which assumption is most reasonable?

5. Referring to Prob. 1, find the velocity of propagation of sound in soft steel, and in copper. The following values for density and Young's Modulus may be used:

	Soft steel	Copper
Density, g. per cm.^{3}	7.70	8.89
Young's Modulus, dynes per cm.^{2}	20×10^{11}	10×10^{11}

6. Remembering that the adiabatic elasticity of air is 1.40 times the pressure, find the velocity of sound along a speaking tube. Density of air is 0.00120 g. per cm.^{3} when the barometric pressure is 76.0 cm. Hg. and the temperature is 20°C.

7. Each of the lines and the cable of Probs. 2, 3, and 4 are terminated at a load with resistance of 500 ohms. Plot voltage and current distribution along the line at an instant shortly after the second reflection of a traveling wave at the load. The traveling wave originates in a battery connected to the sending end of the line. Neglect loss along the line; use the second assumption of Prob. 4.

8. What kind of device at the end of a steel bar would prevent reflection of sound waves at the end of the bar? How would a speaking tube be terminated to prevent reflection of sound at the end? (Note: This latter question is important in loud-speaker design.)

9. With the conditions of Prob. 7, but with a 1-μf condenser replacing the resistance load, plot current and voltage at the load as a function of time. The lines are each 93 miles long.

10. A transmission line is uniformly charged, from end to end, to voltage E. Both ends are open. One end is then suddenly short-circuited. Plot current at the short-circuited end as a function of time. Plot both voltage and current at the mid-point of the line as functions of time. Neglect loss.

11. A transmission line (uncharged) is open-circuited at both ends. A battery of constant voltage E is suddenly connected across the line at a point one-third of the length from one end. Plot battery current as a function of time. Plot voltage at one end of the line as a function of time. Neglect loss.

12. A transmission line is terminated in resistance equal to $2Z_0$. The internal impedance of the battery (connected as in Fig. 72) is also $2Z_0$. Plot current and voltage along the line shortly after the first, second, third, and fourth reflections.

13. A transmission line is terminated in resistance equal to $\frac{1}{2}Z_0$. The internal impedance of the battery (connected as in Fig. 72) is $2Z_0$. Plot current and voltage along the line shortly after the first, second, third, and fourth reflections.

14. Plot battery current in Fig. 73 as a function of time. Do the same for an open-circuited line with moderate losses.

15. Repeat Prob. 10, giving approximate curves for current and voltage if there is a moderate amount of line loss. Show how the steady state is approached.

16. A transmission line is terminated in a series-resonant circuit of inductance and capacitance with a natural period much less than the time required for a wave to travel the length of the line. Sketch current and voltage along the line at several instants after reflection. A qualitative solution is sufficient.

17. Simulating the result of lightning, charge is placed on one section of a transmission line. That section (isolated by a disconnecting switch at each end) is uniformly charged to voltage E, and the rest of the line is uncharged. Charge is suddenly allowed to flow from the charged section to the rest of the line (by simultaneously closing the disconnecting switches). Plot voltage and current at several later instants to show the waves that travel in both directions.

CHAPTER X

LAPLACE TRANSFORMATION

1. The Transformation Method. The Laplace transformation is an extremely useful mathematical device that turns transients problems into steady-state problems. Differential equations are transformed into algebraic equations, and the solution then requires nothing more than algebraic manipulation rather than the operations of calculus.

Transformation as a method is thoroughly familiar in electric-circuit theory, although it is not always called by that name.

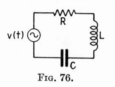

FIG. 76.

Indeed, the use of vectors and complex quantities to describe alternating-current phenomena is a simple example of transformation. In the next few pages we shall review complex vectors and Fourier series as a means of introducing the Laplace transformation. Familiar ideas will be expressed in unfamiliar terms. We shall be doing an easy job the hard way in Secs. 2 through 5. The details in these sections are not important; it is the new point of view that really matters.

2. The Vector Transformation. As an example, let us consider the circuit of Fig. 76. The differential equation is

$$Ri(t) + L\frac{d}{dt}i(t) + \frac{1}{C}\int i(t)\,dt = v(t) \qquad (563)$$

Since this is to be a steady-state problem, the voltage is

$$v(t) = V_m \cos\,(\omega t + \theta_1)$$

and the current $i(t) = I_m \cos\,(\omega t + \theta_2)$. Equation (563) can therefore be written

$$RI_m \cos\,(\omega t + \theta_2) + L\frac{d}{dt}I_m \cos\,(\omega t + \theta_2)$$

$$+ \frac{1}{C}\int I_m \cos\,(\omega t + \theta_2)\,dt = V_m \cos\,(\omega t + \theta_1) \quad (564)$$

Let us assume voltage is known, and the problem is to find current. This requires finding I_m and θ_2. The usual method is not to struggle with Eq. (564) but to write a new equation in terms of "vector" quantities:

$$RI + j\omega LI + \frac{1}{j\omega C}I = V \tag{565}$$

V and I in this equation are complex quantities. Having magnitude and angle, they may be written as $V_m \epsilon^{j\theta_1}$ and $I_m \epsilon^{j\theta_2}$ (another equivalent notation is V_m/θ_1 and I_m/θ_2), and with this expansion Eq. (565) becomes

$$RI_m \epsilon^{j\theta_2} + j\omega L(I_m \epsilon^{j\theta_2}) + \frac{1}{j\omega C}(I_m \epsilon^{j\theta_2}) = V_m \epsilon^{j\theta_1} \tag{566}$$

There are various ways of justifying the change from Eq. (564) to Eq. (566). For our present purpose, we wish to look upon it as a *transformation* defined as follows: If a time function of voltage or current has the form

$$f(t) = F_m \cos (\omega t + \theta) \tag{567}$$

the corresponding complex quantity or "vector" is of the form

$$F = F_m \epsilon^{j\theta} \tag{568}$$

That is,

$$F_m \cos (\omega t + \theta) \qquad \text{transforms to} \qquad F_m \epsilon^{j\theta} \tag{569}$$

Accepting this definition, it can be shown by differentiation and integration (as will be done in detail for the more general case, in Sec. 4) that

$$\frac{d}{dt} F_m \cos (\omega t + \theta) \qquad \text{transforms to} \qquad j\omega F_m \epsilon^{j\theta}$$

and $\tag{570}$

$$\int F_m \cos (\omega t + \theta)\, dt \qquad \text{transforms to} \qquad \frac{1}{j\omega} F_m \epsilon^{j\theta}$$

Making this transformation, Eq. (564) yields Eq. (566).

The next step is to solve Eq. (566), the *transformed equation*, for $I_m \epsilon^{j\theta_2}$, the *transform of current*:

$$I_m \epsilon^{j\theta_2} = \frac{V_m \epsilon^{j\theta_1}}{R + j\left(\omega L - \dfrac{1}{\omega C}\right)} \tag{571}$$

The quantity in the denominator will be called the *impedance function* and be represented by Z:

$$Z = R + j\left(\omega L - \frac{1}{\omega C}\right) \tag{572}$$

Since Z is a complex quantity, it is conveniently written with a magnitude and an angle:

$$Z = |Z|\epsilon^{j\varphi} \tag{573}$$

where

$$|Z| = \sqrt{R^2 + \left(\omega L - \frac{1}{\omega C}\right)^2} \quad \text{and} \quad \varphi = \tan^{-1}\frac{\omega L - 1/\omega C}{R} \tag{574}$$

Equation (571) can now be put in the familiar form:

$$I_m\epsilon^{j\theta_2} = \frac{V_m\epsilon^{j\theta_1}}{Z} = \frac{V_m\epsilon^{j\theta_1}}{|Z|\epsilon^{j\varphi}} = \frac{V_m}{|Z|}\,\epsilon^{j(\theta_1-\varphi)} \tag{575}$$

But $I_m\epsilon^{j\theta_2}$ is not the current in the circuit. Through long experience with steady-state problems we have come to accept $I_m\epsilon^{j\theta_2}$, a complex number, as representing current, but in reality the solution is not finished until the actual current is expressed as a function of time. The transformation of (569) is applied to Eq. (575) in an inverse manner: $\epsilon^{j\theta_2}$ transforms back to $\cos(\omega t + \theta_2)$ and $\epsilon^{j(\theta_1-\varphi)}$ to $\cos(\omega t + \theta_1 - \varphi)$, giving:

$$i(t) = I_m \cos(\omega t + \theta_2) = \frac{V_m}{|Z|} \cos(\omega t + \theta_1 - \varphi) \tag{576}$$

This process, called *inverse transformation*, completes the solution.

To summarize, there are three steps in the solution:

1. By direct transformation, change the differential equation to an algebraic equation.

2. Solve the algebraic equation.

3. By inverse transformation, find the desired current.

The transformation of Pair (569) is limited to time functions that are steady and sinusoidal. This is the familiar transformation used for sine-wave problems. Sometimes, however, it is necessary to find the current in a circuit when the applied voltage, although periodic, is not merely sinusoidal. In such a problem, since $v(t)$ is not sinusoidal, Pair (569) does not apply.

3. The Fourier-series Transformation. It is common knowledge that the best procedure, when the voltage is periodic but not sinusoidal, is to express the voltage in terms of a Fourier series and then to solve for the current in terms of another Fourier series.

Let us formalize this procedure as a transformation. The transformation is defined by the pair of equations [analogous to Eqs. (567) and (568)]:

$$F(\omega) = \frac{\omega_1}{2\pi}\int_0^{2\pi/\omega_1} f(t)\epsilon^{-j\omega t}\, dt \tag{580}$$

$$f(t) = \sum_{\omega/\omega_1=-\infty}^{+\infty} F(\omega)\epsilon^{j\omega t} \tag{581}$$

In Eqs. (580) and (581), ω/ω_1 can be any integer; that is, $\omega = n\omega_1$ where n is an integer. Equation (581) says that a time function $f(t)$ is equal to the sum[1] of an infinite series of exponential terms. When ω is given values equal to multiples of ω_1 (ω_1 is the fundamental frequency), using negative as well as positive multiples of ω_1, these values combine in pairs to give sine and cosine functions of time. (Examples will be given below to show how this works.) These sine and cosine terms are the fundamental and harmonic components of $f(t)$. The direct-current component is that for which $\omega = 0$.

The coefficients of the fundamental- and harmonic-frequency terms are given by $F(\omega)$. This F, like the F of Eq. (568), is complex and expresses both amplitude and phase of the harmonic to which it applies. It is written $F(\omega)$ to indicate that it has different values for the different frequency components of the Fourier series. That is, the amplitude and phase of one harmonic component are not the same as the amplitude and phase of another harmonic component.

When a known $f(t)$ is introduced into Eq. (580), the corresponding $F(\omega)$ results. This is the *direct transformation*, and $F(\omega)$ is the Fourier-series transform of $f(t)$.

[1] There are certain restrictions on Fourier-series expansion, as is well known, but for a time function representing any physical phenomenon, such as voltage or current, it is only necessary to note that the series converges to the function except at discontinuities, and at discontinuities to the mid-point of the discontinuity.

Equation (580) is reasonably familiar. Although it is not identical with the most usual form of integral for finding the coefficients of the terms of Fourier series, it is essentially the same. The time function $f(t)$ is multiplied by an oscillatory term, and the product is then integrated. Equation (580) analyzes a complicated wave into its components of different frequencies and, by obvious analogy to the spectral analysis of visible light, this equation is sometimes called the "prism transformation."

Equation (581) synthesizes the components of different frequencies to regain the original time function $f(t)$. The transformations of Eqs. (580) and (581) are called *inverse* transforma-

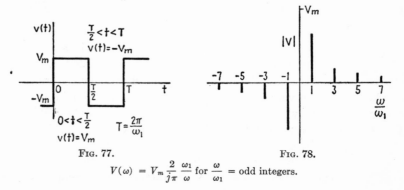

Fig. 77.   Fig. 78.

$$V(\omega) = V_m \frac{2}{j\pi} \frac{\omega_1}{\omega} \text{ for } \frac{\omega}{\omega_1} = \text{odd integers.}$$

tions, because if either is applied to a function, and then the other to the result, the original function is regained.

Examples of Transformation. *a.* Consider the square wave of Fig. 77. Its expression as a function of time is given with the figure; two equations are required, for the function equals V_m through the first half-period and $-V_m$ through the second half-period.

To find $V(\omega)$, Eq. (580) is used:

$$V(\omega) = \frac{\omega_1}{2\pi} \left[\int_0^{\pi/\omega_1} V_m \epsilon^{-j\omega t} \, dt + \int_{\pi/\omega_1}^{2\pi/\omega_1} (-V_m)\epsilon^{-j\omega t} \, dt \right]$$
$$= \frac{V_m}{j2\pi} \frac{\omega_1}{\omega} (\epsilon^{-j\pi\frac{\omega}{\omega_1}} - 1)^2 \tag{582}$$

This expression gives $V(\omega)$ for integer values of ω/ω_1. Let us consider even and odd integer values separately.

For any even integer value of ω/ω_1, including 0, $\epsilon^{-j\pi\omega/\omega_1} = 1$ and $V(\omega)$ consequently equals zero. For any odd integer value, positive or negative, $\epsilon^{-j\pi\omega/\omega_1} = -1$ and for these frequencies

$$V(\omega) = \frac{2V_m}{j\pi}\frac{\omega_1}{\omega}, \qquad \frac{\omega}{\omega_1} = \cdots -3, -1, +1, +3, \cdots \quad (583)$$

This is the transform of the square wave, and Fig. 78 is a diagram of its "spectrum." The frequencies present are odd multiples of the fundamental frequency. The amplitudes diminish in inverse proportion to the frequencies. Even harmonics are not present in the square wave, nor is there a zero-frequency component.

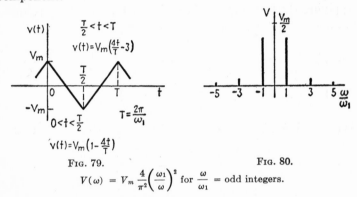

Fig. 79.

Fig. 80.

$$V(\omega) = V_m\frac{4}{\pi^2}\left(\frac{\omega_1}{\omega}\right)^2 \text{ for } \frac{\omega}{\omega_1} = \text{odd integers.}$$

Using the inverse transformation of Eq. (581) to synthesize the time function of the square wave,

$$v(t) = \frac{2V_m}{j\pi}\left(\cdots -\frac{1}{3}\epsilon^{-j3\omega_1 t} - \epsilon^{-j\omega_1 t} + \epsilon^{j\omega_1 t} + \frac{1}{3}\epsilon^{j3\omega_1 t} + \cdots\right)$$

$$= V_m\frac{4}{\pi}\left(\sin\omega_1 t + \frac{1}{3}\sin 3\omega_1 t + \cdots\right) \quad (584)$$

This expansion of a square wave can be found in any mathematical handbook.

b. Consider the triangular wave of Fig. 79. Equations to describe the wave during each half-period are given with the figure. These are substituted into Eq. (580), for $f(t)$, to find $F(\omega)$. One equation is required for the first half-period and another for the second, as in Eq. (582). The result of the integration is

$$V(\omega) = V_m\left[\frac{1 - \epsilon^{-j2\pi\frac{\omega}{\omega_1}}}{j2\pi}\frac{\omega_1}{\omega} + \frac{1}{\pi^2}\left(\frac{\omega_1}{\omega}\right)^2(\epsilon^{-j\pi\frac{\omega}{\omega_1}} - 1)^2\right] \quad (585)$$

For any even integer value of ω/ω_1, $V(\omega) = 0$. For all odd integer values of ω/ω_1,

$$V(\omega) = V_m \frac{4}{\pi^2}\left(\frac{\omega_1}{\omega}\right)^2, \qquad \frac{\omega}{\omega_1} = \cdots -3, -1, +1, +3, \cdots$$

(586)

This is the transform of the triangular wave, and Fig. 80 is a diagram of its "spectrum." Again only odd harmonics are present; their amplitudes diminish as the squares of their frequencies.

Applying the inverse transformation of Eq. (581), the triangular time function is given as

$$v(t) = V_m \frac{4}{\pi^2}\left(\cdots + \frac{1}{9}\epsilon^{-j3\omega_1 t} + \epsilon^{-j\omega_1 t} + \epsilon^{+j\omega_1 t} + \frac{1}{9}\epsilon^{+j3\omega_1 t} + \cdots \right)$$

$$= V_m \frac{8}{\pi^2}\left(\cos \omega_1 t + \frac{1}{9} \cos 3\omega_1 t + \cdots \right)$$

(587)

This expression, also, is commonly listed in mathematical tables.

TABLE 1.   FOURIER-SERIES TRANSFORMATION

Pair	Time function, $f(t)$ (during the interval from $t = 0$ to $t = 2\pi/\omega$)	Transform, $F(\omega)$ (for integer values of ω/ω_1)	See equation No.
	Definition		
1	$f(t) = \displaystyle\sum_{\frac{\omega}{\omega_1} = -\infty}^{\infty} F(\omega)\epsilon^{j\omega t}$	$F(\omega) = \dfrac{\omega_1}{2\pi}\displaystyle\int_0^{2\pi/\omega_1} f(t)\epsilon^{-j\omega t}\, dt$	580 581
	Transformation of Operations		
2	$\dfrac{d}{dt}f(t)$	$j\omega F(\omega)$	589
3	$\displaystyle\int f(t)\, dt$	$\dfrac{1}{j\omega}F(\omega)$	592
	Transformation of Functions		
4	$f(t) =$ square wave of unit amplitude	$F(\omega) = \dfrac{2}{j\pi}\dfrac{\omega_1}{\omega} \quad \left(\dfrac{\omega}{\omega_1}\text{odd}\right)$	583
5	$f(t) =$ triangular wave of unit amplitude	$F(\omega) = \dfrac{4}{\pi^2}\left(\dfrac{\omega_1}{\omega}\right)^2 \quad \left(\dfrac{\omega}{\omega_1}\text{odd}\right)$	586

Equations (583) and (586) give the result of transforming two specific time functions by the Fourier-series transformation. They are entered, for reference, as Pairs 4 and 5 of Table 1.

4. Transformation of Operations. Certain operations always transform to certain other operations, regardless of the function to which they are applied. Thus, differentiation of the time function transforms to multiplication by $j\omega$. An example of this was seen in Eq. (570).

To show this relation, start with Eq. (581) and differentiate:[1]

$$f(t) = \sum F(\omega)\epsilon^{j\omega t} \tag{588}$$

$$\frac{d}{dt}f(t) = \frac{d}{dt}\sum F(\omega)\epsilon^{j\omega t} = \sum \frac{d}{dt}F(\omega)\epsilon^{j\omega t}$$

$$= \sum j\omega F(\omega)\epsilon^{j\omega t} \tag{589}$$

As Eq. (588) relates $f(t)$ to its transform $F(\omega)$, so Eq. (589) relates $\frac{d}{dt}f(t)$ to its transform $j\omega F(\omega)$. This general relation is entered in Table 1, line 2.

---

[1] We are here skating on thin mathematical ice. Term-by-term differentiation of a finite Fourier series is permissible, but term-by-term differentiation of an infinite Fourier series may yield an infinite series that does not converge. It is mathematically better to reach the same conclusion from the direct transformation:

$$F(\omega) = \frac{\omega_1}{2\pi}\int_0^{2\pi/\omega_1} f(t)\,\epsilon^{-j\omega t}\,dt \tag{590}$$

Integrating by parts, with $f(t) = u$ and $\epsilon^{-j\omega t} = dv$ in the standard formula

$$\int_a^b u\,dv = \left[uv\right]_a^b - \int_a^b v\,du:$$

$$F(\omega) = -\frac{1}{j\omega}\left[f\left(\frac{2\pi}{\omega_1}\right) - f(0)\right] + \int_0^{2\pi/\omega_1} \frac{1}{j\omega}\epsilon^{-j\omega t}\frac{d}{dt}f(t)\,dt$$

or

$$j\omega F(\omega) = \int_0^{2\pi/\omega_1} \frac{d}{dt}f(t)\epsilon^{-j\omega t}\,dt + f(0) - f\left(\frac{2\pi}{\omega_1}\right) \tag{591}$$

For a periodic function, $f(0) = f(2\pi/\omega_1)$, and the last two terms may be omitted [unless there is a discontinuity of $f(t)$ at $t = 0$]. When the last two terms are omitted, comparison of Eq. (590) with Eq. (591) shows that if $F(\omega)$ is the transform of $f(t)$, $j\omega F(\omega)$ is the transform of $\frac{d}{dt}f(t)$.

Integration transforms to multiplication by $1/j\omega$ [as in Eq. (570)]. Integrating Eq. (581):

$$\int f(t)\, dt = \int \sum F(\omega)\epsilon^{j\omega t}\, dt = \sum \int F(\omega)\epsilon^{j\omega t}\, dt$$

$$= \sum \frac{1}{j\omega}F(\omega)\epsilon^{j\omega t} \tag{592}$$

This general relation is also entered in Table 1.

The use of these function-transform pairs and operation-transform pairs is best shown by an example.

5. Solution of a Steady-state Problem.   The general method of solution of a circuit problem by transformation was shown in Sec. 2.   The steps are (1) Transform the differential equation of the circuit to obtain an equation of the form $I(\omega) \cdot Z(\omega) = V(\omega)$. (2) Solve for the transform of current $I(\omega) = V(\omega)/Z(\omega)$.   (3) Use the inverse transformation to find $i(t)$ from $I(\omega)$.

Examples.   A square wave of voltage (as in Fig. 77) is applied to a pure inductance, as in Fig. 81.   Find the steady-state current.

The differential equation of this simple arrangement is

$$L\frac{d}{dt}i(t) = v(t) = \text{the square wave of Fig. 77} \tag{593}$$

Apply Pair 2 of Table 1 to the left side of this equation, and Pair 4 to the right side, getting

$$j\omega L I(\omega) = \frac{2}{j\pi}\frac{\omega_1}{\omega}V_m \tag{594}$$

The second step is to solve for the current transform $I(\omega)$:

$$I(\omega) = -\frac{2}{\pi}\frac{\omega_1}{\omega^2}\frac{V_m}{L} = -\frac{\pi}{2}\frac{V_m}{\omega_1 L}\cdot\frac{4}{\pi^2}\left(\frac{\omega_1}{\omega}\right)^2 \tag{595}$$

The third and final step is to find the current from its transform.   From Pair 5 of Table 1 we see that the right-hand member of Eq. (595) is a constant times the transform of the triangular wave.   Taking the inverse transform of each side of Eq. (595):

$$i(t) = -\frac{\pi}{2\omega_1 L}\cdot\text{(the triangular wave of Fig. 79)} \tag{596}$$

Thus a solution of a steady-state circuit problem is obtained by transformation methods.   A check of this result is easily obtained, for Eq. (593) can be solved by integration and the result is the triangular wave of Eq. (596); in problems that are slightly more complicated, however, solution by transformation is the only practicable method.

As another example, let resistance be added to the inductance of Fig. 81, as in Fig. 82. The voltage remains a square wave. The differential equation is then

$$Ri(t) + L\frac{d}{dt}i(t) = v(t) = \text{the square wave} \tag{597}$$

Direct transformation yields:

$$RI(\omega) + j\omega LI(\omega) = \frac{2}{j\pi}\frac{\omega_1}{\omega}V_m \tag{598}$$

Solving for current:

$$I(\omega) = \frac{2}{\pi}\frac{\omega_1 V_m}{j\omega(R + j\omega L)} \tag{599}$$

The final step in the solution is inverse transformation of Eq. (599) to find the time function of current, $i(t)$. This cannot be done from our table of transform pairs because the function of ω of Eq. (599) is not to be found in our table. A much longer table would be needed for practical use. (This

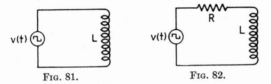

FIG. 81.   FIG. 82.

same problem is discussed from other points of view in Secs. 10 and 11 of Chap. VI.)

6. The Laplace Transformation. In the previous pages we have considered the transformation of periodic functions based on the Fourier-series equation:

$$F(\omega) = \frac{\omega_1}{2\pi}\int_0^T f(t)\epsilon^{-j\omega t}\,dt \tag{600}$$

where T is $2\pi/\omega_1$, the time of one cycle of the fundamental frequency.

The Laplace transformation is defined by

$$F(s) = \int_0^\infty f(t)\epsilon^{-st}\,dt \tag{601}$$

which looks very much like Eq. (600). The most important differences are that the upper limit of integration is not T, but ∞; and s is a continuous variable, whereas, in Eq. (600), ω could have only those particular values (corresponding to harmonic frequencies) that are integer multiples of ω_1. The purpose of the next three paragraphs is to show that the Laplace transformation can be considered to be an extension of the Fourier-series transformation.

1. The Fourier series can describe a function through as long a time as is desired, and T in Eq. (600) can be any finite length of time. In Eq. (601) the integration is extended to infinity.

2. The greater the value of T, the lower the fundamental frequency, for $T = 2\pi/\omega_1$. The lower the fundamental frequency, the less the difference in frequency between one harmonic and the next. If the interval covered by the Fourier series is extended without limit, and T approaches infinity, the fundamental frequency approaches zero. The harmonic frequencies then approach each other so closely that they tend to merge into a continuous function of frequency. In Eq. (601), s is a continuous function of frequency.[1]

3. The constant $\omega_1/2\pi$ which appears in Eq. (600) is omitted from Eq. (601). It has been moved and will reappear as $ds/2\pi$ in Eq. (603). This move is not significant, but is made for convenience.

Certain mathematical conditions must be mentioned at this point. It should be explicitly stated that the Laplace transformation is to be applied only to functions of time that are zero until $t = 0$. That is the time at which integration begins in Eq. (601), and the integral cannot take into account anything that happens before that time.

---

[1] This s is an algebraic variable. It is not an operator. Any other letter could be used instead of s. Some authors use p instead of s, others use λ. In this book, p has been used as an operator, which must not be confused with the algebraic variable s even though s and p appear in similar expressions, such as $Z(s)$ and $Z(p)$. We have used λ as an algebraic variable in earlier chapters, and could continue to use it here, but we will instead choose to use s as being the more customary symbol for the Laplace transformation variable.

The question naturally arises, what kind of a quantity is s? It is dimensionally the same as frequency. It is complex and is often (although somewhat inaccurately) spoken of as "complex frequency." In Sec. 21, s will be expanded into real and imaginary components, $s = \sigma + j\omega$. Compare Eqs. (185), on page 96, wherein λ_1 and λ_2 are specific values of s that make $Z(s) = 0$. In time functions, s appears in terms of the form ϵ^{st}, which corresponds to an oscillation, the frequency of which is determined by ω, the imaginary part of s. The meaning of s will be discussed more fully in Secs. 21 to 24.

Although comparison of Eq. (601) with Eq. (600) suggests that s should be imaginary, this is not necessarily true. (Imaginary s would give the Fourier-integral transformation.) For the Laplace transformation, s may have any complex value for which the integral of Eq. (601) is finite.[1]

7. The Inverse Laplace Transformation. Equation (601) is the direct Laplace transformation, analogous to Eq. (600). The inverse Fourier-series transformation [Eq. (581)] is

$$f(t) = \sum_{-\infty}^{+\infty} F(\omega)\epsilon^{j\omega t} \tag{602}$$

and the analogous inverse Laplace transformation is

$$f(t) = \frac{1}{2\pi j}\int_{c-j\infty}^{c+j\infty} F(s)\epsilon^{st}\,ds \tag{603}$$

The integral of Eq. (603) is analogous to the summation of Eq. (602); it will be recalled that integration is, by definition, the limit of a summation. The quantity c is a real constant [it is a particular value of σ, and may arbitrarily be assigned any value that is permissible for σ in Eq. (601)]. It is not necessary to discuss the meaning of Eq. (603) until later, for, as a matter of fact, we do not need to use it. Our work can all be done with the equation for the direct transformation.

8. Laplace Function-transform Pairs. Before the Laplace transformation method can be useful for the solution of problems, a table of transform pairs is needed. This, Table 2, will be very like Table 1, but of course the pairs will be different for they are

---

[1] The restriction that must be placed on s to make the integral finite is dependent on the nature of the function $f(t)$. For usual functions of t, it is sufficient to say that the real component of s must be positive.

Let σ be the real part of s. If σ is positive, ϵ^{-st} is very small for large values of t. On the other hand, if σ is negative, ϵ^{-st} increases exceedingly rapidly with increasing t. In the latter case, the integral of Eq. (601) would be infinite, and hence useless, unless $f(t)$ should be a function that grows small with increasing t even more rapidly than ϵ^{-st} grows large. For any $f(t)$, there is a limit on what σ may be. This is discussed in Sec. 26. For the present, it is enough to specify that σ is to be positive, and we can then apply Eq. (601) to any $f(t)$ that diminishes with time, or that is constant, or periodic, or that increases with time less rapidly than does an exponential function.

Table 2. Laplace Transformation

Pair	Time function, $f(t)$ [for positive time, $f(t)$ is given below; for negative time, $f(t) = 0$]	Laplace transform, $F(s)$	See equation No.
	Definition		
A	$f(t) = \dfrac{1}{2\pi j}\displaystyle\int_{c-j\infty}^{c+j\infty} F(s)\epsilon^{st}\,ds$	$F(s) = \displaystyle\int_0^\infty f(t)\epsilon^{-st}\,dt$	601 603
	Transformation of Operations		
B	If $f(t)$ transforms to $F(s)$, then $af(t)$ transforms to $aF(s)$		
C	$f_1(t) + f_2(t)$ transforms to $F_1(s) + F_2(s)$		
D	$\dfrac{d}{dt}f(t)$ transforms to $sF(s) - f(0)$		622
E	$\displaystyle\int_0^t f(t)\,dt$ transforms to $\dfrac{1}{s}F(s)$		624
F	$\epsilon^{\alpha t}f(t)$ transforms to $F(s - \alpha)$		692
	Transformation of Functions		
1	$f(t) = 1$ (unit step of Fig. 83)	$F(s) = \dfrac{1}{s}$	604
2	$f(t) = t$	$F(s) = \dfrac{1}{s^2}$	605
3	$f(t) = \epsilon^{-\alpha t}$	$F(s) = \dfrac{1}{s + \alpha}$	606
4	$f(t) = \dfrac{1}{\alpha}(1 - \epsilon^{-\alpha t})$	$F(s) = \dfrac{1}{s(s + \alpha)}$	608
5	$f(t) = \dfrac{1}{\lambda_1 - \lambda_2}(\epsilon^{\lambda_1 t} - \epsilon^{\lambda_2 t})$	$F(s) = \dfrac{1}{(s - \lambda_1)(s - \lambda_2)}$	698
6	$f(t) = t\epsilon^{-\alpha t}$	$F(s) = \dfrac{1}{(s + \alpha)^2}$	610
7	$f(t) = \epsilon^{wt}$	$F(s) = \dfrac{1}{s - w}$	613
8	$f(t) = \dfrac{1}{\omega}\sin \omega t$	$F(s) = \dfrac{1}{s^2 + \omega^2}$	612
9	$f(t) = \cos \omega t$	$F(s) = \dfrac{s}{s^2 + \omega^2}$	616
10	$f(t) = \dfrac{1}{\omega}\epsilon^{-\alpha t}\sin \omega t$	$F(s) = \dfrac{1}{(s + \alpha)^2 + \omega^2}$	618
11	$f(t) = \epsilon^{-\alpha t}\cos \omega t$	$F(s) = \dfrac{s + \alpha}{(s + \alpha)^2 + \omega^2}$	

TABLE 2. LAPLACE TRANSFORMATION.—*(Continued)*

Pair	Time function, $f(t)$	Laplace transform, $F(s)$	See equation No.
	Transformation of Functions—(Continued)		
12	$\dfrac{1}{\lambda_1\lambda_2} + \dfrac{\epsilon^{\lambda_1 t}}{\lambda_1(\lambda_1 - \lambda_2)} + \dfrac{\epsilon^{\lambda_2 t}}{\lambda_2(\lambda_2 - \lambda_1)}$	$\dfrac{1}{s(s - \lambda_1)(s - \lambda_2)}$	676
13	$\dfrac{\alpha}{\lambda_1\lambda_2} + \dfrac{\lambda_1 + \alpha}{\lambda_1(\lambda_1 - \lambda_2)}\epsilon^{\lambda_1 t}$ $+ \dfrac{\lambda_2 + \alpha}{\lambda_2(\lambda_2 - \lambda_1)}\epsilon^{\lambda_2 t}$	$\dfrac{s + \alpha}{s(s - \lambda_1)(s - \lambda_2)}$	681
14	$\dfrac{\epsilon^{\lambda_1 t}}{(\lambda_1 - \lambda_2)(\lambda_1 - \lambda_3)}$ $+ \dfrac{\epsilon^{\lambda_2 t}}{(\lambda_2 - \lambda_1)(\lambda_2 - \lambda_3)}$ $+ \dfrac{\epsilon^{\lambda_3 t}}{(\lambda_3 - \lambda_1)(\lambda_3 - \lambda_2)}$	$\dfrac{1}{(s - \lambda_1)(s - \lambda_2)(s - \lambda_3)}$	
15	$\dfrac{1}{\alpha^2 + \omega^2}\left(\epsilon^{-\alpha t} + \dfrac{\alpha}{\omega}\sin\omega t - \cos\omega t\right)$	$\dfrac{1}{(s + \alpha)(s^2 + \omega^2)}$	703
16	$\sin(\omega t + \theta)$	$\dfrac{s\sin\theta + \omega\cos\theta}{s^2 + \omega^2}$	

based on Eq. (601) instead of Eq. (600). In preparing such a table, let us begin by selecting a number of time functions that might reasonably be useful to represent voltages or currents and find their transforms as functions, not of ω, but of s. The variable s is related to frequency, as will be discussed later.

Pair 1. A time function as simple as any is the unit step function, or "switch-closing function," of Fig. 83. To find its transform, it is substituted into Eq. (601). Since its value is 1 for the entire range of time between the upper and lower limits of the integral, Eq. (601) becomes merely

$$F(s) = \int_0^\infty \epsilon^{-st}\,dt = -\frac{1}{s}\left[\epsilon^{-st}\right]_0^\infty = \frac{1}{s} \tag{604}$$

This provides the transform pair numbered 1 in Table 2.

Pair 2. Another simple time function is that of **Fig. 84.** Through the entire range of the integration, $f(t) = t$, so

$$F(s) = \int_0^\infty t\epsilon^{-st}\, dt = -\left[\frac{st+1}{s^2}\epsilon^{-st}\right]_0^\infty = \frac{1}{s^2} \qquad (605)$$

This gives Pair 2 of the table.

Pair 3. Many transient phenomena are exponential, and it is probable that the transform of the discontinuous exponential

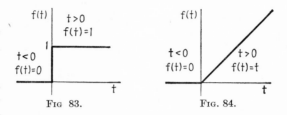

Fig 83.　　　　　　　Fig. 84.

function of Fig. 85 will be useful. Substituting into the transformation formula:

$$F(s) = \int_0^\infty \epsilon^{-\alpha t}\epsilon^{-st}\, dt$$
$$= \int_0^\infty \epsilon^{-(s+\alpha)t}\, dt = \frac{1}{s+\alpha} \qquad (606)$$

This is Pair 3 of Table 2.　(α is positive real.)

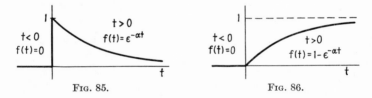

Fig. 85.　　　　　　　Fig. 86.

Pairs 4 *and* 5. It is not necessary to integrate to find the transform of the rising time function of Fig. 86. This time function is the sum of two functions for which transforms have already been found:

$$f(t) = 1 - \epsilon^{-\alpha t} \qquad (607)$$

It is well known from integral calculus that the integral of the sum of two functions is the sum of the integrals of the functions, and from this it follows that the transform of the sum of two time functions is the sum of the transforms of the functions taken individually. This is written symbolically as Pair C of Table 2.

Using Pairs 1 and 3 as the transforms of the two terms of Eq. (607):

$$F(s) = \frac{1}{s} - \frac{1}{s + \alpha} = \frac{\alpha}{s(s + \alpha)} \qquad (608)$$

This is Pair 4, except that the constant is transposed, for convenience, in the table. (Use Pair B of Table 2 to transpose.)

Pair 5 is found similarly; its derivation is now obvious.

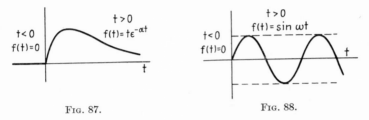

FIG. 87.   FIG. 88.

Pair 6. The surge of Fig. 87 is the response of a critically damped circuit. Its transform, Pair 6 of the table, is found by integration.

Since

$$f(t) = t\epsilon^{-\alpha t} \qquad \text{for} \qquad t > 0 \qquad (609)$$

we write

$$F(s) = \int_0^\infty t\epsilon^{-\alpha t}\epsilon^{-st}\, dt$$

$$= -\left[\frac{(s + \alpha)t + 1}{(s + \alpha)^2}\epsilon^{-(s+\alpha)t}\right]_0^\infty = \frac{1}{(s + \alpha)^2} \qquad (610)$$

Pairs 7 and 8. The transform of the discontinuous sine function of Fig. 88 can readily be found by integration. However, it can also be treated as a sum of known terms, and this proves to be the easier way:

$$f(t) = \sin \omega t = \frac{1}{2j}(\epsilon^{j\omega t} - \epsilon^{-j\omega t}) \qquad (611)$$

$$F(s) = \frac{1}{2j}\left(\frac{1}{s - j\omega} - \frac{1}{s + j\omega}\right)$$

$$= \frac{\omega}{s^2 + \omega^2} \qquad (612)$$

This gives Pair 8, but it cannot be considered to be established without a little further study of the process. Pair 3 was used in its derivation. Now Pair 3 was derived for an exponential with a positive real value of the coefficient α, and we have used it in Eq. (612) for exponentials having positive and negative imaginary values of the coefficient. Is this permissible?

It can be shown that it is permissible. Find the transform of a function $f(t) = \epsilon^{wt}$. This function is to be given no physical interpretation, and w can have any value, real, imaginary, or complex. The transform is

$$F(s) = \int_0^\infty \epsilon^{wt}\epsilon^{-st}\,dt = \int_0^\infty \epsilon^{(w-s)t}\,dt \tag{613}$$

The integral will have a value if the real part of s is greater than the real part of w. This is more apparent if we write the real and imaginary parts of $w - s$ separately.

If $w - s = \text{Re}\,(w - s) + j\,\text{Im}\,(w - s)$,

$$F(s) = \int_0^\infty \epsilon^{\text{Re}(w-s)t}\epsilon^{j\text{Im}(w-s)t}\,dt \tag{614}$$

The exponential with an imaginary exponent is cyclic and does

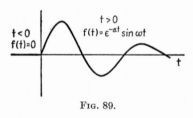

FIG. 89.

not affect the existence of the integral, so we may conclude that if $\text{Re}\,(w - s)$ is negative, the integral has a finite value, whereas if it is positive, the integral does not. Transform Pair 7 is therefore established if $\sigma > \text{Re}\,w$. Since we have stipulated that σ is to be positive, Pair 7 is valid for imaginary values of w, for which $\text{Re}\,w = 0$, and Eq. (612) is justified.

Pair 9. Having justified the use of imaginary exponents by deriving Pair 7, the transform of the discontinuous cosine function can also be found as the sum of exponential functions:

$$f(t) = \cos \omega t \text{ if } t > 0, \qquad f(t) = 0 \text{ if } t < 0$$
$$= \tfrac{1}{2}(\epsilon^{j\omega t} + \epsilon^{-j\omega t}) \tag{615}$$

$$F(s) = \frac{1}{2}\left(\frac{1}{s - j\omega} + \frac{1}{s + j\omega}\right) = \frac{s}{s^2 + \omega^2} \tag{616}$$

This is Pair 9.

Pairs 10 *and* 11. The damped sine appears in many transients problems (Fig. 89). Its transform is most readily found by considering its exponential components:

$$f(t) = \epsilon^{-\alpha t} \sin \omega t$$

$$= \epsilon^{-\alpha t} \frac{\epsilon^{j\omega t} - \epsilon^{-j\omega t}}{2j}$$

$$= \frac{1}{2j}(\epsilon^{(-\alpha+j\omega)t} - \epsilon^{(-\alpha-j\omega)t}) \tag{617}$$

$$F(s) = \frac{1}{2j}\left(\frac{1}{s + \alpha - j\omega} - \frac{1}{s + \alpha + j\omega}\right) = \frac{\omega}{(s + \alpha)^2 + \omega^2} \tag{618}$$

This gives transform Pair 10. The transform of the discontinuous damped cosine is obtained similarly, and is given in Pair 11.

9. Operation-transform Pairs. Considering the analogy between the Fourier-series transformation and the Laplace transformation, it is not surprising that multiplication of the Laplace transform by $1/s$ corresponds to integration of the time function, much as multiplication by $1/j\omega$ corresponded to integration of the Fourier series. Similarly, multiplication of the Laplace transform by s is equivalent to differentiation of the time function, provided initial conditions are properly taken into account.

The relation between differentiation of the time function and multiplication by s is given as Pair D of Table 2 and may be proved as follows. Since

$$F(s) = \int_0^\infty f(t)\epsilon^{-st} \, dt \tag{619}$$

$$sF(s) = s\int_0^\infty f(t)\epsilon^{-st} \, dt = \int_0^\infty f(t)s\epsilon^{-st} \, dt \tag{620}$$

Using the formula for integration by parts, $\int u \, dv = uv - \int v \, du$, let $f(t) = u$ and $s\epsilon^{-st} \, dt = dv$. Then $v = -\epsilon^{-st}$, and $du = \frac{d}{dt}f(t) \, dt$. These are substituted into the integral of Eq. (620), with 0 and ∞ the limits of integration, giving

$$sF(s) = -\left[\epsilon^{-st}f(t)\right]_0^\infty + \int_0^\infty \left[\frac{d}{dt}f(t)\right]\epsilon^{-st} \, dt \tag{621}$$

Substituting the limits for t in the first term gives $0 + f(0)$, using the symbol $f(0)$ to designate the value of $f(t)$ when $t = 0$. Hence

$$sF(s) - f(0) = \int_0^\infty \left[\frac{d}{dt}f(t)\right]\epsilon^{-st} \, dt \tag{622}$$

Comparison of this equation with Eq. (619) establishes Pair D.

The term $f(0)$ is a constant. It is the initial value[1] of the time function, at $t = 0$. For cos ωt, for example, it is 1. For sin ωt, it is 0. For the step function of Fig. 83, or the discontinuous exponential of Fig. 85, it is 1.

In physical problems, $f(0)$ in this transform pair helps provide for the effect of initial conditions. This will be seen in examples of the next section.

Pair E of the table, relating integration to multiplication by $1/s$, is obtained in a similar manner. Multiplying each side of Eq. (619) by $1/s$:

$$\frac{1}{s}F(s) = \int_0^\infty f(t)\frac{1}{s}\epsilon^{-st}\,dt \tag{623}$$

Use the formula for integration by parts, letting $\frac{1}{s}\epsilon^{-st} = u$ and $f(t)\,dt = dv$. With integration from 0 to ∞, the product uv in the formula vanishes, leaving

$$\frac{1}{s}F(s) = \int_0^\infty \left[\int_0^t f(t)\,dt\right]\epsilon^{-st}\,dt \tag{624}$$

By comparison with Eq. (619), $\frac{1}{s}F(s)$ and $\int_0^t f(t)\,dt$ are the transform pair we are seeking.

Pair C in the table has already been explained. In Pair B, a is any constant. The proof, using the definition of $F(s)$ in Pair A, is obvious, for $f(t)$ and $F(s)$ may be multiplied by the same constant. Both of these pairs are simple, but extremely important.

10. Examples of Circuit Problems. We are now prepared to solve by Laplace transformation a great variety of problems that relate to networks with constant lumped parameters.

Example 1. Equation (6), page 15, relates to a circuit of inductance and resistance. There is no applied voltage, but an initial current i_0 is allowed to die gradually away. The differential equation is

$$Ri(t) + L\frac{d}{dt}i(t) = 0 \tag{625}$$

---

[1] Because of the way the lower limit is approached in Eq. (620), our $f(0)$ is the value approached by $f(t)$ as zero time is approached from the positive side (not from the negative side). This distinction is important for functions that are discontinuous at $t = 0$.

This can be transformed, using pairs of Table 2, to

$$RI(s) + L[sI(s) - i(0)] = 0 \tag{626}$$

Solving for current,

$$I(s) = \frac{Li(0)}{Ls + R} = \frac{i_0}{s + (R/L)} \tag{627}$$

Inverse transformation then gives the current:

$$i(t) = i_0\epsilon^{-\frac{R}{L}t} \tag{628}$$

The direct transformation uses transform Pairs B and D (with i and I written for f and F to indicate that the function is current), and Pair **3** gives the inverse transformation. Note that the initial current is automatically taken into account.

Example 2. Equation (3), page 20, is for an inductive circuit with battery voltage suddenly applied; there is no initial current:

$$Ri(t) + L\frac{d}{dt}i(t) = E \qquad i(0) = 0 \tag{629}$$

Transforming as before, using Pair 1 for the transform of the constant voltage E,

$$RI(s) + L[sI(s) - i(0)] = \frac{E}{s} \tag{630}$$

$$I(s) = \frac{E}{L}\frac{1}{s(s + R/L)} \tag{631}$$

By inverse transformation, using Pair 4 from the table,

$$i(t) = \frac{E}{R}(1 - \epsilon^{-\frac{R}{L}t}) \tag{632}$$

which agrees with Eq. (26), page 21.

Example 3. Equation (50), page 37, is for a circuit of condenser and resistance to which a battery voltage is suddenly applied:

$$Ri(t) + \frac{1}{C}\int_0^t i(t)\, dt = E \tag{633}$$

Transform, using Pairs B, E, and 1:

$$RI(s) + \frac{1}{sC}I(s) = \frac{E}{s} \tag{634}$$

$$I(s) = \frac{E}{s(R + 1/sC)} = \frac{E}{R}\frac{1}{s + 1/RC} \tag{635}$$

Inverse transformation with Pair 3 gives

$$i(t) = \frac{E}{R}\epsilon^{-\frac{1}{RC}t} \tag{636}$$

which is the same as Eq. (54) obtained in Chap. II.

Example 4.   Initial charge on a condenser is taken into account if the circuit equation is written fully and correctly.   Thus, Eq. 75 (page 47) is for a condenser with initial charge q_0 which is to be discharged through another condenser and a resistance.   There is no applied voltage:

$$\frac{q_0}{C_1} + \frac{1}{C_1}\int_0^t i(t)\,dt + \frac{1}{C_2}\int_0^t i(t)\,dt + Ri(t) = 0 \tag{637}$$

By direct transformation, using Pairs 1, E, and B,

$$\frac{q_0}{sC_1} + \frac{I(s)}{sC_1} + \frac{I(s)}{sC_2} + RI(s) = 0 \tag{638}$$

Solving,

$$I(s) = -\frac{q_0}{RC_1}\frac{1}{s+\alpha} \tag{639}$$

where, for convenience, we let

$$\alpha = \frac{1}{R}\frac{C_1+C_2}{C_1C_2} \tag{640}$$

By inverse transformation:

$$i(t) = -\frac{q_0}{RC_1}\epsilon^{-\alpha t} \tag{641}$$

This is in agreement with Eq. (82) of Chap. II.

Example 5.   When battery voltage is suddenly applied to a circuit containing all three parameters—resistance, inductance, and capacitance—and initially at rest, the circuit equation is Eq. (103), page 77:

$$Ri(t) + L\frac{di(t)}{dt} + \frac{1}{C}\int_0^t i(t)\,dt = E \tag{642}$$

By direct transformation:

$$RI(s) + L[sI(s) - i(0)] + \frac{I(s)}{sC} = \frac{E}{s} \tag{643}$$

Solving for $I(s)$ and making $i(0) = 0$,

$$I(s) = \frac{E}{L}\frac{1}{s^2 + s\dfrac{R}{L} + \dfrac{1}{LC}} \tag{644}$$

Here we encounter a somewhat new situation, for nothing quite like this function of s appears in Table 2.   However, there are two transforms that seem related, in Pairs 5 and 10, and possibly the present function can be changed to match one of those.   The denominator of Eq. (644) is a quadratic expression in s; it can be factored and written in the form $(s - \lambda_1)(s - \lambda_2)$, where λ_1 and λ_2 are the two roots of the quadratic [λ_1 and λ_2, that is, are the two values of s that make $s^2 + s(R/L) + 1/LC = 0$].   By the usual formula:

$$\lambda_1 = -\frac{R}{2L} + \sqrt{\frac{R^2}{4L^2} - \frac{1}{LC}} \qquad \lambda_2 = -\frac{R}{2L} - \sqrt{\frac{R^2}{4L^2} - \frac{1}{LC}} \tag{645}$$

Written in factored form, Eq. (644) is

$$I(s) = \frac{E}{L}\frac{1}{(s - \lambda_1)(s - \lambda_2)} \tag{646}$$

Since this differs from the transform of Pair 5 of Table 2 only by a constant, that pair can be used in making the inverse transformation to obtain the desired current as a function of time.   Then

$$i(t) = \frac{E}{L}\frac{\epsilon^{\lambda_1 t} - \epsilon^{\lambda_2 t}}{\lambda_1 - \lambda_2} = \frac{E}{\sqrt{R^2 - 4L/C}}(\epsilon^{\lambda_1 t} - \epsilon^{\lambda_2 t}) \tag{647}$$

This agrees with the classic solution given in Eqs. (148) and (149) of Chap. IV, as, of course, it must.   It describes a surge of current.

The trigonometric form of solution is often more convenient if a circuit has so little resistance that the current is oscillatory.   For an oscillatory solution, Pair 10 of the table looks more promising.   Equation (644) can be made to resemble the transform of Pair 10 by "completing the square" in the denominator:

$$I(s) = \frac{E}{L}\frac{1}{s^2 + s\dfrac{R}{L} + \dfrac{R^2}{4L^2} + \dfrac{1}{LC} - \dfrac{R^2}{4L^2}} = \frac{E}{L}\frac{1}{\left(s + \dfrac{R}{2L}\right)^2 + \left(\dfrac{1}{LC} - \dfrac{R^2}{4L^2}\right)} \tag{648}$$

If we let $\alpha = R/2L$ and $\omega^2 = 1/LC - R^2/4L^2$, we can use Pair 10 to give the current:

$$i(t) = \frac{E}{\omega L}\epsilon^{-\alpha t} \sin \omega t \tag{649}$$

and this agrees with Eq. (190) of Chap. IV.

Finally, there is the possibility that the denominator of Eq. (644) is a perfect square; this is true if $R^2/4L^2 = 1/LC$.   Either of the above mathematical forms then reduces to

$$I(s) = \frac{E}{L}\frac{1}{\left(s + \dfrac{R}{2L}\right)^2} \tag{650}$$

With this function of s, Pair 6 is clearly applicable, and inverse transformation gives:

$$i(t) = \frac{E}{L}t\epsilon^{-(R/2L)t} \tag{651}$$

This will be recognized as current in a critically damped circuit, and it is in agreement with Eq. (160) of Chap. IV.

11. The Excitation Function and the Impedance Function.

The transform of the differential equation of a circuit always contains a factor that is related to the circuit impedance.   Five examples have just been given.   Let us, for each, examine the transform of the left-hand side of the circuit equation.

For Example 1, it is $[R + sL]I(s) - Li(0)$.

For Example 2, it is the same, but $i(0)$ is zero.

For Example 3, it is $\left[R + \dfrac{1}{sC}\right]I(s)$.

For Example 4, it is $\left[R + \dfrac{1}{sC_1} + \dfrac{1}{sC_2}\right]I(s) + \dfrac{q_0}{sC_1}$.

For Example 5, it is $\left[R + sL + \dfrac{1}{sC}\right]I(s)$.

The ordinary alternating-current steady-state impedance of the circuit of Examples 1 and 2 is $R + j\omega L$.

For Example 3, it is $R + 1/j\omega C$.

For Example 4, it is $R + 1/j\omega C_1 + 1/j\omega C_2$.

For Example 5, it is $R + j\omega L + 1/j\omega C$.

The quantity in brackets in each of the transforms listed above is identical with the circuit impedance if s is substituted for $j\omega$. Not only is this true for these specific examples, but it can be seen from the nature of operation-transform pairs that it will be true for every network. (This statement is based on the similarity of the Laplace transformation and the vector transformation of Sec. 2.) This gives an easy way of writing the Laplace transform of the equation of a circuit or network without requiring that the differential equation be written at all.

Let us call the **impedance** of a circuit Z. The familiar steady-state impedance is a function of $j\omega$, and may be written $Z(j\omega)$. The Laplace transform of any circuit equation contains an expression that differs from $Z(j\omega)$ only in having $j\omega$ removed and s substituted. This expression will be called $Z(s)$. As seen above, each transform contains a product $Z(s) \cdot I(s)$.

In Examples 1 and 4, as listed above, there are other terms besides $Z(s) \cdot I(s)$; these other terms have to do with initial conditions. When we solve for $I(s)$, as we have done in every problem, these terms, representing initial conditions, are transposed to the other side of the equation. Thus, a formal statement of the transform of any circuit equation is

$$Z(s) \cdot I(s) = V(s) + \text{terms accounting for initial energy} \quad (652)$$

If, for convenience, we write W to mean "terms accounting for initial energy," we have

$$I(s) = \frac{V(s) + W}{Z(s)} \quad (653)$$

where

$$W = \sum_{\text{coils}} Li(0) - \sum_{\text{condensers}} \frac{v(0)}{s}$$

In case there is initially no current in any coil and no charge on any condenser, W is zero. But for each coil in the circuit that is initially carrying current, there is a term (in W) of the form $Li(0)$; and for each condenser with initial charge, there is a term of the form $-v(0)/s$, wherein $v(0)$ is the initial voltage across the condenser.

The numerator of Eq. (653), containing terms to account for initial energy as well as the transform of the applied voltage, is called the **excitation function** of the circuit.

The important thing about Eq. (653) is that it can usually be written by inspection of the circuit, without any necessity for previously writing the differential equation of the circuit. From the known applied voltage, the voltage transform $V(s)$ can be found (from a table, or otherwise). The terms of W can be written from the initial conditions. $Z(s)$ is found from the ordinary impedance of the circuit. Thus, Eq. (653) can be the starting point in solving most problems. This will be made clearer by a few examples.

Before proceeding with examples, it will be well to comment on the algebraic sign of the terms, components of W, which account for initial stored energy. Terms of the form $Li(0)$ are positive if the initial current is positive; this is reasonable, for such an initial current adds to the current produced by a positive applied voltage. On the other hand, terms accounting for initial charge on a condenser have a negative sign. Positive charge is defined as the charge placed on a condenser by a positive current; this produces a voltage across the condenser that opposes a positive applied voltage. If $v(0)$ is the initial voltage across a condenser, and it opposes the applied voltage, the corresponding term in W is $-v(0)/s$.

Example 1. The voltage-regulator circuit (Chap. I, Sec. 12) consists of resistance and inductance in series, the applied voltage being E. A contactor in the circuit operates at time $t = 0$; current at this instant is $i(0) = i_0$, and for all times later than $t = 0$ the resistance in the circuit is R and the inductance is L. Find current.

Refer to Eq. (653). In the numerator, $V(s)$, the transform of the constant applied voltage E, is, by Pair 1 of Table 2, E/s. The only term arising from initial energy in the circuit is Li_0. For the denominator, the impedance of the circuit is $R + j\omega L$. Hence we write

$$I(s) = \frac{E/s + Li_0}{R + sL} \tag{654}$$

This is easily manipulated into recognizable functions of s:

$$I(s) = \frac{E}{L}\frac{1}{s(s + R/L)} + i_0\frac{1}{s + R/L} \tag{655}$$

Pairs 3 and 4 of Table 2 give the desired time function:

$$i(t) = \frac{E}{R}(1 - \epsilon^{-\frac{R}{L}t}) + i_0\epsilon^{-\frac{R}{L}t} = \left(i_0 - \frac{E}{R}\right)\epsilon^{-\frac{R}{L}t} + \frac{E}{R} \tag{656}$$

The solution is thus completed. It may be compared with the classical solution on page 24 for the same voltage-regulator problem.

Example 2. In the network of Fig. 90 (the keying circuit of a radiotelegraph transmitter), the switch S is closed until steady current flows. Switch S is then opened. Find current in the circuit after S is opened.

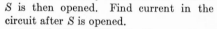

Fig. 90.

Refer to Eq. (653). In the numerator we have $V(s) = E/s$, the transform of the constant applied voltage. To this will be added a term $Li(0)$ because of the initial current in the coil, and inspection of the circuit shows that $i(0) = E/(R + r)$. Also, a term $-v(0)/s$ will be included to account for initial energy in the condenser. In this circuit, $v(0)$, the initial voltage across the condenser, is $ri(0)$.

In the denominator of Eq. (653), write the impedance of the circuit: $Z(p) = sL + R + 1/sC$. This gives

$$I(s) = \frac{E/s + Li(0) - v(0)/s}{sL + R + 1/sC} \tag{657}$$

Rearrangement of the right-hand member gives recognizable terms:

$$I(s) = \frac{E - v(0) - \alpha Li(0)}{L}\frac{1}{(s + \alpha)^2 + \omega^2} + i(0)\frac{s + \alpha}{(s + \alpha)^2 + \omega^2} \tag{658}$$

wherein

$$\alpha = \frac{R}{2L} \quad \text{and} \quad \omega = \sqrt{\frac{1}{LC} - \frac{R^2}{4L^2}}$$

Pairs 10 and 11 yield the required current as a function of time:

$$i(t) = \frac{E - v(0) - \alpha Li(0)}{\omega L}\epsilon^{-\alpha t}\sin \omega t + i(0)\epsilon^{-\alpha t}\cos \omega t \tag{659}$$

Since $v(0)$ and $i(0)$ are known, this completes the solution. (This example is part of Prob. 8, page 184.)

12. Driving-point and Transfer Impedances.   A network that is made up of several circuits has associated with it several impedance functions.   If voltage is applied in circuit 1 of any network, the ratio of the applied voltage, which we shall call V_1, to the current in circuit 1, called I_1, is the driving-point impedance Z_{11}.   The ratio of this voltage applied in circuit 1 to the current it causes in Circuit 2 is the transfer impedance Z_{12}.

Let us first restrict ourselves to consideration of networks in which there is excitation in only one circuit.   That is, voltage is applied in only one circuit (which we shall call circuit 1), and while there may be initial stored energy in the coils or condensers of circuit 1, there is no initial stored energy in any of the elements of any of the other circuits.

For a network thus excited in circuit 1 only, the current transform of circuit 1 is

$$I_1(s) = \frac{V_1(s) + W_1}{Z_{11}(s)} \tag{660}$$

This is a generalization of Eq. (653); like Eq. (653), it can be set up by inspection of the network, making use of familiar steady-state impedance relations.

To find current in circuit 2 of the same network, we use the transfer impedance function:

$$I_2(s) = \frac{V_1(s) + W_1}{Z_{12}(s)} \tag{661}$$

This also can be written by inspection.

In general, for a network excited only in circuit m, the current transform of circuit n is

$$I_n(s) = \frac{V_m(s) + W_m}{Z_{mn}(s)} \tag{662}$$

An example will show how the method is used.

Example.   In the circuit of Fig. 91 (which is the same as Fig. 30, page 131), there is no initial current.   Find current in circuit 1 after the switch is closed.

For this network,

$$Z_{11}(j\omega) = j\omega L_1 + R_1 + \frac{R_{12}(R_2 + j\omega L_2)}{R_{12} + R_2 + j\omega L_2} \tag{663}$$

$$Z_{12}(j\omega) = Z_{11}\frac{R_{12} + R_2 + j\omega L_2}{R_{12}} \tag{664}$$

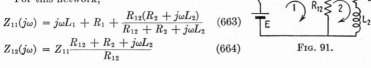

Fig. 91.

Using Eq. (660),

$$I_1(s) = \frac{E/s + 0}{sL_1 + R_1 + \dfrac{R_{12}(R_2 + sL_2)}{R_{12} + R_2 + sL_2}} \qquad (665)$$

The first step of the solution is to put this equation into more familiar form in order to find its inverse transform:

$$I_1(s) = \frac{E}{L_1} \frac{s + R_{22}/L_2}{s\left[s^2 + s\left(\dfrac{R_{22}}{L_2} + \dfrac{R_{11}}{L_1}\right) + \dfrac{R_{11}R_{22} - R_{12}{}^2}{L_1 L_2} \right]} \qquad (666)$$

The function of s of Eq. (666) is still not one for which the transform is known, but at least it is reasonably simple. The parenthesis in the denominator is a quadratic form which can be factored. If we call the roots of the quadratic λ_1 and λ_2, and write α for R_{22}/L_2 in the numerator, we obtain

$$I_1(s) = \frac{E}{L_1} \frac{s + \alpha}{s(s - \lambda_1)(s - \lambda_2)} \qquad (667)$$

[λ_1 and λ_2 are given in terms of circuit constants in Eq. (231).]

Referring to Eq. (661), the current transform for circuit 2 is

$$I_2(s) = \frac{E/s}{Z_{12}(s)} = \frac{E/s}{Z_{11}(s)\dfrac{R_{12} + R_2 + sL_2}{R_{12}}}$$

$$= \frac{ER_{12}}{L_1 L_2} \frac{1}{s\left[s^2 + s\left(\dfrac{R_{22}}{L_2} + \dfrac{R_{11}}{L_1}\right) + \dfrac{R_{11}R_{22} - R_{12}{}^2}{L_1 L_2} \right]} \qquad (668)$$

This is similar to the current transform for circuit 1, but simpler. The denominator is the same, so λ_1 and λ_2 have the same values in Eq. (669) as in Eq. (667):

$$I_2(s) = \frac{ER_{12}}{L_1 L_2} \frac{1}{s(s - \lambda_1)(s - \lambda_2)} \qquad (669)$$

To complete the solution for currents in circuit 1 and circuit 2, Eqs. (667) and (669) must be changed to time functions by inverse transformation. Since our previous work has not yielded any functions of s of similar form, it is necessary to explore new methods. An extremely powerful means is the method of partial fractions. Let us investigate this general method, and then return to the final steps of solution of this problem.

13. Partial-fraction Expansion.

Example 1. The function of s in Eq. (669) is the product of three simple factors. If these appeared as a sum, instead of a product, each could be transformed separately, and Pair C of Table 2 would apply. There is no easy way to handle a product, however, even though each factor of the product could be transformed without trouble if it stood alone.

Fortunately, the method of partial fractions permits us to change the product to a sum. Let us assume that it is possible to expand the product into a sum as follows:

$$F(s) = \frac{1}{s(s - \lambda_1)(s - \lambda_2)} = \frac{A}{s} + \frac{B}{s - \lambda_1} + \frac{C}{s - \lambda_2} \qquad (670)$$

If this latter form were possible, and A, B, and C were constants, the transform of each term could easily be found. Let us explore the possibility of evaluating A, B, and C.

If Eq. (670) is true, it must be possible to put the three terms of the right-hand member over a common denominator and, by equating numerators, write

$$1 \equiv A(s - \lambda_1)(s - \lambda_2) + Bs(s - \lambda_2) + Cs(s - \lambda_1) \qquad (671)$$

This is written as an identity, for we want it to be true for all values of s. If it is true for all values of s, it is true for $s = 0$. If we substitute $s = 0$ into Eq. (671), the second and third terms of the right-hand member are zero, and there results

$$A = \frac{1}{\lambda_1 \lambda_2} \qquad (672)$$

This is the only value of A that will satisfy Eq. (671) when $s = 0$; hence it is the only possible value for A if Eq. (671) is to be an identity.

We also want Eq. (671) to be true if $s = \lambda_1$. Letting $s = \lambda_1$, the first and third terms become zero, and there results

$$B = \frac{1}{\lambda_1(\lambda_1 - \lambda_2)} \qquad (673)$$

This is the necessary value of B.

Similarly, letting $s = \lambda_2$, there results

$$C = \frac{1}{\lambda_2(\lambda_2 - \lambda_1)} \qquad (674)$$

Collecting these expressions in Eq. (670):

$$F(s) = \frac{1}{\lambda_1 \lambda_2} \frac{1}{s} + \frac{1}{\lambda_1(\lambda_1 - \lambda_2)} \frac{1}{s - \lambda_1} + \frac{1}{\lambda_2(\lambda_2 - \lambda_1)} \frac{1}{s - \lambda_2} \qquad (675)$$

The inverse transformation is now performed by using Pairs 1 and 7 of Table 2, giving

$$f(t) = \frac{1}{\lambda_1 \lambda_2} + \frac{\epsilon^{\lambda_1 t}}{\lambda_1(\lambda_1 - \lambda_2)} + \frac{\epsilon^{\lambda_2 t}}{\lambda_2(\lambda_2 - \lambda_1)} \qquad (676)$$

Equations (670) and (676) provide Pair 12 of the table. (Merely to save space, the symbols "$f(t) =$" and "$F(s) =$" are omitted from this rather lengthy pair in the table, and from succeeding pairs also, but the meaning is the same as for the first 11 pairs in which these symbols are included.)

Example 2.   The function of s in Eq. (667), the current transform for circuit 1 in the foregoing example, can be expanded into partial fractions in a similar manner.   It is written

$$F(s) = \frac{s + \alpha}{s(s - \lambda_1)(s - \lambda_2)} = \frac{A}{s} + \frac{B}{s - \lambda_1} + \frac{C}{s - \lambda_2} \qquad (677)$$

Equating numerators:

$$A(s - \lambda_1)(s - \lambda_2) + Bs(s - \lambda_2) + Cs(s - \lambda_1) = s + \alpha \qquad (678)$$

Letting s assume successively the three root values of 0, λ_1, and λ_2, we find:

$$A = \frac{\alpha}{\lambda_1\lambda_2} \qquad B = \frac{\lambda_1 + \alpha}{\lambda_1(\lambda_1 - \lambda_2)} \qquad C = \frac{\lambda_2 + \alpha}{\lambda_2(\lambda_2 - \lambda_1)} \qquad (679)$$

Hence, in Eq. (677),

$$F(s) = \frac{\alpha}{\lambda_1\lambda_2}\frac{1}{s} + \frac{\lambda_1 + \alpha}{\lambda_1(\lambda_1 - \lambda_2)}\frac{1}{s - \lambda_1} + \frac{\lambda_2 + \alpha}{\lambda_2(\lambda_2 - \lambda_1)}\frac{1}{s - \lambda_2} \qquad (680)$$

and, transforming,

$$f(t) = \frac{\alpha}{\lambda_1\lambda_2} + \frac{\lambda_1 + \alpha}{\lambda_1(\lambda_1 - \lambda_2)}e^{\lambda_1 t} + \frac{\lambda_2 + \alpha}{\lambda_2(\lambda_2 - \lambda_1)}e^{\lambda_2 t} \qquad (681)$$

This result is put in storage in Table 2 as Pair 13.

Application.   Returning, now, to the example of circuit analysis in the preceding section, we can find the current in circuit 1, $i_1(t)$, by applying Pair 13 to Eq. (667).   Indeed, that completes the solution for current, α, λ_1, and λ_2 being known.

In the same way, the use of Pair 12 with Eq. (669) gives $i_2(t)$.

The results here obtained by Laplace analysis may be compared with the classic solution of the same problem in Chap. V.   A little algebraic manipulation shows that the steady-state currents are the same as in Eqs. (235) and (236), and the transient coefficients can be compared with Eqs. (246) and (252).   There is no question that the Laplace method, after it has once been mastered, will give answers to such problems more quickly and easily than will the classic method.

14. Partial-fraction Expansion: General.   The method of expansion into partial fractions has been illustrated by examples; it can be generalized as follows.   If $P_1(s)/P_2(s)$ is a proper fraction in which $P_2(s)$ is a polynomial of nth degree in s, the fraction can be expanded in the form

$$\frac{P_1(s)}{P_2(s)} = \frac{A}{s - \lambda_1} + \frac{B}{s - \lambda_2} + \frac{C}{s - \lambda_3} + \cdots + \frac{N}{s - \lambda_n} \qquad (682)$$

wherein λ_1, λ_2, . . . , λ_n are the n roots of $P_2(s) = 0$, provided these roots are all different. Then (by equating numerators):

$$A = \frac{P_1(\lambda_1)}{(\lambda_1 - \lambda_2)(\lambda_1 - \lambda_3) \cdots (\lambda_1 - \lambda_n)} \tag{683}$$

$$B = \frac{P_1(\lambda_2)}{(\lambda_2 - \lambda_1)(\lambda_2 - \lambda_3) \cdots (\lambda_2 - \lambda_n)}, \text{ etc.} \tag{684}$$

wherein $P_1(\lambda_1)$ is the result of writing λ_1 for s in $P_1(s)$. Note that $P_1(\lambda_1)$ is a number, whereas $P_1(s)$ is a polynomial.

If two or more of the roots of $P_2(s) = 0$ are identical, the form of expansion is slightly changed. If $\lambda_2 = \lambda_1$, omit from Eq. (682) the term $B/(s - \lambda_2)$ and write $B/(s - \lambda_1)^2$ in its place. If it is also true that $\lambda_3 = \lambda_2 = \lambda_1$, omit $C/(s - \lambda_3)$ also, substituting $C/(s - \lambda_1)^3$. The numerators A, B, C, etc., are evaluated by equating numerators, the derivatives (with respect to s) of the numerators, and, if necessary, higher derivatives also.

Any college algebra book will give a more comprehensive discussion of the expansion of proper fractions into partial fractions. A variety of methods and forms of expansion are available. Circuit analysis will hardly ever lead to a function of s that is an improper fraction. If this should happen, however, the numerator of the improper fraction would be divided by the denominator to give a polynomial in s and a proper-fraction remainder.

Examples of partial-fraction expansion are given in the preceding Sec. 13.

15. Derivation by Integration. Any ordinary network-analysis problem can be handled by partial-fraction expansion, but there are sometimes easier ways to find the time function corresponding to a new function of s. In Eq. (669), for instance, we are called on to find the transform of $1/s(s - \lambda_1)(s - \lambda_2)$. Let us suppose this is a new function and its transform is yet to be found.

In considering means of handling this new form, we find in our table the somewhat similar function $1/(s - \lambda_1)(s - \lambda_2)$, which differs from the new function only by a factor $1/s$. This suggests making use of Pair E of Table 2.

From Pair 5 we know that if

$$F(s) = \frac{1}{(s - \lambda_1)(s - \lambda_2)}$$

then

$$f(t) = \frac{1}{\lambda_1 - \lambda_2}(\epsilon^{\lambda_1 t} - \epsilon^{\lambda_2 t}) \qquad (685)$$

Pair E says that we can multiply $F(s)$ by $1/s$ if we integrate $f(t)$. That is, the inverse transform of $1/s(s - \lambda_1)(s - \lambda_2)$ is

$$\int_0^t f(t)\, dt = \frac{1}{\lambda_1 - \lambda_2} \int_0^t (\epsilon^{\lambda_1 t} - \epsilon^{\lambda_2 t})\, dt$$

$$= \frac{1}{\lambda_1 - \lambda_2}\left[\frac{1}{\lambda_1}(\epsilon^{\lambda_1 t} - 1) - \frac{1}{\lambda_2}(\epsilon^{\lambda_2 t} - 1) \right]$$

$$= \frac{1}{\lambda_1 \lambda_2} + \frac{\epsilon^{\lambda_1 t}}{\lambda_1(\lambda_1 - \lambda_2)} + \frac{\epsilon^{\lambda_2 t}}{\lambda_2(\lambda_2 - \lambda_1)} \qquad (686)$$

Thus we have derived Pair 12 by integration, a very simple step.

16. Derivation by Differentiation. It seems that it should be possible to derive new pairs by differentiation, as has just been done by integration. This can indeed be done, but with one important qualification.

If $f(t)$ is the inverse transform of $F(s)$, then the derivative of $f(t)$ is the inverse transform of $sF(s)$, *provided $f(0) = 0$.* It is evident from Pair D of the table that this is so. Expressed in other words, a time function can be differentiated, and its transform correspondingly multiplied by s, *if* the time function is zero at time zero.

As an example, let us apply Pair D to Pair 8. The time function of Pair 8 is transformed by differentiation to give:

$$\frac{d}{dt}\left(\frac{1}{\omega} \sin \omega t \right) = \cos \omega t \qquad (687)$$

The function of s must correspondingly be multiplied by s:

$$s\left(\frac{1}{s^2 + \omega^2} \right) = \frac{s}{s^2 + \omega^2} \qquad (688)$$

Since $\sin \omega t$ is zero when $t = 0$, it follows that $f(0)$ in Pair D is zero. Pair 9 for the cosine is thereby derived from Pair 8 for the sine.

If a time function is not zero when $t = 0$, Pair D can still be applied, but the term $f(0)$ of Pair D must then be included in the result. The time function $\cos \omega t$ of Pair 9, for example, can be differentiated to obtain a new pair, but the new transform will contain the term $f(0) = \cos 0 = 1$ (see Prob. 17).

In differentiating to produce new transform pairs, it is not always easy to know whether $f(0) = 0$. Consider the time function of Pair 13, for instance. It is often more convenient to inspect the transform than the time function. If multiplication by s results in a proper fraction (if, that is, the degree of s in the numerator does not become as high as the degree in the denominator), $f(0) = 0$, and such multiplication by s corresponds to simple differentiation of the time function.

Thus, Pair 3 can be obtained from Pair 4 by differentiating the time function and multiplying $F(s)$ by s, for $1/(s + \alpha)$ is a proper fraction. Multiplication of Pair 3 by s, however, gives an improper fraction, so for this operation $f(0)$ is not zero (see Prob. 18). The value of $f(0)$ is actually $\epsilon^0 = 1$, as illustrated in Fig. 85.

17. Translation. Another simple means of deriving new pairs is based on the following simple theorem. If $F(s)$ is the transform of $f(t)$, then $F(s - \alpha)$ is the transform of $\epsilon^{\alpha t}f(t)$. The quantity α can be real, imaginary, or complex.

To prove this theorem, we start with the definition of the Laplace transformation:

$$F(s) = \int_0^\infty f(t)\epsilon^{-st}\, dt \qquad\qquad (689)$$

The function that occurs in the theorem is obtained by writing

$$F(s) = \int_0^\infty \epsilon^{\alpha t}f(t)\epsilon^{-\alpha t}\epsilon^{-st}\, dt = \int_0^\infty \epsilon^{\alpha t}f(t)\epsilon^{-(s+\alpha)t}\, dt \quad (690)$$

Let $s + \alpha = s'$, from which $s = s' - \alpha$. Equation (690) can then be written

$$F(s' - \alpha) = \int_0^\infty [\epsilon^{\alpha t}f(t)]\epsilon^{-s't}\, dt \qquad\qquad (691)$$

In Eq. (691), s' is a complex quantity that can take any value for which the integral has meaning. The same can be said of s, but s does not appear in Eq. (691). Hence we need not distinguish between s' and s, and the prime can be dropped:

$$F(s - \alpha) = \int_0^\infty [\epsilon^{\alpha t}f(t)]\epsilon^{-st}\, dt \qquad\qquad (692)$$

As $F(s)$ in Eq. (689) is the transform of $f(t)$, so $F(s - \alpha)$ in Eq. (692) is the transform of $\epsilon^{\alpha t} f(t)$. Thus the theorem is proved, and the result is preserved as Pair F of Table 2.

This change of variable is called translation because $F(s - \alpha)$ is a function similar to $F(s)$, but produced by values of s that are greater by α. Let values of s, real and complex, be represented by points in a plane, as in Fig. 92a; the value of s at any point in the plane gives a certain value to $F(s)$, and s at another point at a distance $+\alpha$ gives the same value to $F(s - \alpha)$.

The change of a function from $F(s)$ to $F(s - \alpha)$ amounts to translation of the function F through a distance α. If $F(s)$ has poles (that is, if the function becomes infinite) at certain values of s, the function $F(s - \alpha)$ has poles at values of s that are greater by α. As an example, the function $F(s) = \dfrac{1}{s - w}$ has a pole at $s = w$; if $s - \alpha$ is substituted for s, we obtain the function $F(s - \alpha) = \dfrac{1}{s - \alpha - w}$, which has a pole at $s = \alpha + w$.

The theorem states that translation of the function of s through α corresponds to multiplying the time function by $\epsilon^{\alpha t}$. This principle can be used to change known transform pairs into new forms, as in the following example.

Example. Assume that the only function-transform pair available is Pair 1, which says that if $f(t) = 1$, $F(s) = 1/s$. It is desired to find the time function that is the inverse transform of $1/(s - \lambda_1)(s - \lambda_2)$.

The function $1/s$ has only one pole, and that one at the origin where $s = 0$, as indicated in Fig. 92a. We are interested in a function with two poles, one at $s = \lambda_1$ and one at $s = \lambda_2$, and no pole at $s = 0$, as in Fig. 92d. The first step is to move the one pole of $1/s$ away from the origin by using the translation theorem just developed. Since

$$f(t) = 1 \qquad \text{transforms to} \qquad F(s) = 1/s \qquad (693)$$

it follows from the theorem, or from Pair F, that

$$\epsilon^{\alpha t} \qquad \text{transforms to} \qquad \frac{1}{s - \alpha} \qquad (694)$$

This function has a pole at $s = \alpha$. Figure 92b shows the pole, after translation, for a case in which α is real and negative.

Next, Pair E of Table 2 is used to produce a second pole. Applying Pair E to Eq. (694):

$$\int_0^t \epsilon^{\alpha t}\, dt = \frac{1}{\alpha}(1 - \epsilon^{\alpha t}) \qquad \text{transforms to} \qquad \frac{1}{s(s - \alpha)} \qquad (695)$$

This function, as in Fig. 92c, has a pole at the origin as well as a pole at $s = \alpha$. We do not want a pole at the origin, but we do want a pole at λ_1, so we translate through λ_1. Applying again Pair F of Table 2, since

$$-\frac{1}{\alpha}(1 - \epsilon^{\alpha t}) \qquad \text{transforms to} \qquad \frac{1}{s(s - \alpha)} \qquad (696)$$

it follows that

$$-\frac{\epsilon^{\lambda_1 t}}{\alpha}(1 - \epsilon^{\alpha t}) \qquad \text{transforms to} \qquad \frac{1}{(s - \lambda_1)(s - \lambda_1 - \alpha)} \qquad (697)$$

If we let $\lambda_1 + \alpha = \lambda_2$, this may be written

$$\frac{1}{\lambda_1 - \lambda_2}(\epsilon^{\lambda_1 t} - \epsilon^{\lambda_2 t}) \qquad \text{transforms to} \qquad \frac{1}{(s - \lambda_1)(s - \lambda_2)} \qquad (698)$$

The two poles of this function, λ_1 and λ_2, are shown in Fig. 92d. Thus, producing poles by integration and shifting them by translation, we have arrived at the transform pair that was required.

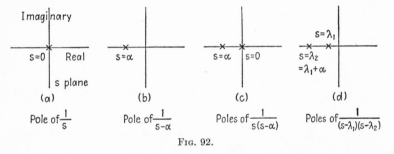

FIG. 92.

This is an illustration of a general method of procedure. Using integration, differentiation, and translation (Pairs D, E, and F), one can derive any of the pairs of Table 2 or, indeed, any pair for which $F(s)$ is a rational function. For each particular problem under consideration, it must be decided whether this method or the method of splitting into partial fractions is the more promising. Sometimes one will be easier, sometimes the other.

18. Response to Alternating Voltage. Although the examples of foregoing sections have considered only constant applied voltages, the transform method is perhaps even more advantageous for other forms of voltage.

Example 1. Alternating voltage is suddenly applied to a circuit of resistance and inductance. Find the current.

The circuit impedance function is $Z(s) = R + sL$. Let the applied voltage be $v(t) = E \sin \omega t$. Its transform (by Pair 8) is $V(s) = \omega E / (s^2 + \omega^2)$.

Assume that there is no initial current in the circuit; then, using Eq. (653),

$$I(s) = \frac{\omega E/(s^2 + \omega^2)}{R + sL} = \frac{E}{L}\frac{\omega}{(s + R/L)(s^2 + \omega^2)} \tag{699}$$

Here is an unfamiliar function of s; its inverse transform must be found before the solution can be completed. There are several possible ways of proceeding, but Eq. (699) looks enough like Pair 8 of Table 2 to be encouraging. From Pair 8,

$$\frac{\omega}{s^2 + \omega^2} \qquad \text{transforms to} \qquad \sin \omega t \tag{700}$$

This function of s has a pair of poles at $s = \pm j\omega$; the function of Eq. (699) also has a pair of poles at $\pm j\omega$, but it has another pole besides. Its third pole is at $s = -R/L$, which may for convenience be called $-\alpha$.

We wish to get a pole at $-\alpha$ into the pair of Eq. (700). Since poles are conveniently produced at the origin, let us proceed as in Fig. 93. Starting

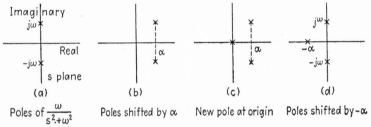

(a) Poles of $\dfrac{\omega}{s^2+\omega^2}$ (b) Poles shifted by α (c) New pole at origin   (d) Poles shifted by $-\alpha$

Fig. 93.

with the function of Eq. (700), which has the poles shown in Fig. 93a, translate the function (to the right in the s plane if α is real and positive) by writing $s - \alpha$ for s. Then produce a new pole at the origin by multiplying by $1/s$. Finally translate the function back again (to the left in the s plane) by writing $s + \alpha$ for s. The result will be the required function of Eq. (699).

The corresponding operations on the time function are as follows: We start with Eq. (700). To translate, apply Pair F of Table 2, giving

$$\frac{\omega}{(s - \alpha)^2 + \omega^2} \qquad \text{transforms to} \qquad \epsilon^{\alpha t} \sin \omega t \tag{701}$$

(This has, indeed, already been obtained as Pair 10 of Table 2.) Next, apply Pair E:

$$\frac{\omega}{s[(s - \alpha)^2 + \alpha^2]} \qquad \text{transforms to} \qquad \int_0^t \epsilon^{\alpha t} \sin \omega t \, dt \tag{702}$$

$$= \frac{\omega}{\alpha^2 + \omega^2}\left[1 + \epsilon^{\alpha t}\left(\frac{\alpha}{\omega} \sin \omega t - \cos \omega t\right) \right]$$

Now apply Pair F again:

$$\frac{\omega}{(s + \alpha)(s^2 + \omega^2)} \qquad \text{transforms to} \qquad \frac{\omega}{\alpha^2 + \omega^2}\left(\epsilon^{-\alpha t} + \frac{\alpha}{\omega} \sin \omega t - \cos \omega t\right) \tag{703}$$

This completes the solution of the example, for we can now write the inverse transform of Eq. (699) as

$$i(t) = \frac{E\omega}{L(R^2/L^2 + \omega^2)}\left(\epsilon^{-\frac{R}{L}t} + \frac{R}{\omega L}\sin \omega t - \cos \omega t\right) \qquad (704)$$

[This is a special case of Fig. 43 and Eq. (381) of Chap. VI.]   Equation (703) gives us Pair 15 for the table.

Example 2.   A pulse of voltage, described by $v(t) = Et\epsilon^{-\gamma t}$ is applied to a circuit of resistance and inductance in series.   This is not a periodic voltage; it is a single surge of the "artificial lightning" type used for high-voltage testing of insulation (see Fig. 50 and Sec. 9 of Chap. VI).

The current is found by writing $I(s) = V(s)/Z(s)$, there being no initial stored energy.   The transform of the applied voltage is given by Pair 6 of Table 2: $V(s) = E/(s + \gamma)^2$.   The circuit impedance function is

$$Z(s) = R + sL$$

Hence the transform of current is

$$I(s) = \frac{E}{L(s + \gamma)^2(s + R/L)} \qquad (705)$$

The time function, the inverse transform of Eq. (705), can be found by the method used in the previous example, employing translation and integration, or it can be found by expansion into partial fractions.   It is often necessary to decide which of these two methods to use.   In this example, they are about equally promising, so let us split into partial fractions for the purpose of illustrating that method.

The function of s of Eq. (705) has one second-order pole (corresponding to a double root of the denominator) and one first-order pole.   Following the rule of Sec. 14, let us expand it in the form:

$$\frac{1}{(s + \gamma)^2(s + \alpha)} = \frac{A}{s + \gamma} + \frac{B}{(s + \gamma)^2} + \frac{C}{s + \alpha} \qquad (706)$$

Clearing of fractions:

$$A(s + \gamma)(s + \alpha) + B(s + \alpha) + C(s + \gamma)^2 \equiv 1 \qquad (707)$$

There are several ways of solving for A, B, and C.   The most direct, if not the quickest, is as follows.   First collect terms:

$$s^2(A + C) + s[A(\gamma + \alpha) + B + 2C\gamma] + (A\gamma\alpha + B\alpha + C\gamma^2) \equiv 1 \qquad (708)$$

This is written as an identity to emphasize that the left member must equal the right member for all values of s, which is possible only if the coefficients of like powers of s are equal.   Hence

$$A + C = 0 \qquad (709)$$
$$A(\gamma + \alpha) + B + 2C\gamma = 0 \qquad (710)$$
$$A\gamma\alpha + B\alpha + C\gamma^2 = 1 \qquad (711)$$

These three equations can now be solved simultaneously for A, B, and C. The solution is simple if determinants are used, and gives

$$A = -\frac{1}{(\alpha - \gamma)^2} \qquad B = \frac{1}{\alpha - \gamma} \qquad C = \frac{1}{(\alpha - \gamma)^2} \qquad (712)$$

The transform of each term of the right-hand member of Eq. (706) is easily found. Performing this transformation, and at the same time inserting the values of A, B, and C:

$$f(t) = -\frac{\epsilon^{-\gamma t}}{(\alpha - \gamma)^2} + \frac{t\epsilon^{-\gamma t}}{\alpha - \gamma} + \frac{\epsilon^{-\lambda t}}{(\alpha - \gamma)^2} \qquad (713)$$

Finally, then, using this transform of Eq. (706), we have as the solution of our problem, the current in the circuit,

$$i(t) = \frac{E}{L(\alpha - \gamma)^2}[(\alpha - \gamma)t\epsilon^{-\gamma t} - \epsilon^{-\gamma t} + \epsilon^{-\alpha t}] \qquad (714)$$

Noting that $\alpha = R/L$, this is seen to be the same as Eq. (426), page 210, another solution of the same problem.

19. Superposition of Voltages. If voltage is applied in more than one circuit of a network, the principle of superposition is used. First assume that one voltage source is active and all others inactive. The inactive voltage sources are considered to carry current but not to supply voltage; in other words, the other batteries or generators are replaced by short-circuits. Determine the current produced in each branch of the network. In a similar manner, find the current produced in each branch by each of the voltage sources in turn acting alone. Finally, add the individual currents to obtain the total current.

If there is initial energy stored in coils or condensers, the terms representing energy storage in these elements are to be treated like the terms representing voltage sources. Thus, in Eq. (662), voltage is applied in circuit m, and there is initial energy storage in circuit m only. Terms representing initial stored energy (terms represented by W_m) are added to the transform of the applied voltage in Eq. (662). If there were initial stored energy in circuit k also, superposition would be used; the inverse transform of Eq. (662) would give the current in circuit n, owing to excitation in circuit m, and to this would be added another component of current in circuit n, determined by assuming V_m and W_m both zero and taking into account only the initial energy in circuit k and the applied voltage, if any, in circuit k.

Formal expression of this method is obtained by writing differential equations for each circuit and transforming them to obtain

$$z_{11}(s)I_1(s) + z_{12}(s)I_2(s) + \cdots = V_1(s) + W_1$$
$$z_{21}(s)I_1(s) + z_{22}(s)I_2(s) + \cdots = V_2(s) + W_2 \quad (715)$$
$$\cdot \cdot \cdot \cdot \cdot \cdot \cdot \cdot \cdot \cdot \cdot \cdot \cdot \cdot \cdot \cdot \cdot \cdot \cdot \cdot \cdot \cdot \cdot \cdot \cdot \cdot$$

These are simultaneous algebraic equations, and there are as many equations as there are circuits in the network; z_{11}, z_{22}, etc., are the self-impedance functions[1] of circuits 1, 2, etc., and z_{12}, z_{13}, etc., are the mutual impedance functions between circuits 1 and 2, circuits 1 and 3, etc.

Solution of this family of equations gives $I_1(s)$ or any of the other currents in terms of the applied voltages and impedances. Thus,

$$I_n = \frac{(V_1 + W_1)M_{1n} - (V_2 + W_2)M_{2n} + \cdots}{D} \quad (716)$$

wherein D is the determinant of the set of equations:

$$D = \begin{vmatrix} z_{11} & z_{12} & z_{13} & \cdot \cdot \cdot \\ z_{21} & z_{22} & z_{23} & \cdot \cdot \cdot \\ z_{31} & z_{32} & z_{33} & \cdot \cdot \cdot \\ \cdot \cdot \cdot \cdot \cdot \cdot \cdot \cdot \cdot \end{vmatrix} \quad (717)$$

and M_{mn} is the minor of the mth row and the nth column.

This generalized solution may appear a little formidable, but if Eq. (716) is studied a term at a time it will be seen to be a statement of the superposition principle. The first term gives the component of current in circuit n resulting from excitation in circuit 1; the second term gives the component from excitation in circuit 2, etc. After each has been determined independently, the components are added to give total current in circuit n.

---

[1] It should be emphasized that Z_{11} of Eq. (660) is not the same as z_{11} of Eq. (715). Z_{11} is the driving-point impedance of the network, whereas z_{11} is the self-impedance of circuit 1 alone—the impedance that would be measured if all other circuits were open. Also, Z_{12}, the transfer impedance, must not be confused with z_{12}, the mutual impedance. Z_{11}, Z_{12}, etc., can be expressed in terms of z_{11}, z_{12}, etc. From Eq. (716), Z_{1n}, $= D/M_{1n}$ and other driving-point and transfer impedances are found correspondingly.

20. The Inverse Transformation. In the preceding sections, Laplace transformation has served as a tool to solve differential equations. The direct transformation has been used to change a differential equation into an algebraic equation, and algebraic methods have then yielded an expression that is the transform of the desired solution. In the foregoing problems, in which we have been solving for current, we have first obtained an expression for $I(s)$. Inverse transformation is then necessary to give the desired $i(t)$.

We have not used any straightforward means of finding $i(t)$ from $I(s)$, but rather we have hunted through our table of Laplace transforms to see if we could find a suitable pair already derived. If a pair is found with the correct function of s, the time function of the pair gives the solution of the problem. It is to be noted that the table is prepared by performing the *direct* transformation on a variety of time functions, with the hope that the functions of s thus obtained will match those that arise in the solution of problems. We have not used Eq. (603) for performing the inverse transformation, but instead we have accomplished the inverse transformation by retracing the direct transformation.

The straightforward means of performing the inverse transformation, given in Eq. (603), is[1]

$$f(t) = \frac{1}{2\pi j} \int_{c-j\infty}^{c+j\infty} F(s) \epsilon^{st} \, ds \qquad (718)$$

It is not really necessary to discuss this inverse transformation (and the rest of the chapter can be omitted by those who care to do so), but its consideration introduces a number of new ideas that are not only interesting but also turn out to be extremely powerful in advanced methods of analysis.

It will be helpful in discussing Eq. (718) to consider:
1. The variable s.
2. The function ϵ^{st}.
3. The path of integration and the limits.
4. The function $F(s)$.

---

[1] Proof that this is indeed the inverse transformation may be found in treatises on the Laplace transformation. It is merely suggested here by showing that Eq. (603) is analogous to the inverse operation of Fourier-series analysis.

21. The Variable s. As in our previous work, s is a complex variable with a meaning akin to frequency. Being complex, it will have a real and an imaginary component, and we may write $s = \sigma + j\omega$; σ and ω are thus defined as the components of s.

Figure 94a shows the s plane. The real and imaginary components of s, σ and ω, are measured along the horizontal and vertical axes. Any complex value of s is represented by a point in this plane.

22. The Function ϵ^{st}. The nature of ϵ^{st} depends on whether s is real, imaginary, or complex. If s is real, $\omega = 0$, and the point representing s lies on the horizontal axis of Fig. 94a. With real s, $\epsilon^{st} = \epsilon^{\sigma t}$; this is a real exponential time function, with a rate of

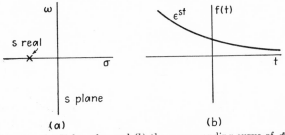

(a)   (b)

FIG. 94.   (a) Value of s, and (b) the corresponding curve of ϵ^{st}.

growth or decay that is determined by σ. In Fig. 94a, s is represented by a point on the axis to the left of the origin; the corresponding time function, shown in Fig. 94b, grows smaller with time. If s lay to the right of the origin, the time function would increase with time.

If s is imaginary, it is represented by a point on the vertical axis, and the corresponding time function ϵ^{st} is complex. In our work, imaginary values of s appear in pairs; if one is $+j\omega$ the other is $-j\omega$. If s has such a pair of imaginary values, ϵ^{st} has a pair of values that add to give a real oscillation: $\epsilon^{j\omega t} + \epsilon^{-j\omega t} = 2 \cos \omega t$. A pair of imaginary values for s is shown in Fig. 95a, and the corresponding cosine time function in Fig. 95b.

When s is complex, the complex values appear in conjugate pairs. Let one value of s be $s_1 = \sigma_1 + j\omega_1$; the other value of the pair will be $s_2 = \sigma_1 - j\omega_1$. One value corresponds to a point in the upper half of the complex s plane and the other to its mirror-image in the lower half of the plane. Such a pair is shown in Fig.

96a. The corresponding values for ϵ^{st} add to give an oscillation that is either increasing or decreasing with time:

$$\epsilon^{s_1 t} + \epsilon^{s_2 t} = \epsilon^{(\sigma_1 + j\omega_1)t} + \epsilon^{(\sigma_1 - j\omega_1)t}$$
$$= \epsilon^{\sigma_1 t}(\epsilon^{j\omega_1 t} + \epsilon^{-j\omega_1 t}) = 2\epsilon^{\sigma_1 t}\cos\omega_1 t$$

A pair of points in the left half of the plane (σ negative) corresponds to a decreasing (damped) oscillation. A pair in the right

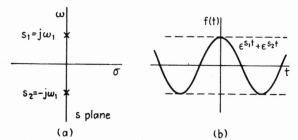

Fig. 95. (a) A pair of values of s, and (b) a curve of $\epsilon^{s_1 t} + \epsilon^{s_2 t}$.

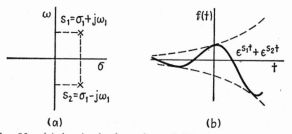

Fig. 96. (a) A pair of values of s, and (b) a curve of $\epsilon^{s_1 t} + \epsilon^{s_2 t}$.

half of the plane (σ positive), as in Fig. 96, corresponds to an increasing oscillation. The distance of the pair to the left or right of the vertical axis indicates the amount of damping. The distance of each of the pair above and below the horizontal axis is proportional to the frequency of the oscillation. It is for this reason that the s plane is sometimes called the **complex-frequency plane.**

23. The Integral. The integral of Eq. (718) represents a summation of oscillations. The values to be given to s in the course of the integration lie along the dash line of Fig. 97. The real part of s is held constant ($\sigma = c$) during the integration, while the value of ω is varied from $-\infty$ to $+\infty$.

Integration includes all negative values of ω as well as all positive values.   These can be considered in pairs.   The integration therefore includes values of s in conjugate pairs.   Since the integration sums pairs of the form ϵ^{st} with conjugate values of s, and since such pairs comprise oscillations, the integration is, as stated above, a summation of oscillations.

The path of integration is a vertical straight line as in Fig. 97. The value of c, the displacement of the path of integration from the vertical axis, can be any desired quantity, with the following provision.   There are certain values of s that make $F(s)$ infinite; these, the poles of $F(s)$, are fixed points in the complex s plane.   The path of integration must lie to the right of all poles of $F(s)$. Unless this restriction is placed upon c, Eq. (718) is not the inverse Laplace transformation.   The necessity for this restriction will be explained in Sec. 26.

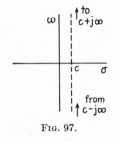

Fig. 97.

24. The Function $F(s)$.   For each conjugate pair of values of s, $F(s)\epsilon^{st}$ is an oscillation.   For a given value of s, $F(s)$ is merely a number; it is, in general, complex, and it gives the value of $F(s)\epsilon^{st}$ at zero time.   We may say of the oscillation:

1. The imaginary part of s determines its frequency.

2. The real part of s determines its rate of increase (or decay).

3. The magnitude of $F(s)$ gives its amplitude at zero time.

4. The angle of $F(s)$ gives its phase at zero time.

5. The oscillation extends through all time, negative and positive.

The integral of Eq. (718), then, sums an infinity of such oscillations of different frequencies to obtain a time function $f(t)$.   As the various harmonic terms of a Fourier series have different amplitudes and phases, so the different oscillatory components of the Laplace integral have different amplitudes and phases.

Clearly, the value of the integral of Eq. (718) depends on the nature of the function $F(s)$.   It is a remarkable fact that the value of the integral can be determined from information about $F(s)$ at the poles, those singular points at which $F(s)$ becomes infinite, and at those points only.   All that one must know about $F(s)$ elsewhere is that it is an analytic function (meaning that it possesses a unique derivative at every point).   The functions of s

arising in circuit analysis are rational functions, and all rational functions satisfy this requirement.

In Fig. 93, and throughout Sec. 17, we gave particular attention to the poles of the complex functions. This was sufficient because, as we shall now see, all the information that we need about a function is comprised in its behavior at the poles. If we know where in the s plane the poles are located, and how the function approaches infinity at these poles, we have all the information needed to evaluate the integral of Eq. (718).

In explanation, it is necessary to introduce certain relations concerned with integration in the complex plane.

1. Ordinary integration is a special case of integration in the complex plane in which the path of integration is along the axis of

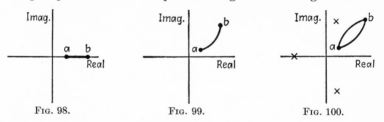

Fig. 98.   Fig. 99.   Fig. 100.

reals. Thus, integration from a to b means that the variable of integration is to be given successively all real values from a to b, and the path of integration is that shown in Fig. 98. It is obvious that integration from a to b and back to a again, retracing the path of integration to the starting point, will give zero as the result of the integration. This is true regardless of the function being integrated.

2. If integration is from any point a to any other point b in the complex plane, the values that are to be assumed successively by the variable may be specified by showing the path of integration, as in Fig. 99. Here, also, integration from a to b and back to a again, retracing the same path, gives zero for the integral of any function.

3. If integration follows one path from a to b but returns from b to a along a different path, as in Fig. 100, the integral around the closed path is still zero *provided* the function being integrated does not become infinite at any point on or within the closed path of integration. Thus, the function being integrated may have poles (indicated by x in Fig. 100) anywhere outside the loop, and the

integral is zero—but if there were a pole within the path of integration, the integral around that path would not be zero.

4. If there is a pole within the closed path of integration, the value of the integral about the closed path is found as follows. Let us say the function being integrated is $F(s)$ and it has a pole at $s = s_1$. If the pole is a first-order pole, the product $(s - s_1)F(s)$ is not infinite but finite at $s = s_1$. (This is the meaning of a *first-order* pole.) When one such first-order pole is enclosed within the path of integration, as shown in Fig. 101, and integra-

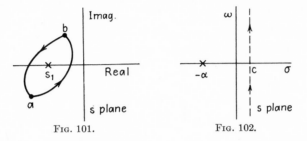

FIG. 101.   FIG. 102.

tion is performed by following the path in a counterclockwise direction, the result of the integration is

$$\oint F(s) \ ds = 2\pi j[\lim_{s \to s_1} (s - s_1)F(s)] \tag{719}$$

(The quantity in brackets is called the "residue" at the pole.)

5. If more than one pole is enclosed within the path of integration, the integral is $2\pi j$ times the sum of the residues at the several poles.

6. The residues at multiple-order poles are readily evaluated, but the method need not be given here.

25. Contour Integration. We are now prepared to evaluate the integral of Eq. (718), the inverse Laplace transformation, in specific examples.

Example 1. $F(s)$ is $1/(s + \alpha)$; find $f(t)$. By Eq. (718),

$$f(t) = \frac{1}{2\pi j} \int_{c-j\infty}^{c+j\infty} \frac{\epsilon^{st}}{s + \alpha} ds \tag{720}$$

This integrand has one pole, at $s = -\alpha$, as shown in Fig. 102. The path of integration is also shown in the figure.

It is difficult to integrate along this path of integration (or at least it would be with a more complicated integrand), but it is easy with the following artifice. The path of integration can be closed by a half-circle to the left, as suggested in Fig. 103; the half-circle must be infinitely large. The closed path, shown by the dash line, will surround the pole at $-\alpha$, and we find the value of the integral around the *closed* path by using Eq. (719):

$$\oint \frac{\epsilon^{st}}{s+\alpha}\,ds = 2\pi j\left[\lim_{s\to-\alpha}\ (s+\alpha)\frac{\epsilon^{st}}{s+\alpha}\right] = 2\pi j\epsilon^{-\alpha t} \qquad (721)$$

The integral required, however, is the integral along the vertical straight line only and not the integral along the entire closed path. Fortunately, the integral along the infinite half-circle can be shown to be zero provided t in Eq. (721) is positive: if t is *positive*, and the real part of s has a very large

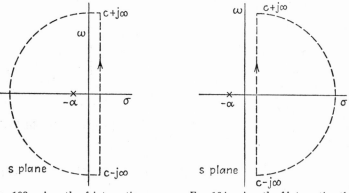

Fig. 103. A path of integration that can be used for positive time.

Fig. 104. A path of integration that can be used for negative time.

negative value, ϵ^{st} is vanishingly small, and thus the integrand is zero in Eq. (721) for all of the infinite half-circle that lies far to the left. It can be shown that the two ends of the half-circle, one infinitely far up and the other infinitely far down, also contribute nothing to the integral. This leaves us with the useful conclusion that the integral along the vertical line is the same as the integral along the entire closed path, and hence is $2\pi j\epsilon^{-\alpha t}$.

Having now evaluated the integral of Eq. (720) for positive values of t, it follows that

$$f(t) = \epsilon^{-\alpha t} \qquad (t > 0) \qquad (722)$$

It remains to find $f(t)$ for negative time.

The path of integration shown in Fig. 103 is useless for negative values of time, for if t is negative and the real part of s is also negative, ϵ^{st} is very large and the integral along the semicircle to the left, as in Fig. 103, is certainly not negligible. However, when t is *negative*, ϵ^{st} is extremely small if the real part of s is large and *positive*, and this suggests that we abandon the path of integration shown in Fig. 103 and try that of Fig. 104. Closing the path of integration thus, with an infinite half-circle to the *right*, where

σ is large and positive, it can be shown that the half-circle contributes nothing to the integral for any *negative* value of time. Finally, since the path of integration of Fig. 104 surrounds no poles, the integral around the closed path is zero. Since the integral along the half-circle is zero for all negative values of time, the integral along the vertical straight line is also zero for negative time. This gives, in Eq. (720),

$$f(t) = 0 \qquad (t < 0) \tag{723}$$

The problem is now complete. The inverse Laplace transformation (integrating by the method of residues) has given $f(t)$ for both negative time and positive time, as Eqs. (722) and (723). The result is, happily, the same as that given in Pair 3 of Table 2.

Example 2. $F(s) = 1/s$; find $f(t)$. This function of s has one pole at $s = 0$, the origin. By Eqs. (718) and (719)

$$f(t) = \lim_{s \to 0} s\frac{\epsilon^{st}}{s} = \lim_{s \to 0} \epsilon^{st} = 1 \tag{724}$$

for all positive time. As before, since the path of integration of Fig. 104 encloses no poles, $f(t) = 0$ for negative time. This agrees with Pair 1 of Table 2.

Example 3. $F(s) = s/(s^2 + \beta^2)$; find $f(t)$. This function has two poles, for it may be written

$$F(s) = \frac{s}{s^2 + \beta^2} = \frac{s}{(s + j\beta)(s - j\beta)} \tag{725}$$

Contour integration following the path of Fig. 103 encloses a pole at $s = -j\beta$ and a pole at $s = +j\beta$. The integral is $2\pi j$ times the sum of the residues, so by Eqs. (718) and (719)

$$f(t) = \lim_{s \to j\beta} (s - j\beta)\frac{s\epsilon^{st}}{(s + j\beta)(s - j\beta)} + \lim_{s \to -j\beta} (s + j\beta)\frac{s\epsilon^{st}}{(s + j\beta)(s - j\beta)}$$

$$= \frac{j\beta\epsilon^{j\beta t}}{2j\beta} + \frac{(-j\beta)\epsilon^{-j\beta t}}{(-2j\beta)} = \cos \beta t \tag{726}$$

This is the inverse transformation of Pair 9 of Table 2.

These three examples are perhaps enough to show the method which can be applied without difficulty to find $f(t)$ from $F(s)$ in other pairs of Table 2.

Integration in the complex plane is useful as a method, but it is even more valuable as a concept. Among the conclusions of major significance are the following:

1. If $F(s)$ has a first-order pole at the origin, it transforms to an $f(t)$ that is constant for positive time and zero for negative time—a step function, as in Fig. 83.

2. If $F(s)$ has a first-order pole on the real axis, as in Fig. 105a, $f(t)$ is a simple exponential function for positive time and zero for negative time, as in Fig. 85.   If the pole is left of the origin, the exponential function $f(t)$ decreases with time; if the pole is to the right of the origin, $f(t)$ is increasing.[1]

3. If $F(s)$ has a pair of poles on the imaginary axis, at $+j\omega$ and $-j\omega$, as in Fig. 105b, $f(t)$ is a sinusoidal function (an undamped oscillation) for positive time and is zero for negative time, as in Fig. 88.

4. If $F(s)$ has a conjugate complex pair of poles at $\sigma + j\omega$ and $\sigma - j\omega$, as in Fig. 105c, $f(t)$ is the product of a sinusoidal function

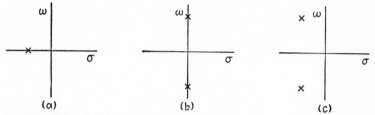

Fig. 105.   Poles of $F(s)$.   See Figs. 85, 88, and 89 for corresponding time functions, $f(t)$.

and an exponential function for positive time, and zero for negative time (see Fig. 89).   If the poles are in the left-half plane, $f(t)$ is a decreasing (or damped) oscillation; if the poles are in the right-half plane, $f(t)$ is increasing with time.

5. If $F(s)$ has a number of poles or pairs of poles, $f(t)$ is the sum of the corresponding time functions.

26. Extension of $F(s)$.   The function $F(s)$ is defined by Eq. (601).   This equation is an infinite integral and, as was stated in Sec. 6, it has no meaning unless σ, the real part of s, is sufficiently large and positive.   It is now possible to make a more definite statement (which, however, we shall not attempt to prove). $F(s)$ is defined by Eq. (601) for every value of s that lies farther to the right in the complex plane than does any pole of $F(s)$. Equation (601) cannot be evaluated to find $F(s)$ for any value of s

---

[1] It was seen in Sec. 22 that if s is real, the function ϵ^{st} is a continuous exponential function of time as in Fig. 94b.   It is here stated that if $F(s)$ has a pole at s_1, and s_1 is real, the function $\dfrac{1}{2\pi j}\displaystyle\int_{c-j\infty}^{c+j\infty} F(s)\epsilon^{st}\,ds$ is a *discontinuous* exponential function of time as in Fig. 85.   These two facts must not be confused with each other.

that lies to the left of a pole of $F(s)$.   In all the region to the left of such a pole, $F(s)$ is, as yet, undefined.

How, then, could we undertake to integrate an expression containing $F(s)$ along the closed path of Fig. 103, a path which extends into the left-hand region where $F(s)$ is undefined?   The justification follows:

1. $F(s)$ is analytic in the right-hand region.
2. $F(s)$ is undefined in the left-hand region.
3. We wish to integrate in the left-hand region.
4. We can integrate only if $F(s)$ is an analytic function.
5. We therefore define $F(s)$ in the left-hand region as an analytic function.
6. There is only one function that is analytic in the left-hand region, and that is, at the same time, a continuation of the known $F(s)$ in the right-hand region.   We define $F(s)$ in the left-hand region as this function.

This is definition "by analytic continuation," and it is accomplished by letting the same formula that describes the function in the right-hand region of the s plane describe it in the left-hand region also ("extension through preservation of form").   Thus, if $F(s)$ is $1/(s - w)$ in the right-hand region, we let it be $1/(s - w)$ in the left-hand region also; $F(s)$ is then analytic everywhere except at $s = w$.

With $F(s)$ defined in the right-hand region by Eq. (601), and in the left-hand region by analytic continuation, our use of contour integration is justified.

27. Current and Voltage at Negative Time.   It is interesting to notice that the inverse transformation always yields a time function that is zero for negative time.   When $f(t)$ is evaluated by Eq. (718), using contour integration as in Fig. 104, the result for negative time is always zero.   The path of integration, being closed to the right, as it is for negative time, surrounds no poles, for it is stipulated that the value of c shall be great enough to place the path of integration to the right of all poles.   This, indeed, is the reason that such a limitation must be placed on c. It is now clear why $F(s)$ cannot be the Laplace transform of a time function with any value but zero for negative time.

It is worth emphasizing that the inverse Laplace transformation, in the integral of Eq. (718), expresses a current or a voltage that begins suddenly, at the instant of closing a switch, as the sum of oscillations that are entirely continuous and that existed long before the switch was closed.   As Gardner[1] says:

> The integral states these facts in a surprising way. . . . Until time $t = 0$ is reached, these components have had the proper amplitude and phase exactly to annul one another.   Beyond this point, without the slightest change in amplitude or phase, they give as their sum the actual current existent in the circuit.   One may protest against the artificiality of this concept, but must concede its great power in reducing all transient phenomena to terms of the steady state—which is so well understood, and easily calculated.

28. Review of the Chapter.   This chapter is presented in three parts.   The first five sections are introductory; they are to show that Laplace transformation is not entirely different from more familiar processes, and particularly that it is similar to Fourier-series analysis.   Sections 6 through 19 provide the working tools of the Laplace transformation method.   Sections 20 through 27 relate to the mathematics of the inverse transformation, and rather advanced concepts of extraordinary value and interest are introduced.

Throughout the chapter, the mathematics is sketchy, but it is not careless.   Mathematical niceties are omitted, some with mere passing reference and some without mention.   There is no attempt to be comprehensive, and mathematical statements are permitted to be incomplete for the sake of brevity.   They are not, however, permitted to be inexact.

Volumes have been written on what is omitted from this chapter, and it seems that the most fitting conclusion is to refer the reader to books in which he may find answers to questions that have, it is hoped, been raised in his mind.

GARDNER, M. F., and J. L. BARNES, "Transients in Linear Systems," John Wiley & Sons, Inc., New York, 1942.   (Definitive.)

BUSH, V., "Operational Circuit Analysis," John Wiley & Sons, Inc., New York, 1929.   (Early, but excellently written.)

CAMPBELL, G. A., and R. M. FOSTER, "Fourier Integrals for Practical Applications," D. Van Nostrand Company, Inc., New York, 1948. (Extensive tables.)

JAEGER, J. C., "An Introduction to the Laplace Transformation," John Wiley & Sons, Inc., New York, 1949.   (Good, brief, readable.)

---

[1] GARDNER, M. F., Operational Calculus, *Elec. Eng.*, **53**, 1339, 1934.

LAPLACE TRANSFORMATION   355

CARSLAW, H. S., "Introduction to the Theory of Fourier's Series and Integrals," Dover Publications, 1930. (Advanced.)

CHURCHILL, R. V., "Modern Operational Mathematics in Engineering," McGraw-Hill Book Company, Inc., New York, 1944.

GOLDMAN, S., "Transformation Calculus and Electrical Transients," Prentice-Hall, Inc., New York, 1949.

Problems

1. Current in a circuit is $i = 15 \cos \omega t$ and the voltage across the circuit is $v = 90 \cos (\omega t - \pi/4)$. Transform current and voltage to complex quantities of the form of Eq. (567). Find Z of the circuit.

2. Voltage applied to a circuit is $170 \cos \omega t$. The circuit consists of 12 ohms resistance and 0.25 henry inductance in series. Frequency is 60 cycles per sec. Find V. Find Z. Find I, and transform to $i(t)$.

3. A voltage wave is defined by $v(t) = t$ from $t = -\pi/\omega_1$ to $t = +\pi/\omega_1$. The wave is periodic; that is, $v(t) = v(t + 2\pi)$. Find $V(\omega)$ using the transformation of Eq. (580). (Note: Integration can be from $-\pi/\omega_1$ to π/ω_1 if this is more convenient.) Add this pair to Table 1.

4. Show that $V(\omega)$ of Prob. 3, transformed by Eq. (581), gives the formula for a saw-tooth wave:

$$v(t) = \frac{2}{\omega_1} \sin \omega_1 t - \frac{1}{\omega_1} \sin 2\omega_1 t + \frac{2}{3\omega_1} \sin 3\omega_1 t - \frac{1}{2\omega_1} \sin 4\omega_1 t + \cdots$$

5. Find the Laplace transforms of the following voltages and currents, all of which are zero until $t = 0$:

a. $v(t) = 17$

b. $i(t) = 8t$

c. $v(t) = 10 - 10\epsilon^{-5t}$

d. $v(t) = 10 - 8\epsilon^{-4t}$

e. $i(t) = 9 \sin 377t$

f. $v(t) = 6 \sin (377t - \pi/6)$

6. Find the inverse Laplace transforms (current or voltage) of the following:

a. $V(s) = \dfrac{1}{3s}$

b. $I(s) = \dfrac{1}{4s + 12}$

c. $I(s) = \dfrac{5}{s^2 + 9}$

d. $I(s) = \dfrac{5}{s^2 + 5s}$

e. $V(s) = \dfrac{2}{s^2 + 6s + 8}$

f. $V(s) = \dfrac{s + 4}{s^2 + 4}$

7. Find the inverse Laplace transform of $F(s) = \dfrac{s}{(s + \alpha)^2}$

8. Find the Laplace transform of $f(t) = t^2$.

9. Derive Pair 5 of Table 2 by the method of partial fractions.

10. Derive Pair 4 of Table 2 by using Pair E.

11. Derive Pair 11 of Table 2 by using Pair D.

12. Derive Pair 11 of Table 2 by applying Pair E. Pair 1 is also used in the course of the derivation.

13. Derive Pair 14 of Table 2.

14. Derive Pair 16 of Table 2.

15. Solve Eq. (657) for current in such a way as to obtain $i(t)$ as the sum of exponential terms (not trigonometric). This is the practical form with high resistance.

16. Apply Pair D of Table 2 to Pair 13, and compare the result with another pair of the table.

17. Apply Pair D of Table 2 to Pair 9 and to Pair 16.

18. Apply Pair D of Table 2 to Pair 3 and to Pair 1.

19. Using integration and translation as in Sec. 17, derive Pair 6 and Pair 8. For each, begin with Pair 1.

20. Find the inverse transform of $I(s)$ in Eq. (705) by translation and integration as in Sec. 17. Compare as to ease of solution with Example 2, Sec. 18.

21. Identify the "natural" and "forced" components of current in Eq. (714), which correspond to the "transient" and "steady-state" components of a current produced by a suddenly applied periodic voltage.

22. Find the inverse transform of

$$\frac{s}{(s - \lambda_1)(s - \lambda_2)}$$

23. In Fig. 30, page 131, the switch is closed. The branch R_{12} is disconnected. Steady current $E/(R_1 + R_2) = i_0$ then flows. The branch R_{12} is suddenly reconnected. Find i_1 thereafter, using Laplace transformation. (Note: The algebra in this solution is rather lengthy; this is typical of such problems.)

24. Plot, as in Fig. 105, the poles of $F(s)$ for the time functions of Figs. 83, 86, and 84. Note that the latter does not have a *first-order* pole (it has a *second-order* pole).

25. By inverse transformation, using the method of residues to integrate in the complex plane, find $f(t)$ from the $F(s)$ of Pair 4. Repeat for the $F(s)$ of Pair 5; of Pair 8; of Pair 11; and of Pair 16.

26. How are the five conclusions on pages 351 and 352 reached? Relate to the discussion of Sec. 22.

27. How are the poles of $I(s)$, as in Fig. 105, related to the "zeros" of $Z(s)$; that is, to the values of s that make impedance zero, as discussed in Sec. 18 of Chap. IV?

28. Most of the problems following other chapters of the book can be solved by Laplace transformation.

INDEX

A

Alternating-current impedance, 70
Alternating voltage, application of, 185, 339
  non-sinusoidal, 206
Analogues, 4
Analytic continuation, 353
Angular velocity, natural, 77, 99
Arresters, lightning, 244, 303

B

Barnes., J. L., 354
Bewley, L. V., 291, 301
Bush, V., 257, 300, 354

C

Campbell, G. A., 354
Capacitance, 34
  mutual, 157
Carslaw, H. S., 355
Churchill, R. V., 355
Circuits, coupled resonant (*see* Resonant circuits)
  differentiating and integrating, 216
  with RC, 40, 47, 54, 326
    with constant voltage, 35, 325
    with sine-wave voltage, 194
    time constant, 54, 55
  with RL, 14, 16, 324
    with constant voltage, 13, 18, 20, 32, 60, 325
    with non-periodic voltage, 208
    with non-sinusoidal voltage, 206
    with sine-wave voltage, 186, 339
    time constant, 55
    with variable L, 245, 251, 258

Circuits, with RLC, 117
  with constant voltage, 65, 69, 75, 81, 109, 124, 326
  with sine-wave voltage, 198, 201, 218
  with several meshes (*see* Networks)
  sweep, linear, 51, 184
  oscillograph, 46
Coefficients, solution for, 87, 110, 135, 137, 163
Complementary function, 60–62, 69, 209
Complex frequency, 316, 346
Complex plane, integration in, 348
  contour, 349
Component, steady-state, 19, 63, 69, 185
  transient, 19, 61, 62, 69, 123, 185, 205
Corona, 303
Coupled resonant circuits (*see* Resonant circuits)
Coupling, coefficient of, 220
Crests of wave, 105
Critical resistance, 76, 84
Critically damped surge, 84, 327

D

Damping, 101
  critical, 84, 327
Damping factor, 98
Decrement, logarithmic, 108
  natural, 99
Decrement factor, 98
Determinants, 165
Differential analyzer, 257
Differential equations (*see* Equations)
Differentiating circuit, 216

357